Readings in Vertebrate Zoology

Edited by
Richard S. Peterson
University of California—Santa Cruz

MSS EDUCATIONAL PUBLISHING COMPANY, INC.
19 EAST 48th STREET, NEW YORK, N. Y. 10017

596.08
P 485

This is a custom-made book of readings prepared
for the courses taught by the editor. For information about our program, please write to:

  MSS Educational Publishing Company, Inc.
        19 East 48th Street
        New York, New York 10017

MSS wishes to express its appreciation to the
authors of the articles in this collection for
their cooperation in making their work available in this format.

CONTENTS

PREFACE

This volume is a potpourri of research papers on the biology of vertebrate animals. It was compiled with the idea that undergraduate students in zoology can benefit from the experience of grappling with original research, rather than always being separated from the real investigator by a textbook compiler or editor. Original papers are generally available in libraries, but for maximum benefit an entire class should read a paper and discuss it and single library copies of technical articles could never accommodate a whole class.

The papers in this volume are exciting. They are firsthand reports of original research, mostly on wild animals. None is a review or popularized story. Many of the papers are technical and may require considerable digestion before the author's excitement percolates through to the reader, but the careful student will be rewarded as he shares the development of a new idea, or a new view of an old one, with the biologist who did the work.

John Steinbeck wrote in _Sea of Cortez_ that "The true biologist deals with life, with teeming, boisterous life, and learns from it, learns that the first rule of life is living." The teeming, boisterous, and all too often chaotic nature of the animals described in these papers will be obvious. But it may require reading between-the-lines, and some broad acquaintance with zoological studies, to understand how these

1

papers reflect the living, thinking biologist-authors behind them. In some papers, glimmers of the living man may shine through in the introductions, or discussions. Certainly the insights are more frequent than in other, more laboratory-oriented scientific writings.

Scientific papers are brief. The costs of printing and other necessities (including the time available to readers) have forced authors to eliminate decorative editorializing and speculation, and confine themselves to factual observations and rigorous interpretations. Sometimes this boiling-down process tends to obscure the feelings of the man behind the paper. If the reader bears in mind that the author probably took up his pen primarily because he had something of vital fascination to say, the excitement of the work should finally stand out.

The purpose of this volume is, then, to introduce the reader to original research on vertebrates. Each paper contains original observations, mostly on birds and mammals, much of it done in the field during the 1960's. A scattering of current work is represented, but there has been no attempt to cover every aspect of vertebrate biology. A basic textbook on organismal biology, and one dealing specifically with vertebrates, are indispensable companions to this volume.

Richard S. Peterson

Santa Cruz, July 1969

A TRAFFIC SURVEY OF *MICROTUS-REITHRODONTOMYS* RUNWAYS

By Oliver P. Pearson

Patient observation of the comings and goings of individual birds has long been one of the most rewarding activities of ornithologists. The development in recent years of inexpensive electronic flash photographic equipment has made it possible and practical for mammalogists to make similar studies on this aspect of the natural history of secretive small mammals. The report that follows is based on photographic recordings of the vertebrate traffic in mouse runways over a period of 19 months. Species, direction of travel, time, temperature and relative humidity were recorded for each passage. In addition, many animals in the area were live-trapped and marked to make it possible to recognize individuals using the runways.

THE APPARATUS

Two recorders were used. Each consisted of an instrument shelter and a camera shelter. Each instrument shelter was a glass-fronted, white box containing an electric clock with a sweep second hand, a ruler for measuring the size of photographed individuals, a dial thermometer and a Serdex membrane hygrometer. The ends of the box were louvered to provide circulation of air as in a standard weather station. This box was placed along one side of the runway, across from the camera shelter, so that the instruments were visible in each photograph (Plate I). The camera shelter was a glass-fronted, weather-proof box containing a 16-mm. motion picture camera synchronized to an electronic flash unit. In one of the recorders the camera was actuated by a counterweighted treadle placed in the mouse runway immediately in front of the instrument shelter (Plate I, bottom). An animal passing along the runway depressed the treadle, thereby closing an electrical circuit through a mercury-dip switch. This activated a solenoid that pulled a shutter release pin so arranged that the camera made a single exposure. The electronic flash fired while the shutter was open. This synchronization was easily accomplished by having the film-advance claw close the flash contact. The camera would repeat exposures as rapidly as the treadle could be depressed, but at night about three seconds were required for the flash unit to recharge sufficiently to give adequate light for the next exposure.

JOURNAL OF MAMMALOGY, 1959, Vol. 40, pp. 169-180.

The other recorder was actuated by a photoelectric cell instead of by a treadle. A beam of deep red light shone from the camera shelter across the runway and was reflected back from a small mirror in the instrument shelter to a photoelectric unit in the camera shelter. When an animal interrupted the light beam, the photoelectric unit activated a solenoid that caused the camera to make a single exposure, as in the other recorder.

To avoid the possibility of frightening the animals it would be desirable to use infra-red–sensitive film and infra-red light, but standard electronic flash tubes emit so little energy in the infra-red that this is not practical. Instead, I used 18 layers of red cellophane over the flash tube and reflector to give a deep red flash of light. Wild mice, like many laboratory rodents, are probably insensitive to deep red light. I found no evidence that the flash, which lasts for only 1/1000th of a second, frightened the mice. A muffled clunk made by the mechanism also seemed not to alarm the mice unduly.

When the camera diaphragm was set to give the proper exposure at night, daytime pictures were overexposed, since the shutter speed was considerably slower than 1/30th of a second. To reduce the daytime exposure, a red filter was put on the camera lens. The filter did not affect night exposures because red light from the flash passed the red filter with little loss. In addition, on one of the cameras the opening in the rotary shutter was reduced to give a shorter exposure.

Both recorders function on 110-volt alternating current. The treadle-actuated one could be adapted to operate from batteries. The units continue to record until the motion picture camera runs down or runs out of film. One winding serves for several hundred pictures. The film record can be studied directly by projecting the film strip without making prints.

The camera shelter and instrument shelter had overhanging eaves to prevent condensation of frost and dew on the windows. A small blackened light bulb was also kept burning in the camera shelter to raise the temperature enough to retard fogging on the glass. Animals were encouraged to stay in their usual runway by a picket fence made of twigs or slender wires. No bait was used.

A few individual animals could be recognized in the pictures by scars or molt patterns, but most had to be live-trapped and marked. Using eartags and fur-clipping I was able to mark distinctively (Plate I, bottom) all of the mice captured at any one station. The clipping remained visible for days or months depending upon the time of the next molt.

The apparatus produces photographic records such as those shown in the lower pictures in Plate I. These can be transposed into some form as Fig. 2.

THE STUDY AREA

The study centered around a grassy-weedy patch surrounding a brush pile in Orinda, Contra Costa County, California (Plate I). The runways wound through a 20 × 20-foot patch of tall weeds (*Artemisia vulgaris, Hemizonia* sp. and *Rumex crispus*) and under the brush pile. The weeds were surrounded by and somewhat intermixed with annual grasses. Oaks and other trees, as well as a house and planting, were 50 feet away.

Summer climate in this region is warm and sunny with official mean daily maximum temperatures rising above 80°F. in late summer. Official temperatures occasionally reach 100°, and temperatures in the small instrument shelters used in this study sometimes exceeded this. Nights in summer are usually clear and with the mean daily minimum temperature below 52° in each month. About 27 inches of rain fall in the winter and there is frost on most clear nights. The mean daily maximum temperature in January, the coldest month, is 54°, and the mean daily minimum 31°.

PROCEDURE

I placed the first recorder in operation on January 29, 1956, and the second on October 19, 1956. Except for occasional periods of malfunction and a few periods when I was away they continued to record until the end of the study on September 10, 1957. Approximately 778 recorder-days or 111 recorder-weeks of information were thus obtained. The monthly distribution of records was as follows: January, 54 days; February, 70; March, 90; April, 80; May, 84; June, 67; July, 52; August, 88; September, 48; October, 33; November, 52; and December, 60.

The recorders were placed at what appeared to be frequently used *Microtus* runways, usually situated on opposite sides of the weedy patch 20 to 30 feet apart. For one period of four months one of the recorders was placed at a similar weedy patch 70 yards away. Early in the study it was discovered that a neighbor's Siamese cat sometimes crouched on the camera shelter waiting for mice to pass along the exposed runway in front of the instrument shelter. Consequently, a 2½-foot fence of 2-inch-mesh wire netting was set up enclosing most of the weedy patch. This prevented further predation by cats at the center of the study area, although cats continued to hunt outside of the fence a few yards away from the recorders. The only other tampering with predation was the removal of two garter snakes on April 11, 1957.

RESULTS

Traffic in individual runways.—The recorders were operated at eighteen different stations. At seven of these apparently busy runways a traffic volume higher than a few passages per day never developed, and so the recorders were moved within two weeks. Perhaps the mice originally using these runways had abandoned them or had been killed shortly before a recorder was moved to their runway, or perhaps the disturbance of placing a recorder caused the mice to divert their activities to other runways. At the other eleven stations a satisfactory volume of traffic was maintained for three to more than twenty weeks. A station was abandoned and the recorder moved when the traffic had decreased to a few passages per day. Subsequently, I found that even this little activity does not indicate that the mice are going to abandon the runway,

5

for on several occasions traffic in a runway dropped this low and then climbed again to high levels. At one recorder the total number of passages in consecutive weeks was 183, 84, 26, 75 and 203. The runway represented in Fig. 1 was one of those used most consistently, but even it shows marked daily and weekly fluctuations. It is probable that after a few weeks of disuse during the season when grass and weeds are growing rapidly, a runway would not be reopened, but during the rest of the year an abandoned runway remains more or less passable and probably more attractive to mice than the surrounding terrain.

Figure 1 summarizes the traffic in one of the busiest runways. On the first night there were an unusual number of records of harvest mice whose curiosity may have been aroused by the apparatus. Obviously they were not frightened away. After a short time traffic increased to a high level and remained high until the middle of November, when passages by *Microtus* decreased sharply. During the week before the decrease, seven marked individuals provided most of the *Microtus* traffic. One of these individuals, an infrequent passerby, disappeared at the time of the decrease, but the other six remained nearby for at least another week and continued to pass occasionally. Those *Microtus* that disappeared later were replaced by others so that even the infrequent passages in late November and early December were being provided by seven marked individuals. The decrease of *Microtus* traffic was caused, therefore, not by deaths but by a change in runway preference. Several of these same individuals were using another runway 20 feet away in mid-January, February and March.

Three to six marked *Reithrodontomys*, depending upon the date, were providing most of the harvest-mouse traffic in the runway represented in Fig. 1. The average number of passages per day of animals of all kinds was eighteen. In the ten other most successful runways, the average number of passages per day ranged from two to nineteen.

Figure 2 gives a detailed accounting of the traffic at a single recording station for six days. One can judge from this figure the kind of information (excluding

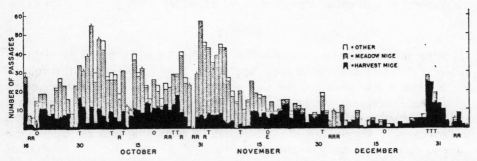

FIG. 1.—Traffic volume along one runway for 16 weeks. Meaning of symbols under the base line: T= live-trapping carried out for part of this day; O= full moon; E= total eclipse of the moon; R= rain. Columns surmounted by a vertical line represent days for which the recording was incomplete; the heights of the various segments of these columns should be considered minimum values.

6

temperatures and humidities) obtained with the recorders and can at the same time catch a revealing glimpse of an aspect of the biology of small mammals that has heretofore been revealed inadequately by trapping and other techniques. It may be seen that the mouse traffic was provided by one female and two male harvest mice and by three male, three female, and one or more unidentified meadow mice; together they gave between 15 and 24 passages each day. No individual passed more than eight times in one day. One harvest mouse (R2) seemed to spend the day to the left and to make a single excursion

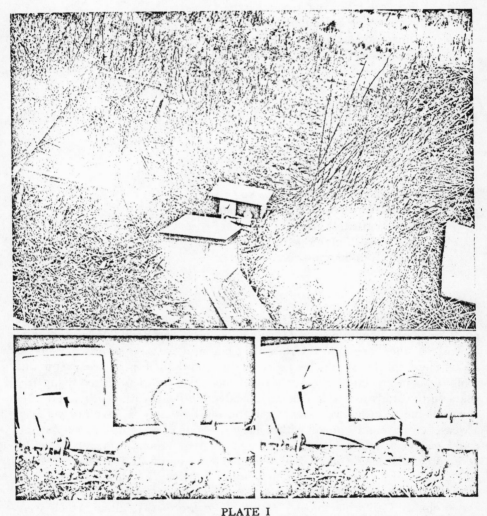

PLATE I

TOP: Camera shelter (foreground) and instrument shelter in position at a mouse runway on the study area. BOTTOM: The kind of records obtained with the recorder; *left*—a meadow mouse marked by clipping two strips of fur on the hips; *right*—a marked harvest mouse crossing the treadle.

to the right each night. Harvest mice first appeared in the evening between 6:37 and 7:22 and none passed after 6:26 in the morning. Five or six *Microtus* passed within a few hours (February 24), and there was nightly near-coincidence of *Reithrodontomys* and *Microtus*.

Traffic in all runways combined.—During the 111 recorder-weeks, the following passages of animals were photographed:

Meadow mouse, *Microtus californicus*	6,077
Harvest mouse, *Reithrodontomys megalotis*	1,753
Bird (see following account)	382
Brush rabbit, *Sylvilagus bachmani*	94
Shrew, *Sorex ornatus*	56
Peromyscus (see following account)	39
Fence lizard, *Sceloporus occidentalis*	33
Garter snake, *Thamnophis* sp.	17
Salamander (see following account)	11
Alligator lizard, *Gerrhonotus* sp.	10
House cat, *Felis domesticus*	6
Newt, *Taricha* sp.	5
Pocket gopher, *Thomomys bottae*	3
Gopher snake, *Pituophis catenifer*	3
Mole cricket, *Stenopelmatus* sp.	2
Ground squirrel, *Citellus beecheyi*	1
Weasel, *Mustela frenata*	1
King snake, *Lampropeltis getulus*	1
Racer, *Coluber constrictor*	1
TOTAL	8,495

On the basis of trapping results in this and in similar habitat nearby, large numbers of meadow mice and harvest mice were expected. The recording of at least 26 other species in the runways came as a pleasant surprise. Whereas all of these species would be expected to record their presence eventually, some of them are rarely seen or trapped near this location. After living five years on the study area, after doing considerable field work nearby, and after checking the recorders twice each day during the study, I have not yet seen a weasel or a ground squirrel within at least a mile of the study area. Weasels could easily escape detection, but large, diurnal ground squirrels must be very rare. The single individual recorded on August 31 may have been a young squirrel emigrating from some distant colony. Noteworthy absences were those of wood rats (*Neotoma fuscipes*), moles (*Scapanus latimanus*), and probably California mice (*Peromyscus californicus*), all of which were common within 100 feet of the recorders. An opossum (*Didelphis marsupialis*) was seen a few feet from one of the recorders but did not appear on the films. No house mice (*Mus musculus*) were detected in the photographs, although it is possible that some passages of *Mus* were listed as of *Reithrodontomys*. House mice were caught occasionally in houses nearby and in a field near a poultry house 200 yards away, but none was caught during frequent live-trapping near the recorders.

The total of 8,495 passages of animals gives an average of 11 passages per day in each runway. A patient, non-selective predator waiting for a single catch at runways such as these could expect, theoretically, a reward each 2.2 hours. The mean weight of animal per passage was about 31 grams, which would yield approximately 40 calories of food. This much each 2.2 hours would be more than enough to support an active mammal the size of a fox.

Meadow mouse.—The 6,077 *Microtus* passages were distributed throughout the day and night as shown in Fig. 3 (above). The hours of above-ground activity, however, were quite different in winter than in summer, so Fig. 3 is only a year-around average somewhat biased by the fact that more *Microtus* were recorded in the spring than in the other seasons. A more detailed analysis of the *Microtus* data will be given in a later report. By marking as many of the mice as possible, it was found that usually four or more individual *Microtus* were using each runway but rarely more than ten. On some occasions more than 60 *Microtus* passages were recorded at a single point in 24 hours.

Harvest mouse.—Harvest mice were almost entirely nocturnal (Fig. 3, center). They not only used the *Microtus* runways, but their passages were frequently intermixed with those of *Microtus* (Fig. 2). On fourteen occasions the two species passed within 60 seconds of each other, and on one occasion

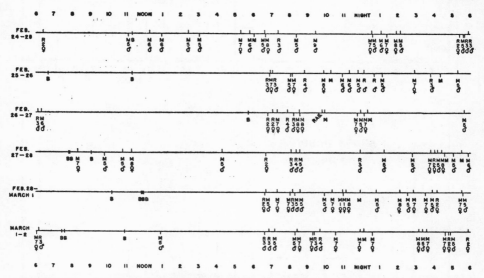

Fig. 2.—A sample record of the total traffic in a single runway over a period of six days. Marks above the base lines indicate passages from right to left, and marks below the base line passages from left to right. R represents *Reithrodontomys*; M, *Microtus*; B, bird (includes brown towhee, wren-tit, and song sparrow); and RAB, brush rabbit. Most of the mice are further identified by number and sex.

a 4-month-old male *Microtus* and a 5-month-old male *Reithrodontomys* appeared in the same photograph.

The history of one runway indicates that traffic by *Reithrodontomys* alone does not keep a *Microtus* runway open. One or more *Microtus* passed almost daily along this runway during February. At the end of the month the *Microtus* disappeared and two *Reithrodontomys* became active in the same runway. Despite an average of 3.3 passages per day by *Reithrodontomys* throughout March and up to mid-April, grass and weed seedlings grew up

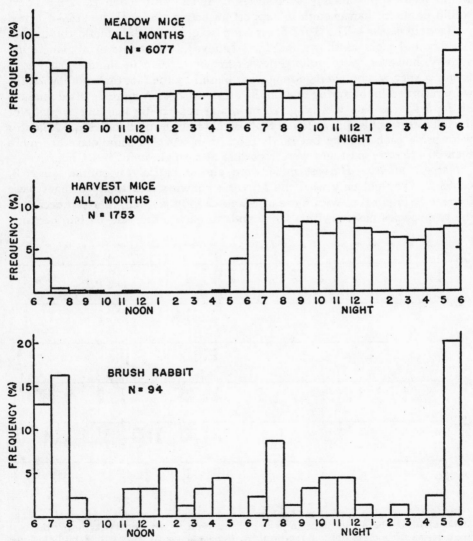

Fig. 3.—Distribution by hours of 6,077 passages of meadow mice (above); 1,753 passages of harvest mice (center); and 94 passages of brush rabbits (below).

in the runway and it began to look unused. By the end of April almost all traffic had ceased.

The *Reithrodontomys* data will be analyzed in a later report.

Birds.—Of the 382 bird records, at least 255 were of sparrows (at least 122 song sparrow; the remainder mostly fox sparrow, white-crowned sparrow and golden-crowned sparrow). Other birds recognized were wren-tit, wren, brown towhee and thrush. On several occasions birds, especially song sparrows, battled their reflections in the window of the instrument shelter. This caused long series of exposures. Each series was counted as a single passage. If the bird stopped for a minute or more and then returned to the battle, this was counted as another passage. All bird records were during daylight hours.

On three occasions a sparrow and an adult *Microtus* appeared in the same photograph. On one of these occurrences a song sparrow was battling its reflection when an adult, lactating *Microtus* came along the runway. The sparrow retreated about 12 inches toward the camera shelter and, as soon as the mouse had passed, returned to the runway.

Brush rabbit.—All except four of the records of brush rabbits were in June and July of 1957, a season when these animals, especially young ones, were abundant. Figure 3 (below) shows that they were most active in the early morning.

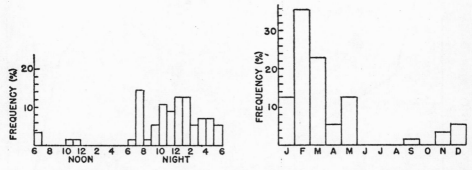

Fɪɢ. 4.—Distribution by hours of 56 passages of shrews (left) and distribution by months of 56 passages of shrews (right).

Shrew.—The dry, weedy habitat chosen was not favorable for shrews, and they were near the minimum weight necessary to depress the treadle of one of the recorders, so that some may have passed along the runway without making a record. The shrews were highly nocturnal (Fig. 4, left) and avoided the surface runways during the dry summer months (Fig. 4, right). Since captive specimens of *Sorex* are rarely inactive for more than one hour (Morrison, Amer. Midl. Nat., 57: 493, 1957), the scarcity of records in the daytime probably means only that the shrews were not moving above ground at this time. They may have been foraging along gopher, mole and *Microtus* tunnels during the daytime.

A shrew was marked on March 4, a few inches from one of the recorders. It was captured 15 feet away on May 30 and 5 feet farther away on June 23. It passed along the study runway five times in the 16-week interval between first and last capture: on March 13, 27, 31, and April 17, and possibly on April 10 (markings obscured). Another shrew was recorded on March 27. Unless baited traps attract shrews from a considerable distance, or the recorder repels them, a trapper setting traps in this runway for a few nights would have had small chance of recording the presence of this individual which apparently was nearby for at least 16 weeks.

Not a single shrew was recorded during the dry summer months of June, July and August. Nevertheless, on July 8 when I was checking the photo-electric recorder at 5:55 AM, a shrew emerged completely from a small hole in

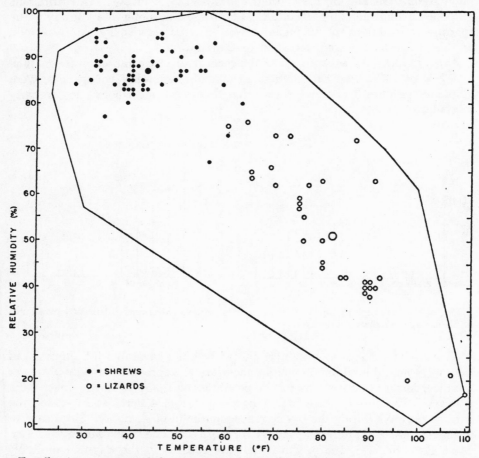

Fig. 5.—A comparison of the temperatures and humidities encountered by shrews and fence lizards in the runways. The larger circles show the position of the mean for each species. The large polygon encloses the range of temperatures and humidities available to the animals during the study.

the ground a few inches from the instrument shelter, twitched his nose rapidly for a few seconds, and retreated down the same hole.' The air temperature was 54° and the relative humidity 78 per cent—normal for this season. Obviously shrews were present on the study area during some or all of the summer months but were not frequenting the surface runways.

Figure 5 shows the temperatures and relative humidities encountered above ground by the shrews on the study area compared with the total range of temperatures and humidities recorded throughout the study. By their nocturnal, winter-time activity shrews encountered the coldest, most humid conditions available in the region. In contrast, the similarly small, insectivorous fence lizards existing in the same habitat managed by their own behavioral patterns to encounter a totally different climate (Fig. 5). The mean of the temperatures recorded at the times of lizard passages was 39° warmer than that recorded for shrew passages, and relative humidity was 36 per cent lower.

This activity pattern of shrews differs from that reported by Clothier (Jour. Mamm., 36: 214–226, 1955) for *Sorex vagrans* in Montana. He found shrews there to be active "both day and night and throughout the year, even during extremely bad weather." It is important to understand, however, that he collected in damp areas near water, where the shrews may not have had to modify their activity to avoid desiccation. Extremely bad weather, for a shrew, is hot dry weather.

Peromyscus.—*Peromyscus truei* was abundant in brushy places and in houses nearby; *P. maniculatus* was scarce. Some of the *Peromyscus* records were clearly of *truei* and some may have been of *maniculatus*, but many could not be identified with certainty. No adult *P. californicus* was recognized although a few young ones may have passed and been listed as *truei*. All passages of *Peromyscus* were at night.

Salamander.—The record includes passages by both *Ensatina escholtzii* and *Aneides lugubris*. They were recorded in October, November, March and April. By being nocturnal and by avoiding the dry season, they encountered in these autumn and spring months about the same microclimate as shrews, but were recorded neither in the winter months nor at temperatures below 39°. A third species, *Batrachoceps attenuatus*, was common in the study area but is so small that it could not be expected to actuate either of the recorders. One *Batrachoceps* electrocuted itself underneath the treadle but has not been included in the records.

Comparison of traps and recorders.—The combination of live-trapping and photographing revealed a failure of small mammals to move between runways only a few feet apart. On several occasions meadow mice and harvest mice were live-trapped a few feet from one of the recorders, were released at the same place, and were recaptured a week or more later not more than a few feet away, yet during the intervening time they failed to pass the recorder. Conversely, some individual mice repeatedly recorded themselves on the films yet could never be induced to enter any of a large number of live traps placed in the same runway and in nearby runways. It is obvious that all mice present do not use all of the active runways close to their home, and it is also obvious that neither the recorders nor traps give a complete accounting of the mice present.

SUMMARY

A motion-picture camera synchronized to an electronic flash unit was used to record the passage of animals along meadow-mouse runways and to record the temperature, relative humidity and time at which they passed. More than 26 species used the runways during 111 weeks of recording. Meadow mice, harvest mice, sparrows, brush rabbits and shrews passed most frequently. The average traffic per day in each runway was 11 passages; on some days there were more than 60 passages. Rarely more than ten meadow mice or six harvest mice used a runway in any one period. Meadow mice and harvest mice used the same runways simultaneously. Traffic by harvest mice alone did not keep the runways open.

Meadow mice were active during the day and night; harvest mice were strongly nocturnal. Brush rabbits were active primarily early in the morning. Almost all shrews were recorded at night and in the winter months. Consequently, they encountered the coldest, most humid conditions available to them. In contrast, the similarly small, insectivorous fence lizards encountered a microclimate that was 39° warmer and 36 per cent less humid. Neither traps nor recorders accounted for all the individuals living nearby.

Museum of Vertebrate Zoology, Berkeley, California. Received October 29, 1957.

INFLUENCE OF WATER BALANCE AND MICROCLIMATE ON THE LOCAL DISTRIBUTION OF THE REDBACK VOLE AND WHITE-FOOTED MOUSE

LOWELL L. GETZ

Department of Zoology, University of Connecticut, Storrs, Connecticut

(Accepted for publication June 20, 1967)

Abstract. A comparison was made of the importance of water balance, as influenced by microclimate, upon the local distribution of the white-footed mouse, *Peromyscus leucopus,* and the redback vole, *Clethrionomys gapperi.* The characteristic habitats of the two species in southern New England are dry upland woods and low swamps, respectively. Temperature and relative humidity in the habitats of the two species differed only from 0800 to 1600 on clear days; at other times they were the same. Daytime relative humidities averaged 75 to 85 and 70 to 80% in swamp and upland sites, respectively. There was no consistent difference in the absolute humidities between the swamp and upland at any season. Air temperatures during the summer were 2 to 3°C lower in the swamp than in the upland; during the winter they were the same in both. Water turn-over rate of *C. gapperi* is approximately 2.2 times that of *P. leucopus* (10.46 and 4.82 g/day, respectively). The difference results primarily from a more dilute urine from *C. gapperi;* the urine of *P. leucopus* is 2.2 times as concentrated as that of *C. gapperi.* Restriction of *C. gapperi* to low, wet areas in southern New England is correlated with the availability of standing water or an accessible water table, not with microclimate. Evaporative water losses of *C. gapperi* are significantly greater than those of *P. leucopus* at absolute humidities of 6.0–12.8 mg/l; they were essentially the same at 16.3 mg/l. *C. gapperi* is only slightly diurnal; living in the drier uplands would increase its water requirements by only 0.02 g/day. The low water requirement for kidney function of *P. leucopus* permits it to live in drier upland wooded situations where free water is normally restricted to that available in food (fruits and insects). *P. leucopus* is strictly nocturnal; microclimates in swamps and uplands are similar at these times and would not be a factor in the water balance or local distribution of this species.

INTRODUCTION

The correlation between water balance and habitats of small mammals has received considerable attention in recent years. Most of these studies have dealt with adaptations for extreme environments such as deserts. Only a few studies have also concerned species living in mesic situations (Chew 1951, Chenoweth 1917, Pruitt, 1953, 1959, Lindeborg 1952, Dice 1922, Getz 1963, 1965, Church 1966). Most of the latter suggest positive correlations between water balance and the moisture regime of the habitats of the species studied. Some further indicated a significant influence of microclimate upon the water balance of certain species (Getz 1963, Chew 1951, Pruitt 1953, 1959, Chenoweth 1917). Others (Getz 1965, Dice 1922) suggested local microclimate conditions were not sufficiently different to place enough of a stress on the water balance of a species to be a factor in its local distributional pattern.

Most of the above studies, however, were essentially laboratory measurements of water balance of the small mammals with only limited field measurements of water availability and microclimate conditions.

The redback vole, *Clethrionomys gapperi,* and the white-footed mouse, *Peromyscus leucopus,* lend themselves to a study of influence of water balance and microclimate on local distributions of small mammals. In general, *C. gapperi* is limited to relatively moist situations such as low, wet swamps; in some regions it may be found in more upland situations, but still appears to be more abundant in moist areas (Gunderson 1959, Manville 1949, Butsch 1954, Burt 1957). Although Odum (1944) and Getz (1962) indicated a high water turn-over rate for this species, the water balance of *C. gapperi* has not been extensively studied. *P. leucopus* is found in all types of wooded situations, but normally attains its highest population densities in drier upland woods (Burt 1957, Getz 1961). The available information concerning the water balance of the white-footed mouse indicates this species to be tolerant of relatively dry situations (Chew 1951, Lindeborg 1952).

A combined field-laboratory study was initiated to determine the influence of microclimate upon the water balance of *P. leucopus* and *C. gapperi* and the possible relationship of these two factors upon their local distributions. Only water balance studies are treated in detail in the present paper.

METHODS

Field Studies

Comparisons of local distributional patterns of *C. gapperi* and *P. leucopus* were made in central Connecticut and northern Vermont. Numerous snap-trap transects and a permanent live-trap study area were established in each region. The permanent study area in Connecticut, 3.5 km north of Storrs, Tolland County, included a dry upland hardwoods and a low mixed deciduous-coniferous swamp; each was typical of the optimum habitat of each species in southern New England. Subsequent publications will describe in detail all the sites included in the local distributional studies.

Microclimate.—Records of microclimate data were obtained in the Connecticut study area (from December 1962 through May 1967) from 16 continuously recording and 6 max-min stations. Four stations each in the swamp and upland contained Bristol Model 4069TH spring driven, thermohumidigraphs which simultaneously recorded temperature and relative humidity 20 cm above the surface. The other stations recorded temperatures 8 cm above the surface or 5 cm below the surface. In addition, spot checks and 2, 24-hr studies were made of temperatures and humidities with a thermistor psychrometer.

Spot checks of soil temperatures (7 cm below the surface) were obtained during various seasons of the year from 10 to 20 sites (5 readings at each site) in each area. A hypodermic thermistor probe connected to a Yellow Springs telethermometer was used.

Water Balance Studies

Except where otherwise indicated all experiments were conducted in constant temperature-humidity rooms at $15 \pm 1°C$ and $75 \pm 5\%$ RH. Animals were maintained in individual $10 \times 15 \times 10$ cm hardware cloth (0.6 cm mesh) cages provided with a food chute and an L-shaped drinking tube attached to an inverted plastic graduated cylinder. The experimental rooms were dark except when the animals were being checked (twice daily). Food consisted of "Old Fashion" rolled oats. All animals were maintained in the experimental conditions for at least a week prior to the start of recording data.

Wild captured and laboratory raised animals were used in the study. All experimental animals and laboratory stock, except the lab raised *C. gapperi*, were captured in the vicinity of Storrs, Tolland Co., Connecticut. The latter were captured in Alger Co., Michigan.

Water consumption

Ad libitum.—Basic consumption of distilled water was determined for 10-day periods. The influence of temperature and humidity on ad libitum consumption were also studied in a constant temperature cabinet at temperatures of 5, 20, and 30°C. During the temperature studies air humidity was maintained at saturation. Consumption was also recorded at humidities of 35, 55, 75, and 95% RH at 20°C. These represented absolute humidities of 6.0, 9.4, 12.8, and 16.3 mg/1. Humidities were maintained by use of supersaturated salt solutions (Winston and Bates 1960).

Minimum consumption.—Ad libitum consumption was first determined for a 10-day period. The quantity of water made available daily to each individual was then reduced in arbitrary steps (normally .02 g/g/day) at 4-day intervals until the animal was unable to maintain its weight after 4 days on a given water ration.

Water deprivation.—Individuals were maintained ad libitum and weighed daily for a 10-day period. Water then was withheld for 48 hr; the animals were weighed at 16, 24, 32, 40, and 48 hr.

Kidney function

Urine production.—Urine production of each individual was measured for 10 days by placing the experimental cages above aluminum foil pans containing 1 cm of mineral oil.

Tolerance to salt water.—The animals were given distilled water for 10 days and then given .10 M NaCl water for 5 days. Salinity was increased in steps of .05 M at 5-day intervals until the animals died. Water consumption was measured daily and weights of the animals recorded when the salinity of the water was changed. The salinities were changed at 10-day intervals in a second group.

Urine concentration.—Samples of urine were obtained daily from animals on ad libitum distilled water until at least 10 g were available from each animal. Samples were frozen as they were collected and kept frozen until tested. Specific gravity was determined by weighing known volumes to the nearest 0.1 mg on a chain balance. The urine samples were oven dried at 100°C for 2 days. The residue was weighed to give another estimate of urine concentration.

Urine samples were taken on the 4th and 5th day (on each molarity of salt water) from animals on the 5-day regime of increasing salinity of drinking water. Another group of samples was taken from *P. leucopus* on the 10-day regimes (8th and 9th days) at salinities of .40, .45, and .50 M.

Individuals of *P. leucopus* and *C. gapperi* were also force-fed water of .65 and .35 M NaCl, respectively (salinities indicated to be slightly above the maximum their kidneys could handle). The animals were deprived of water for 12 hr; 1.0 cc of salt water was then injected directly into the stomach through a small plastic tube attached to a hypodermic syringe at 2 to 4 hr intervals. Urine samples were collected from under mineral oil after each elimination; each sample was kept separate and frozen until tested.

Urine samples were tested for chloride ion concentration (mEq/1) by use of an Aminco-Cotlove chloride titrator with automatic read-out (Cotlove and Nishi 1961).

Fecal water losses

Water content of feces of each species was determined by oven-drying feces.

Evaporative water losses

Direct measurement.—Total (skin and respiratory) water losses were obtained by use of a Haldane open system (Brody 1945). The techniques used have been described previously (Getz 1963). The animal chamber was weighed on a chain balance to the nearest 1 mg both with and without the animal before and after each run. Evaporative losses were measured for 10 fasting individuals of each species at 15, 20, 25, and 30°C. Evaporation from the same 10 individuals was measured at all 4 temperatures. Evaporation was measured during 6-hr runs. All runs were conducted during the period of 0800–1800.

Indirect measurements.—Indirect measurement of water losses were obtained by measuring urine production and fecal water losses. These were subtracted from the total water intake, including consumption, metabolic water production, and free water in the food. The difference between the total water intake and the measured losses was assumed to have been lost via evaporation. Basic data were obtained under the standard conditions of 15°C and 75% RH. Evaporative losses of both species were also measured at absolute humidities of 6.0, 9.4, 12.8, and 16.3 mg/1 at 20°C (the same chamber and methods of controlling humidity were utilized as described above). In addition, evaporative losses of *C. gapperi* were measured at 5, 20, and 30° in a saturated humidity (see also above).

Calculations.—Evaporative losses were calculated in terms of cm^2 body surface area (Pearson 1947).

Oxygen Consumption

Oxygen consumption values were measured at temperatures of 1 to 30°C. A spirometer system modified from that described by Wiegert (1961) was used. The animals were fasted for 8 hr before the start of a run. There was a 1 hr acclimation period to each temperature before oxygen consumption was recorded. Oxygen consumption was measured at temperatures of approximately 1, 5, 10, 15, 20, 25, and 30°C. Repetitive (6 to 8) 1-min readings were taken at each temperature and general activity of the animal noted. Records for obviously active animals were discarded. Data were obtained from 6 adult, wild captured individuals (3 male, 3 female) of each species. Similar data from 1 individual of each species were also obtained during which time the animals had access to rolled oats. These were used to obtain estimates of metabolic water production (see below).

Statistical analysis

Small sample, nonparametric statistical tests were used to determine significances of differences. These included the Mann-Whitney U-test and Wilcoxon matched-pairs sign-ranked test (Siegel 1956).

RESULTS

Microclimate

Only averages of 5-day periods from 23 to 27 February 1964 and 25 to 29 July 1964 plus the spot-checks of soil temperatures are included here (Figs. 1–2; Table 1). Comparisons of the data with the remaining records indicate them to be representative of the general microclimate conditions of the habitats of the two species.

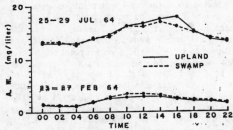

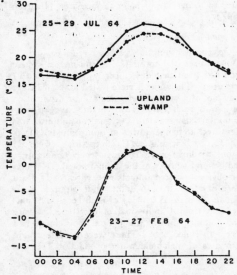

Fig. 1. Absolute humidities 20 cm above the surface in the Connecticut study area. Data represent 5-day averages during the indicated periods.

Fig. 2. Air temperatures 20 cm above the surface in the Connecticut study area. Data represent 5-day averages during the indicated periods.

Temperature and relative humidity in the habitats of the two species differed only from 0800 to 1600 on clear days. In the summer, daytime relative humidities averaged 75 to 85 and 70 to 80% in the swamp and upland sites, respectively. During the winter, relative humidities were slightly lower in both areas; the amount of difference between the two sites was of the same magnitude as during the summer, however. There was no consistent difference in the absolute humidities at any season. Daytime air temperatures during the summer were 2–3°C lower in the swamp than in the upland. Winter temperatures were similar in

both habitats during the day. On overcast days and at night during all seasons there was no significant difference in the microclimates of the habitats of the two species.

Soil temperatures of the swamp averaged approximately 1.0°C lower than those of the upland (Table 1).

WATER BALANCE STUDIES

Water consumption

Ad libitum.—Ad libitum water consumption (at 15°C and 75% RH) was 7.23 g/day (0.315 g/g/day) and 2.85 g/day (0.129 g/g/day) for *C. gapperi* and *P. leucopus* respectively (Table 2). Differences in consumption between *C. gapperi* from Michigan and Connecticut animals were not significant. Female *C. gapperi* consumed 2.07 g/day (0.121 g/g/day) more water than did the males.

Minimum consumption.—*P. leucopus* could

TABLE 1. Average soil temperatures (7 cm below surface) in the Connecticut study area. Five measurements each were taken at 10–20 stations in each area

Date	Time	Upland	Swamp	Difference
15 Oct 62	1430	8.5	7.0	1.5
14 Oct 63	1430	13.0	12.0	1.0
6 Jan 64	1430	2.0	1.0	1.0
4 Jun 65	1545	11.5	10.5	1.0
17 Aug 65	0645	17.5	18.5	1.0
17 Aug 65	1630	19.0	19.0	0
25 Aug 65	0900	15.5	14.0	1.5
25 Aug 65	1600	17.0	16.5	0.5
9 Sep 65	1450	15.5	14.5	1.0
26 Aug 66	1530	18.5	16.5	2.0

TABLE 2. Ad libitum water consumption of *Peromyscus leucopus* and *Clethrionomys gapperi* at 15°C and 75% RH. See text for source of experimental animals

Sex	Source of animals	N	g/day	g/g/day
P. leucopus				
Male	Wild capt	16	3.08	0.137
Male	Lab raised	33	2.85	0.125
Male	Average	49	2.92	0.129
Female	Wild capt	15	2.85	0.138
Female	Lab raised	25	2.70	0.125
Female	Average	40	2.76	0.130
	Average	89	2.85*	0.129**
C. gapperi				
Male	Wild capt	22	6.92	0.297
Male	Lab raised	18	5.63	0.221
Male	Average	40	6.34***	0.263****
Female	Wild capt	17	8.38	0.386
Female	Lab raised	13	8.45	0.381
Female	Average	30	8.41***	0.384****
	Average	70	7.23*	0.315**

Asterisk-pairs represent differences significant at least at the .01 level.

18

N	Ad libitum		Minimum		% of ad libitum	
	g/day	g/g/day	g/day	g/g/day	g/day	g/g/day
P. leucopus 18..................	2.6 (1.2–4.3)	0.118 (0.06–0.22)	0.65 (0.5–1.4)	0.025 (0.02–0.06)	25.0	21.1
C. gapperi 12..................	6.5 (3.4–10.8)	0.248 (0.12–0.40)	4.30 (1.1–7.5)	0.169 (0.06–0.30)	66.1	68.1
Difference........................	3.9ᵃ	0.130ᵃ	3.65ᵃ	0.144ᵃ	41.1ᵃ	47.0ᵃ

ᵃSignificant at 0.1 level.

maintain body weight for at least 4 days on approximately 0.025 g/g/day; this represented a daily ration of 0.65 g (Table 3). The minimum water ration on which *C. gapperi* could maintain its body weight for 4 days was 0.248 g/g/day (6.5 g/day). Differences between total absolute amounts of water consumed by the two species when on ad libitum as compared to minimum consumption requirements are not significantly different. Minimum requirements of female *C. gapperi* were slightly higher than those of males (0.21 and 0.15 g/g/day, respectively; the difference was significant at the .05 level).

Water deprivation.—After 48 hr without water, surviving *C. gapperi* had lost an average of 24.8% (18.7–32.3) of their original body weight. *P. leu-*

copus losses averaged only 15.3% (6.8–20.6) (Fig. 3). The differences in losses between the two species were significantly greater (< .01 level) at each 8-hr period. None of the 19 *P. leucopus* died during the water deprivation or recovery periods. Three of the 13 *C. gapperi* died during the deprivation period (2 at 32 hr, and 1 at 40 hr); an additional 4 died within 2 days after being given access to water.

Influence of humidity upon water consumption.—There was not significant correlation between water consumption and humidity in *C. gapperi* or *P. leucopus*.

Influence of temperature on water consumption.—Water consumption of both species was only slightly less at 30°C than at 5°C. The differences represented 0.3 and 0.9 g/day increases in water requirements for *P. leucopus* and *C. gapperi* respectively at 5° as compared to 30°C.

Kidney function

Urine production.—Urine production when on ad libitum water consumption was 6.71 g/day (0.325 g/g/day) and 1.96 g/day (0.084 g/g/day) in *C. gapperi* and *P. leucopus*, respectively (Table 4).

Urine production was less at absolute humidities of 6.0 and 9.4 than at 12.8 and 16.3 mg/1 (Table 5). This may be a reflection of lesser evaporative water losses at the higher humidities. Comparison of the differences in urine production indicates less difference between the two species at 6.0 mg/1 than at the other humidities.

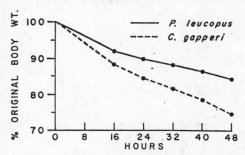

FIG. 3. Rates of weight loss of *Peromyscus leucopus* and *Clethrionomys gapperi* when deprived of water for 48 hr. Averages for 19 and 13 individuals each, respectively.

TABLE 4. Urine production and concentration when on ad libitum water consumption (15°C, 75% RH)

Species	N	Urine production		Concentration	
		g/day	g/g/day	Specific gravityᵃ	Residue (g/g/urine)
P. leucopus.....................	14	1.96 (0.75–4.65)	0.084 (0.038–0.198)	1.0596 (1.0505–1.0729)	0.1661 (0.1250–0.2128)
C. gapperi.....................	17	6.71 (2.85–17.73)	0.325 (0.127–0.980)	1.0200 (1.0057–1.0450)	0.0722 (0.0343–0.1164)
Difference.....................		4.75ᵇ	0.241ᵇ	0.0396ᵇ	0.0939ᵇ

ᵃSpecific gravity distilled water=0.9865.
ᵇSignificant at .01 level.

TABLE 5. Influence of absolute humidity on urine production (20°C)

Species	N	6.0 mg/1 AH		9.4 mg/1 AH		12.8 mg/1 AH		16.3 mg/1 AH	
		g/day	g/g/day	g/day	g/g/day	g/day	g/g/day	g/day	g/g/day
C. gapperi	7	6.30 (2.21-14.61)	0.294 (.092-.680)	7.84 (2.85-19.06)	0.369 (.097-.829)	9.32 (2.69-16.08)	0.483 (.094-.869)	8.37 (3.59-16.18)	0.431 (.130-.981)
P. leucopus	4	0.79 (.61-.90)	0.039 (.023-.053)	1.05 (.28-1.49)	0.054 (.014-.088)	1.54 (1.13-2.08)	0.079 (.058-.111)	1.33 (1.10-1.55)	0.068 (.049-.094)
Difference		5.51	0.255	6.79	0.315	7.78	0.404	7.04	0.363

No difference in urine production was observed in *C. gapperi* at temperatures of 5, 20, and 30°C. Comparable data are not available for *P. leucopus*.

Tolerance to salt water.—*P. leucopus* was able to survive on much higher salinities than was *C. gapperi* (Figs. 4 and 5). None of the *P. leucopus* had died before all individuals of *C. gapperi* were dead; approximately half the *P. leucopus* survived to .45 M.

Concentrating power of the kidneys.—The specific gravity and residue of the urine of the two species while on ad libitum water consumption indicated the urine of *P. leucopus* to be approximately 2.2–2.3 times as concentrated as that of *C. gapperi* (Table 4).

A close correlation between the Cl⁻ content of the drinking water and urine was observed in both species (Fig. 6). These data indicate *C. gapperi* to be able to produce a maximum Cl⁻ concentration of 240 mEq/1 and *P. leucopus* 570 mEq/1. When force-fed water of a salinity obviously higher than the kidneys could handle (.65 and .35 M NaCl, *P. leucopus* and *C. gapperi*, respectively), the maximum Cl⁻ concentration of the urine was approximately the same as when on ad libitum with increasing salinities. Maximum Cl⁻ concentrations obtained were 565 (454–660) and 274 (198–310) mEq/1 for *P. leucopus* and *C. gapperi*, respectively.

Water consumption on the various salinities was measured to obtain a better estimate of the maximum salinities tolerated. Consumption of *P. leu-*

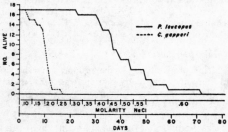

FIG. 4. Survival times of *Peromyscus leucopus* and *Clethrionomys gapperi* when maintained on increasing salinity salt water. Salinities were increased in steps of .05 M at 5-day intervals.

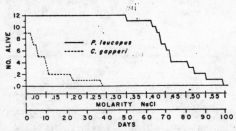

FIG. 5. Survival times of *Peromyscus leucopus* and *Clethrionomys gapperi* when maintained on increasing salinity salt water. Salinities were increased in steps of .05 M at 10-day intervals.

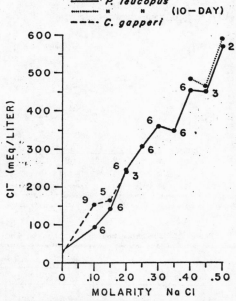

FIG. 6. Relationship between Cl⁻ concentration of urine and salinity of drinking water; 5-day interval between salinity changes of drinking water except as noted. Numbers represent number of individuals in each sample; *P. leucopus* 10-day interval group, 6 individuals at each salinity.

TABLE 6. Summary of water balance of *Peromyscus leucopus* and *Clethrionomys gapperi* when maintained on a diet of rolled oats (15°C and 75% RH)

	P. leucopus			*C. gapperi*		
	g/day	g/g/day	%	g/day	g/g/day	%
Intake						
Consumption....................	3.12	.135	64.7	8.36	.368	79.9
In Food.........................	.50	.020	10.4	.60	.026	5.7
Metabolic.......................	1.20	.051	24.9	1.50	.066	14.4
Total.....................	4.82	.206		10.46	.460	
Loss						
Urine..........................	1.45	.062	30.1	6.90	.304	66.0
Feces..........................	.54	.024	11.2	.53	.023	5.1
Evaporation....................	2.83	.120	58.7	3.03	.133	28.9
Total.....................	4.82	.206		10.46	.460	

copus only gradually increased (if at all) at each salinity up through .35 M. When placed on .40 M, consumption increased markedly. This indicates most individuals were able to obtain sufficient water from salinities up through .35 M. The consumption of *C. gapperi* increased rapidly on each higher salinity; it was not possible to determine the point of maximum increase in consumption.

Fecal water losses

The water content of the feces of *P. leucopus* averaged 43.8%; that of *C. gapperi* was 49.0%. Fecal water loss of the two species was almost identical and constituted a small percentage of their total daily water loss (Table 6).

Evaporative water losses

Direct measurement

Total evaporative water losses were significantly greater from *C. gapperi* at temperatures of 15, 20, and 30°C (Table 7). Losses were the same in both species at 25°C. The maximum difference recorded between the 2 species was 0.8 g/day (at 15°C). There was only a slight indication of correlation between evaporation and temperature in either species. The only differences which were statistically significant were the losses at 20 and 30°C. *C. gapperi* lost 0.5 g/day more water at

TABLE 8. Evaporative water losses of *Peromyscus leucopus* and *Clethrionomys gapperi* at 15°C and 75% RH as determined by indirect measurements. See text for methods

Species	N	g/day	g/cm²/day
P. leucopus........	14	2.86 (1.33–3.96)	0.0422 (0.0160–0.0605)
C. gapperi..........	17	3.54 (2.54–5.62)	0.0661 (0.0354–0.0911)
Difference.:........		0.68[a]	0.0239[b]

[a]Significant at .05 level.
[b]Significant at .01 level.

30°C than at 20°C; *P. leucopus* evaporated approximately 0.7 g/day more water at 30° than at 20°C.

Indirect measurement

Indirect measurements of evaporative water losses at 15°C and 75% RH also indicated *C. gapperi* to have significantly higher evaporative rates than *P. leucopus* (Table 8). The difference between the two species was essentially the same as recorded at 15°C in the direct measurement experiments. The absolute amounts were greater than those obtained in the drier air in the Haldane system, however. The difference is essentially the same in both species (0.0130 and 0.0193 g/cm²/ day). The most probable reason for such a dif-

TABLE 7. Relationship between temperature (°C) and evaporative water losses of *Peromyscus leucopus* and *Clethrionomys gapperi* as determined from direct measurements in a Haldane open system

	N	g/day				g/cm²/day			
		15°	20°	25°	30°	15°	20°	25°	30°
gapperi..........................	10	2.6	2.3	2.6	2.8	0.046	0.041[a]	0.045	0.048[a]
leucopus........................	10	1.8	1.8	2.5	2.5	0.029	0.028[b]	0.038	0.038[b]
ifference........................		0.8	0.5	0.1	0.3	0.017[a]	0.013[a]	0.007	0.010[b]

[a]Significant at .01 level.
[b]Significant at .05 level.

TBLE 9. Influence of absolute humidity on evaporative water losses of *Peromyscus leucopus* and *Clethrionomys gapperi*. (Indirect measurement; 20°C) See text for methods

Species	N	6.0 mg/l		9.4 mg/l		12.8 mg/ 1		16.3 mg/l	
		g/day	g/cm²/day	g/day	g/cm²/day	g/day	g/cm²/day	g/day	g/cm²/day
gapperi	7	3.33	0.060^b (0.050–0.105)	2.90	0.053 (0.027–0.084)	2.32	0.045 (0.023–0.073)	1.54	0.028^b (0.017–0.066)
leucopus	4	2.55	0.040 (0.045–0.050)	2.26	0.036 (0.036–0.054)	1.76	0.028 (0.021–0.052)	1.59	0.025 (0.018–0.034)
Ference		0.78	0.020ª	0.64	0.017	0.56	0.017	0.05	0.003

ªSignificant at .01 level.
Difference significant at .01 level.

ence relates to the amount of activity during trials. The animals would be less active dur; the short direct measurement runs (which re made during their normal periods of inivity; see below) than during the 10-day inect measurement runs. The direct measurents are therefore more indicative of basal rates evaporation.

nfluence of humidity on evaporation.—*C. gapi* had higher evaporative water losses than did *leucopus* at absolute humidities of 6.0, 9.4, and 8 mg/l; at 16.3 mg/l they were essentially the ne (Table 9). The rate of loss in *C. gapperi* reased more rapidly at the lower humidities n it did in *P. leucopus*. At 6.0 mg/l the total erence in evaporation between the two species s approximately 0.8 g/day.

nfluence of temperature on evaporation.—Inct measurements of water losses at 5, 20, and C (in a saturated humidity) were determined y for *C. gapperi*. These data also indicated a ht difference in evaporative losses between 20 30°C (.060 g/cm²/day more at 30° than at C).

Metabolic water production

Ietabolic water production was calculated from es giving grams of water formed per gram of l consumed and grams of water formed per of oxygen consumed when on a given diet iew 1965). Consumption (less fecal losses) of ed oats was measured at 15°C for both species. manufacturer's listing of carbohydrate, fat, protein composition was used to estimate abolic water production when on a rolled oat

Oxygen consumption data at 15°C when the nals were feeding on rolled oats were also used btain an estimate of metabolic water produc

Metabolic water production, when feeding rolled oats, accounted for approximately 14 25% of the total water requirements of *C. beri* and *P. leucopus*, respectively (Table 6).

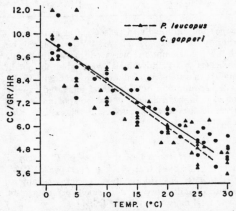

FIG. 7. Relationship between oxygen consumption of *Peromyscus leucopus* and *Clethrionomys gapperi* and ambient temperature. Each point represents an average of 6–8, 1-min measurements of consumption of a given individual at that ambient temperature.

Oxygen Consumption

Oxygen consumption between temperatures of 1–30°C was similar in the two species (Fig. 7). The slightly lower temperatures in the swamp would therefore not result in a significant difference in the metabolic activities between the two species. Both would respond similarly physiologically to the temperature differences in the two' habitats. Influence of temperature on energy requirements and respiratory water losses would therefore be similar in the two species. Based on this limited data, temperature differences in swamps and uplands do not appear to be major factors in the water balance differences of *C. gapperi* and *P. leucopus*.

DISCUSSION

The similarity in the water requirements of the individuals of *C. gapperi* from Michigan and Con necticut indicate the data may be somewhat representative of the species over much of its range. The water requirements of *P. leucopus* also agree favorably with published reports of this species in Illinois and Michigan (Chew 1951, Lindeborg 1952). The conclusions made in this study concerning water requirements therefore pertain more or less to the species in general and are not necessarily restricted to the Connecticut populations.

The primary difference in the water balance of the two species is the greater production of and a less concentrated urine by *C. gapperi* than by *P. leucopus*. This is indicative of a more efficient kidney in *P. leucopus*. *C. gapperi* must consume approximately 4.75 g/day more water than does *P. leucopus* to make up for the difference in kidney requirements.

In addition, the evaporative water losses at lower humidities are greater from *C. gapperi* than from *P. leucopus*. The magnitude of this difference is significant only when based on continuous exposure to given conditions, however. A study of the activity pattern of *C. gapperi* (Getz In Press) indicates this species is essentially nocturnal and displays only a small amount of diurnal activity. There is no significant difference in the microclimate of the swamp and upland area during the night.

Calculations were made of the differences in the potential evaporative water losses between an individual *C. gapperi* living in an upland situation and one living in a swamp. This took into account both the activity pattern and the microclimate of the two situations (Fig. 1–2). On a clear day (which occurs approximately 67% of the time in the vicinity of Storrs, Connecticut; USDA, 1941) there would be only 0.02 g/day more water lost by the individual in the upland than by one living in the swamp.

Microclimate is therefore not a significant factor restricting *C. gapperi* to swamps in southern New England. This species must live in a situation where sufficient water is available either as free water or in succulent food items to accommodate kidney requirements. Free water could consist of standing water, rain (adhering to plants or on the leaf litter), snow, or dew. Field observations eliminated the latter three as important factors. Standing water in depressions and under wind-thrown trees was present in the swamp most of the year, except for the driest parts of the summer. Even at these times, the water table was within 50 cm of the surface. Cavities formed by roots of trees shifting during high winds create tunnels in the substrate which would permit the voles to make their way down to the water table and obtain drinking water throughout the year.

There was no indication that any of the surface vegetation was being utilized even during the periods of peak population densities. It seems most likely that in the present study area the voles were feeding on some type of subterranean food. Whittaker (1962) has indicated *C. gapperi* in New York feeds significantly on the soil fungus *Endogone*.

Studies of usefulness of *Endogone* as a source of water for *C. gapperi* are not available. Utilization of mushrooms as a source of water was observed, however, to see if fungi in general could satisfy the water requirements of *C. gapperi*. Four individuals were maintained on fresh mushrooms as a sole source of water for 14 days without losing weight. If succulent soil fungi such as *Endogone* are readily available, it could serve as a water source in upland habitats.

P. leucopus is strictly nocturnal in habits (Johnson 1926, Bruce 1960, Beheny 1936), it is therefore exposed to essentially the same microclimate conditions regardless of where it is living, swamp or uplands (Figs. 1–2).

Although the water requirements of *P. leucopus* are not great, individuals must obtain approximately 3.12 g/day in addition to metabolic water. Free water is unavailable in the upland areas for extensive periods of time. This means *P. leucopus* must rely primarily on the water in its food. During the late summer and early fall, berries and other succulent fruit are relatively abundant and would afford a sufficient water supply.

During the fall and winter, acorns make up a substantial portion of the food of *P. leucopus* (Hamilton 1939, 1943; field observations during the current study). A study was made to see if *P. leucopus* could maintain body weight using acorns as a source of water. The 6 animals tested slowly lost weight (0.3 g/day) throughout the 14 days they were on experiment. In addition, acorns slowly dehydrate when cached; an experimental group of field-cached acorns lost 50% of their water between October and March. Acorns cached by mice would therefore significantly decrease in their importance as a water source during the winter.

During times when there is no free water available in the form of snow or rain *P. leucopus* must rely on succulent food of some type, however, to obtain the required water. The most likely source of such water is underground roots and tubers or insects. Larvae and adults of the latter are consumed in significant numbers by *P. leucopus* (Hamilton 1939, 1943) and could easily be a significant component of its water supply.

Kidney efficiency therefore appears to be an important factor in the local distribution of *P. leu-*

copus and *C. gapperi*. Although *P. leucopus* is able to live both in lowland and uplands, its low water requirements resulting from an apparently efficient kidney permit it to attain high population densities in the drier uplands. Microclimate or water balance do not appear to be factors in the lower population densities of *P. leucopus* in swamps. I have previously suggested (1961) that food availability is a factor. The field aspects of this study support this conclusion.

It is possible that interspecific aggressiveness could also be a factor in the lower population densities of *P. leucopus* in swamps. If *C. gapperi* were dominant over *P. leucopus,* the latter could be excluded from situations which are suitable for *C. gapperi.* Calhoun (1963) summarized potential social dominance between the two species. In general *P. leucopus* appears to be subordinate to *C. gapperi,* but in some regions *C. gapperi* is either slightly subordinate to *P. leucopus* or there is no evident dominant-subordinate relationship. Even in those regions where one species was dominant over the other, the two species were still sympatric, however. He assumed a territorial type avoidance to be operating, not exclusion of the subordinate species from a given habitat.

In addition, *P. leucopus* population densities may also be low in swampy situations in regions in which *C. gapperi* does not occur (Getz 1961).

Preliminary observations of the social interactions between these two species indicated no definite dominance of either species (unpublished data). During encounters between individuals of the two species there was an obvious avoidance of each other, but nothing that would indicate dominance. Based on the available evidence interspecific competition does not therefore appear to be a factor in the lower population densities of *P. leucopus* in swamps.

ACKNOWLEDGMENTS

Thanks are extended to Donald H. Miller, Jerry J. Franz, Harold Kipperman, Ronnie Elkins, Judith L. Holland, Dana Thorne, Melinda A. Novak, and Kathy Gambling for assisting in the experimental and microclimate work. I also wish to thank Dr. Alan H. Brush for offering valuable suggestions concerning the manuscript. The work was sponsored in part by NSF G 22553 and GB 2242 and by the University of Connecticut Research Foundation.

LITERATURE CITED

Beheny, W. H. 1936. Nocturnal explorations of the forest deer-mouse. J. Mammal. **17**: 225–230.

Brody, S. 1945. Bioenergetics and growth. Reinhold. New York. 1023 p.

Bruce, V. G. 1960. Environmental entrainment of circadian rhythms. Cold Spring Harbor Symp. Quant. Biol. **25**: 29–48.

Burt, W. H. 1957. Mammals of the Great Lakes Region. Univ. Mich. Press. Ann Arbor. 246 p.

Butsch, R. S. 1954. The life history and ecology of the red-backed vole, *Clethrionomys gapperi gapperi* Vigors, in Minnesota. Unpubl. Ph.D. thesis. Univ. Mich.

Calhoun, J. B. 1963. The social use of space, p. 1–187. In W. V. Mayer and R. G. Van Gelder [eds.] Physiological Mammalogy. Academic Press. New York.

Chenoweth, H. E. 1917. The reactions of certain moist forest animals to air conditions and its bearing on problems of mammalian distributions. Biol. Bull. **32**: 183–201.

Chew, R. M. 1951. The water exchanges of some small mammals. Ecol. Monogr. **21**: 215–225.

——. 1965. Water metabolism of mammals, p. 43–178. In W. V. Mayer and R. G. Van Gelder [eds.] Physiological Mammalogy. Academic Press. New York.

Church, R. L. 1966. Water exchanges of the California vole, *Microtus californicus*. Physiol. Zool. **39**: 326–340.

Cotlove, E., and H. H. Nishi. 1961. Automatic titration with direct read-out of chloride concentration. Clinical Chem. **7**: 285–291.

Dice, L. R. 1922. Some factors affecting the distribution of the prairie vole, forest deer mouse and prairie deer mouse. Ecology **3**: 29–47.

Getz, L. L. 1961. Notes on the local distribution of *Peromyscus leucopus* and *Zapus hudsonius*. Amer. Midl. Nat. **65**: 486–500.

——. 1962. Notes on the water balance of the redback vole. Ecology **43**: 565–566.

——. 1963. A comparison of the water balance of the prairie and meadow voles. Ecology **44**: 202–207.

——. 1965. Humidities in vole runways. Ecology **46**: 548–551.

——. In press. Influence of light on the activity of the redback vole. Univ. Conn. Occ. Paps. (Biol. Ser).

Gunderson, H. L. 1959. Red-backed vole habitat studies in central Minnesota. J. Mammal. **40**: 405–412.

Hamilton, W. J., Jr. 1939. American mammals. McGraw-Hill. New York. 434 p.

——. 1943. The mammals of eastern United States. Comstock Publ. Co. Ithaca. 432 p.

Johnson, M. S. 1926. Activity and distribution of certain wild mice in relation to biotic communities. J. Mammal. **7**: 245–277.

Lindeborg, R. G. 1952. Water requirements of certain rodents from xeric and mesic habitats. Contr. Lab. Vert. Biol., Univ. Mich. **58**: 1–32.

Manville, R. H. 1949. A study of small mammal populations in northern Michigan. Misc. Publ. Mus. Zool., Univ. Mich. **73**: 1–83.

Odum, E. P. 1944. Water consumption of certain mice in relation to habitat selection. J. Mammal. **25**: 404–405.

Pearson, O. P. 1947. The rate of metabolism of some small mammals. Ecology **28**: 127–145.

Pruitt, W. O. 1953. An analysis of some physical factors affecting the local distribution of the short-tail shrew (*Blarina brevicauda*) in the northern part of the Lower Peninsula of Michigan. Misc. Publ. Mus. Zool., Univ. Mich. **79**: 1–39.

————. 1959. Microclimates and local distribution of small mammals on the George Reserve, Michigan. Misc. Publ. Mus. Zool., Univ. Mich. 109: 1–27.

Siegel, S. 1956. Nonparametric statistics for the behavioral sciences. McGraw-Hill. New York. 312 p.

USDA. 1941. Climate and man (USDA Yearbook). Govt. Printing Office. Washington, D. C. 1248 p.

Whittaker, J. O., Jr. 1962. *Endogone, Hymenogaster,* and *Melanogaster* as small mammal foods. Amer. Midl. Nat. 67: 152–156.

Wiegert, R. G. 1961. Respiratory energy loss and activity patterns of the meadow vole, *Microtus pennsylvanicus pennsylvanicus.* Ecology 42: 245–253.

Winston, R. W., and D. H. Bates. 1960. Saturated solutions for the control of humidity in biological research. Ecology 41: 232–237.

25

THE FEEDING EFFICIENCY OF INSECTIVOROUS BATS

By Edwin Gould

Griffin (1953) has recently suggested that insectivorous bats use their high frequency sounds not only for avoiding stationary obstacles but also for locating and capturing flying insects. Evaluation of this hypothesis requires accurate information about the sizes and sound reflecting properties of bats' insect prey, and this paper will assemble the pertinent data that I have been able to obtain both from previous papers and from the analysis of many digestive tracts of bats collected for this purpose. In addition to the types of insects captured the rate at which they are taken was measured whenever possible in order to judge whether a process of selective pursuit and capture is involved, or whether a random process akin to "filter feeding" could account for the efficiency actually attained. It would also be desirable to know the distances at which flying insects are detected; but to date no satisfactory methods have been developed for obtaining more than the rough estimate of this quantity included below for the red bat, *Lasiurus borealis.*

I wish to acknowledge my gratitude for advice received from the following entomologists, who identified many of the insect remains from bat stomachs; Asher Treat, John G. Franclemont, Howard Ensign Evans, W. T. M. Forbes, Clifford O. Berg, George Ball, Benjamin Henson, and Charles Wyttenbach.

JOURNAL OF MAMMALOGY, 1955, Vol. 36, pp. 399-407

26

Encouragement and helpful criticism were also provided by Donald R. Griffin. This work was supported financially by contracts between the Office of Naval Research and Cornell University (Zoology Department) and Harvard University (Biological Laboratories).

Data from previous work.—While many studies of bats' feeding habits have been reported, the results are often useless for the present purpose either because the insects could be identified only to order or family, leaving a considerable range of uncertainty as to their actual sizes, or because the identity of the bat itself was in doubt. The most extensive list of insects captured by known species of bats has been assembled by Poulton (1929) who includes many scattered observations reported by others. These records and most others do not give the insect sizes directly, but in such cases typical figures for the species in question have been obtained from Hampson's, CATALOGUE OF THE LEPIDOPTERA PHALAENAE IN THE BRITISH MUSEUM, or other standard entomological references.

The European long-eared bat (*Plecotus auritus*) provided most of the data summarized by Poulton; but this species can not be considered typical of the family Vespertilionidae, for it not only catches moths on the wing but also picks insects off the foliage of trees and bushes. Poulton (*loc. cit.*), Buckhurst (1930), Manwaring (1938), and Nicholson (1937) list 431 individual moths and butterflies of 22 species taken by *Plecotus*. The smallest of these was *Maniola tithonus* with a wingspread of about 30 mm., and the largest was *Vanessa atalanta* with a wingspread of 67 mm. The most common moths in these lists were *Mamestra brassicae*, *Caradrina cubicularis* and *Amphipyra tragopoginis*, with wingspreads of 46, 33, and 38 mm. respectively. Others of similar size were also numerous. The average wingspread of the moths taken by *Plecotus* can be estimated as about 45 mm. from the records presented by these four writers. Most of this data, however, was obtained from moth wings found beneath *Plecotus* roosts; many smaller insects may also be taken and these would not be represented in this compilation.

The noctule (*Nyctalus noctula*), one of the larger European bats, frequently takes beetles of approximately 20 mm. body length. Ryberg (1947) identified *Rhizotrogus solstitialis* and *Melolontha vulgaris* from this bat, while Poulton (*loc. cit.*) lists *M. vulgaris* and *Geotrupes stercorarius*. Eisentraut (1950) states that this species together with *Eptesicus serotinus*, *Myotis myotis* and *Rhinolophus ferrum-equinum* prefer relatively large insects. The closely related but smaller *Nyctalus leisleri* feeds at least to some extent, according to Poulton, on the dung fly, *Scatophaga stercoraria*, with a wingspread of 23 mm. The smaller European bats of the family Vespertilionidae are stated by Eisentraut to prefer Diptera and the smaller Lepidoptera.

The European horseshoe bats of the genus *Rhinolophus* belong to a different family from those mentioned above, and Moehres (1953) has recently shown that these bats use somewhat different types of high frequency sound for orientation, sounds characterized by higher and constant frequencies, longer pulse duration, and more directional emission. Poulton (*loc. cit.*) reports that the greater horseshoe bat (*R. ferrum-equinum*) was found to feed on at least two species of beetles, *Geotrupes spininger* and *Melolontha vulgaris*, 20 and 24 mm.

27

in body length respectively. Eisentraut (*loc. cit.*) states that the lesser horseshoe bat, *R. hipposideros,* like the smaller European Verspertilionidae, select Diptera and the smaller Lepidoptera.

Concerning American bats only a few records provide useful indications of the sizes of insects commonly taken on the wing. Huey (1925) found the remains of nine sphinx moths, averaging 77 mm. wingspread, beneath a roost of the California leaf-nosed bat, *Macrotus californicus* (Phyllostomidae). Poole (1932) mentions finding a small mosquito and a stink bug (*Nezara,* length probably about 16 mm.) in the stomach of a hoary bat, *Lasiurus cinereus* (Vespertilionidae). From the mouth of a Seminole bat (*Lasiurus seminolus*) shot while feeding, Harper (1927) recovered a green fly (*Chlorotabanus crepuscularis,* body length about 14 mm. (Stone, 1938). Orr (1954) lists several insects taken by *Antrozous pallidus,* but this species is known to catch Jerusalem crickets and probably other insects on the ground and it is not possible to determine which of the species listed by Orr were caught on the wing.

Insects taken from bats collected to study feeding efficiency.—During 1953 and 1954 many bats were collected by shooting, by means of trammel nets, or by collecting at roosts shortly after they had returned from feeding. In each case the weight of the bat and its stomach were recorded, together with the elapsed time since the first emergence of the species from its roost (usually observed on the same night, otherwise within a day or two). This time will be called for convenience the "feeding period," although it is of course a maximum time available for feeding, since at many roosts 20 to 30 minutes elapse between the appearance of the first and last bats. Also, the passage of food from stomach to the intestine has been neglected, so that the rates of food accumulation listed below are minima. The *Pipistrellus* and *Lasiurus* were not observed at their roosts, but their time of emergence is unlikely to have differed substantially from the other species. On several evenings insects were also trapped to aid in identifying the insect remains from the bat stomachs. Most of the bats were collected near Mashpee, Massachusetts, but some of the records were obtained near Concord, Provincetown, or Tyringham, Massachusetts; Ithaca, New York; and the Okefenokee Swamp, Georgia. Several bats were collected at the roosts before their evening flights commenced and all had completely empty stomachs.

Since bats are known to fill their stomachs under favorable conditions within a quarter to a half hour after their emergence from the roost (Poulton, 1929; Hamilton, 1930) particular attention was paid to the first few minutes of the feeding period. While the bulk of a bat's stomach contents consists of food too finely chewed for identification, the weight of stomach contents accumulated per unit time gives an indication of the bulk rate of insect capture, while the occasional identifiable fragment indicates at least some of the types of insect taken. Since identification is more likely when the insect is large or has hard parts in its exoskeleton, a list of types identified gives a biased impression of the actual food since the small soft-bodied insects will be much less likely to be recognized. Despite these limitations the results of this collecting program indicate limits to the range of sizes and numbers of insects captured by the species of bats studied.

Myotis lucifugus, the common little brown bat, provided the bulk of the data;

out of 68 of these bats collected, 33 stomachs contained fragments that could be identified as belonging to the orders Coleoptera, Trichoptera, Lepidoptera, Hymenoptera, and Diptera. The identified beetles (Elateridae) ranged from 5 to 8 mm. body length and 10 to 12 mm. wingspread. An ichneumonid, *Cremastus* sp., had a body length of 8 mm. and a wingspread of 11 mm. Among the Chironomidae one *Chironomus* sp. was recovered with a 7 mm. wingspread and a body length of 8 mm. The smallest insect identified (*Metriocnemus mitis*, wingspread 3 mm., weight 0.2 mg.) was taken from the mouth of a *Myotis lucifugus* shot while feeding on the wing. Four of these bats were taken with reasonably full stomachs after 45 to 95 minutes feeding time, the stomach contents weighing 0.9 to 1.15 grams. Since the body weights of these four bats ranged from 5.5 to 8.2 grams, and since the maximum weight of stomach contents recorded from this species was 1.7 grams, their success at catching flying insects was impressive.

During August, 1953, bats were studied at Tyringham, Massachusetts, where they had become accustomed to hunt moths attracted by a light set up by Dr. Asher Treat; while not positively identified these were probably *Myotis lucifugus*, *Lasiurus borealis*, or both. On one occasion the wings of a moth of the family Pyralidae were dropped by a feeding bat; the wingspread of this moth was about 19 mm. and its body length about 10 mm. Another evening a noctuid moth, *Leucamia pseudargyria*, with a wingspread of 41 mm. was pursued by a bat up to a brightly lighted porch screen. Dr. Treat has since written that these bats "will and habitually do attack moths as large as *Crymodes devastator*" (body length about 30 mm., wingspread about 60 mm.).

On Sept. 2, 1953, a silver haired bat, *Lasionycteris noctivagans*, was shot while feeding over the sand dunes at Provincetown, Massachusetts, and from its mouth was recovered the remains of a stable fly, *Stomoxys calcitrans* (body length 7 mm., wing spread 14 mm.).

Twelve big brown bats (*Eptesicus fuscus*) were taken at Concord, Mass., from July 10 to August 7, 1954, after 25 to 112 minutes feeding time. Their weights ranged from 8.3 to 19 grams and all but one were young of the year. One had an empty stomach after 28 minutes, but another had captured 1.4 grams of insects after a feeding time of 33 minutes. The average rate of accumulation of insects, excluding the bat with an empty stomach, was 1.2 grams per hour; and the single adult *Eptesicus* had accumulated food at the average rate of 2.7 grams per hour. One banded big brown bat, released at dusk, was shot exactly 25 minutes later, during which time it had accumulated 0.5 grams of insects.

Most impressive of all were two *Pipistrellus subflavus* collected at Mashpee, Massachusetts, on August 4 and 5, 1953. These bats weighed 5.3 and 6.7 grams, and they had accumulated 1.4 grams and 1.7 grams respectively in 30 minutes of feeding time.

In late August, 1954, several red bats (*Lasiurus borealis*) were observed in the bright lights of a miniature golf course at Falmouth, Massachusetts, feeding actively on moths, beetles and other insects attracted to the lights. These bats did not appear in numbers at the lights until about an hour after dark; their first feeding period was evidently spent elsewhere. On some nights six to ten could be

29

seen at one time within a few feet of each other; sometimes two to four bats would apparently pursue the same insect. On three occasions bats flying relatively straight changed their course suddenly to dart towards and capture a moth estimated to be five or six feet to the right or left of the point where the bat began its sudden turn. Unsuccessful passes at flying moths were frequently observed; sometimes three or four successive attempts would be made. Once two bats made consecutive but unsuccessful attempts to catch a particular moth; only to have a third bat seize the prey. Twice it seemed clear that when one bat actively pursued a moth two others approached from several yards distance and joined in the chase. The high frequency sounds of these red bats followed a pattern generally similar to that described for feeding *Eptesicus* by Griffin (1953). This characteristic sound pattern of a feeding bat may have served to attract the others. The most abundant insect present was the adult of the army worm, *Pseudaletia unipuncta*; and the fact that the bats were feeding on this species was confirmed by a hind wing dropped by a bat while feeding. The average wingspread of several of these moths was 46 mm.

One 8.6 gram Seminole bat, *Lasiurus seminolus*, shot on the outskirts of the Okefenokee Swamp, Georgia on March 21, 1954, after 20 minutes of feeding time, had accumulated 0.5 grams of stomach contents.

The instances in which bats were clearly having a successful early feeding period are summarized in Table 1; and it is evident that rates of accumulation of one to two grams per hour are regularly attained by these bats under favorable conditions.

Discussion.—These rates of insect capture can be used to estimate the number of individual insects captured per unit time. Such estimates, however, require not only identification of an occasional fragment from the stomach contents but quantitative estimates of the proportion of the total catch that was contributed by insects of each size. Since only a very small fraction of the stomach contents escape reduction to an unidentifiable "soup," such assumptions cannot for the present be more than a rough approximation. For example *Myotis lucifugus* was shown to catch insects ranging in size from *Metriocnemus* with a weight of 0.2 mg. to moths weighing approximately 15 mg. The typical hourly catch of one gram for a successful *Myotis* might theoretically consist of 5000 *Metriocnemus* or 67 moths each weighing 15 mg., or any intermediate mixture. While neither of these two extremes is likely, it seems probable for *Myotis* that small insects weighing about one milligram predominate. Otherwise large chitinous pieces would have been found in the stomach contents.

If we assume, rather conservatively, that the one gram hourly catch consists on the average of insects weighing two milligrams, we arrive at an estimate of 500 individual insects captured per hour, or approximately one every seven seconds. Even the improbably high figure of 10 mg. for the average size of the insects captured leads to an estimate of 100 catches per hour, or one every 36 seconds.

Consideration should be given to the possibility that these bats feed by flying through dense swarms of small insects (such as chironomids) with their mouths

30

TABLE 1.—*Rates of insect capture attained by feeding bats. Only the more successful feeders are included*

Species of bat	Age	Body weight (grams)	Feeding period (minutes)	Weight of stomach contents (grams)	Theoretical rate of insect capture (grams/hour)
Myotis lucifugus.....................	Adult	8	45	1.0	1.3
Myotis lucifugus.....................	Adult	8.2	70	1.3	1.1
Myotis lucifugus.....................	Adult	8.2	70	1.0	0.9
Myotis lucifugus.....................	Adult	5.5	95	1.1	0.7
Average of 4 adult *Myotis lucifugus*..		7.5	70	1.1	1.0
Eptesicus fuscus.....................	Young	8.8	62	1.0	1.0
Eptesicus fuscus.....................	Young	9.0	112	1.0	0.5
Eptesicus fuscus.....................	Young	8.4	65	0.7	0.7
Eptesicus fuscus.....................	Young	8.6	60	0.3	0.3
Eptesicus fuscus.....................	Young	8.6	60	0.6	0.6
Eptesicus fuscus.....................	Young	7.6	39	0.5	0.8
Eptesicus fuscus.....•..............	Young	9.0	46	1.4	1.7
Eptesicus fuscus.....................	Young	12.8	25	0.5	1.2
Eptesicus fuscus.....................	Young	9.1	43	1.5	2.1
Eptesicus fuscus.....................	Young	8.3	31	0.7	1.4
Average of 10 young *Eptesicus*......		9.1	58	0.8	1.1
Eptesicus fuscus.....................	Adult	18.9	90	4.0	2.7
Lasiurus seminolus.................	Adult	8.7	20	0.5	1.5
Pipistrellus subflavus...............	Adult	6.7	30	1.7	3.3
Pipistrellus subflavus...............	Adult	5.3	30	1.4	2.7

open, catching insects only by chance in a sort of filter feeding process. In *Myotis lucifugus*, however, the area of the open mouth is only about one square centimeter, and at a typical flight velocity of five meters per second the volume of air filtered would be about 1800 liters per hour. If the average weight of the insects were 2 mg., the average density would have to be 0.28 per liter (one in every 3.6 liters). Smaller insects such as *Metriocnemus* actually found in the mouth of a *Myotis* would have to occur at average densities of 2.8 per liter (one every 0.36 liters). Such densities are possible in swarms, but only during a small fraction of its feeding period could a bat possibly be flying through dense swarms even if these were selectively sought out. Even if one assumed that a bat flew through dense swarms as much as one tenth of the feeding period, the insect densities would have to be ten times the figures mentioned above in order to account for the actual rates of food accumulation on a random basis. Hence most of the prey must be secured by a selective pursuit of individual insects.

It is next necessary to inquire whether perceptible amounts of sound energy would be returned to a bat from such small insects as those captured by *Myotis*. To answer this question one would ideally wish to know: (1) the intensity of sound emitted by the bat, which can be taken as about 100 dynes/cm² (Griffin, 1950); (2) the distance from bat to insect; and (3) the proportion of the sound striking the insect which is reflected or scattered back towards the bat.

Over distances at which most insects are probably detected it is approximately true that the energy decreases as the square of the distance, both as the sound travels towards the insect and as the echo returns to the bat. Since energy is proportional to the square of the sound pressure, the pressure of the returning echo should vary as the square of the distance from the bat to its insect target. On this basis one could theoretically calculate the sound pressures of the echo reaching a bat's ears; but a further complication arises because the smaller insects, at least, have dimensions comparable to the wavelength of the sound emitted by the bat. This results in an extremely complicated, sometimes periodic, relationship between target size and the proportion of the incident sound returning to the bat as an echo (Beranek, 1949, Fig. 313). Any detailed consideration of these matters is beyond the scope of this paper, but two important elementary points are consistent with the assumption that echoes from insects would be audible to the bats.

Even the smallest insects that are known to be captured (*Metriocnemus*) have wingspreads of about 3 mm. This dimension is approximately equal to the shortest wavelengths occuring at the beginning of the pulses that have been detected from this species on occasion. The typical initial frequency of *Myotis* pulses is about 80 kc., corresponding to a wavelength of 4.3 mm. But when a special effort was made to search for higher frequencies still earlier in the pulses (and lower in amplitude as picked up by the microphones) frequencies as high as 120 kc. were recorded (Griffin, 1950). The wavelength of 120 kc. sound is 2.9 mm. A very rapid decline in the energy scattered back to the bat will occur only when the target diameter falls well below one wavelength. Furthermore it is well known that these bats can easily detect wires as small as 0.5 mm. in diameter (Griffin and Galambos, 1941). Hence it is wholly reasonable to assume that echoes from 3 mm. insects would be detectable by *Myotis*, although more detailed analytical studies would be necessary to learn the effective range at which such small targets can be detected.

A second type of evidence that bats could actually hear echoes from insects has recently been obtained from preliminary experiments carried out with Dr. Griffin in which a bat was held in the hand and induced to emit pulses of high frequency sound directed toward an actual insect impaled on the end of a fine wire. Close beside the bat was placed the condenser microphone used to pick up the sound, but the microphone was also pointed towards the insect. Oscillographic records of echoes from the pulses emitted by *Myotis lucifugus* could be obtained from moths such as cecropia (*Platysamia cecropia*) and the common io, (*Automeris io*) at a distance from the bat to microphone of 50 cm. Some echoes were detectable at 50 cm. from a fluttering moth of the army worm, *Pseudaletia unipuncta*, having a wingspread of 35 mm. With the apparatus used, the minimum detectable sound pressure is far above the threshold of hearing of bats, if we assume that at frequencies of about 50 kc. they have a threshold equal to that of the human ear at 1 to 3 kc. The echoes that the apparatus could detect at 50 cm. must therefore be audible to the bats at considerably greater distances; and smaller insects at 50 cm. or less must also reflect echoes audible to the bat.

SUMMARY

An analysis has been made of the insects captured by bats on the wing, based both on a survey of published records and a program of collecting bats to analyze the contents of their digestive tracts. Special attention was paid to the sizes of the insects and to the rates at which insects are caught; and this data is discussed in relation to the hypothesis advanced by Griffin that insects are located and captured by means of the bats' high frequency sounds.

The insects actually identified ranged in size from a 0.2 milligram *Metriocnemus* found in the mouth of a *Myotis lucifugus* to sphinx moths averaging 77 mm. wingspread reported by Huey to be captured by the California leaf-nosed bat *Macrotus californicus*. Even with the single species *Myotis lucifugus* the size of insect prey ranges from *Metriocnemus* with a wingspread of 3 mm. to beetles of the family Elateridae with wingspreads of 10–12 mm.

The rate at which bats fill their stomachs after the beginning of their evening flight indicates an impressive efficiency in catching insects. One gram per hour is not an uncommon rate in *Myotis lucifugus*. Maximum rates recorded were 2.7 grams per hour for *Eptesicus fuscus* and 3.3 grams per hour for *Pipistrellus subflavus*.

Making conservative assumptions regarding the average size of the insects captured by such species as *Myotis lucifugus* it can be shown that a random process akin to filter feeding cannot possibly account for these rates of catching insects. It is therefore probable that individual insects are located, pursued, and captured at rates of the order of one every few seconds.

The sizes of the insects are in all cases nearly equal to, or greater than, one wavelength of the sounds emitted by bats that catch them. Oscillographic records of echoes of bat sounds from insects at 50 cm. have been obtained, and there is good reason to believe such echoes would be audible to the bats. The evidence discussed is therefore consistent with the hypothesis that flying insects are captured by echolocation.

LITERATURE CITED

BAINES, J. M. 1940. Analysis of lepidoptera eaten by bats. Entomologist, 73: 139–40.

BERANEK, L. L. 1949. Acoustic measurements. Wiley, New York. 914 p.

BUCKHURST, A. S. 1930. Moths destroyed by a long eared bat. Entomologist, 63: 238.

COLYER, C. N. 1951. Flies of the British Isles. Frederick Warne and Co. London and New York. 383 p.

CURTIS, J. 1860. Farm insects. Blackie and Son, London. 528 p.

EISENTRAUT, M. 1950. Die Ernährung der Fledermäuse. Zoologische Jahrbücher, 79: 114–177.

ESSIG, E. O. 1929. Insects of western North America. Macmillan Co., New York. 1035 p.

FOWLER, C. 1887. British Coleoptera. L. Reeve and Co. London, vol. 4. 411 p.

FURNEAUX, W. 1897. British butterflies and moths. Longmans, Green and Co., London. 358 p.

GRIFFIN, D. R. 1950. Measurements of the ultrasonic cries of bats. Jour. Acoustical Soc. Amer., 22: 247–255.

————. 1953. Bats sounds under natural conditions with evidence for echolocation of insect prey. Jour. Expt. Zool., 123: 435–466.

GRIFFIN, D. R. AND R. GALAMBOS. 1941. The sensory basis of obstacle avoidance by flying bats. Jour. Expt. Zool., 86: 481–506.

HAMILTON, W. J., JR. 1930. Notes on the mammals of Breathitt County, Kentucky. Jour. Mamm., 11: 306–311.

HAMPSON, G. F. 1903, 1905, 1906, 1908, 1909, 1910, and 1913. Catalogue of the Lepidoptera Phalaenae in the British Museum. British Mus. Nat. Hist., vol. iv, v, vi, vii, viii, ix, x, xi.

HARPER, FRANCIS. 1927. The mammals of the Okefenokee Swamp region of Georgia. Proc. Boston Soc. Nat. Hist., 38: 191-396.

HODGSON, S. B. 1943. Bats feeding on moths at Sallow. Entomologist, 76: 147-48.

————. 1944. Lepidoptera eaten by bats. Entomologist, 77: 62-63.

HUEY, L. M. 1925. Food of the California leaf-nose bat. Jour. Mamm., 6: 196-197.

LANG, H C. 1884. Butterflies of Europe. L. Reeve and Co., London. 396 p.

MANWARING, J. 1939. Lepidoptera taken by bats. Entomologist, 72: 190.

MEYRICK, E. 1927. A revised handbook of British Lepidoptera. Watkins and Doncaster, London. 914 p.

MOEHRES, F. P. 1953. Über die Ultraschallorientierung der Hufeisennasen. Zeitschr. f. vergl. Physiol., 34: 554-555.

NICHOLSON, C. 1937. Moths eaten by bats. Entomologist, 70: 188.

ORR, R. T. 1954. Natural history of the pallid bat, *Antrozous pallidus* (LeConte). Proc. Cal. Acad. Sci., 28: 165-246.

POOLE, E. L. 1932. Breeding of the hoary bat in Pennsylvania Jour. Mamm., 13: 365.

POULTON, E. B. 1929. British insectivorous bats and their prey. Proc. Zool. Soc. London, 1929: 277-303.

RYBERG, O. 1947. Studies on bats and bat parasites. Bokforlaget Svensk Natur., Stockholm. 330 p.

STONE, A. 1938. The horseflies of the subfamily Tabanidae of the Nearctic Region. U.S.D.A., Misc. Publ. 305.

FURTHER STUDIES ON THE FEEDING EFFICIENCY OF BATS

Edwin Gould

An evaluation of the hypothesis that bats use their high frequency sounds for locating and pursuing flying insects (Griffin, Jour. Exp. Zool., 123: 435–466, 1953) has been made by the qualitative and quantitative analyses of bat stomachs (Gould, Jour. Mamm., 36: 399–407, 1955) as measures of the feeding efficiency of insectivorous bats. A conservative estimate was that about 500 insects were captured per hour by *Myotis lucifugus*. A random process of feeding cannot account for such high rates of catching insects. The number of dives per unit time of feeding bats has recently been observed to supplement the evidence based on stomach analysis. The study was made at the edge of a small swale on the outskirts of Baltimore, Maryland, during the summer of 1957. The bats were almost certainly *Myotis lucifugus* because of their size and manner of flight.

TABLE 1.—*Rates of diving by Myotis lucifugus in pursuit of insects, on the evening of July 7*

DURATION OF OBSERVATION, SECONDS	NO. OF DIVES OBSERVED	RATE: NO. OF DIVES/HR.
30	12	1,440
5	4	2,880
20	11	1,980
15	6	1,440
30	13	1,560
20	9	1,620
15	13	3,120*
140	53	1,363
5	2	1,440
33	6	655
10	8	2,880
15	3	720
20	3	540*
Total = 358	Total = 143	$\bar{x}$ = 1,665

*Range.

The dives were counted from the moment a bat came into view until it disappeared and, for convenience, this time will be called the "period of observation." The number of bats observed during any one evening varied from two to five. There was no way of knowing whether the same bat was being observed from one period of observation to the next. Table 1 lists all of the data collected on one favorable night (July 7) in the same order that the dives were observed. Table 2 is a compilation of data from several evenings. The total time in all periods of observation was 2,369 seconds and the total number of dives was 878.

JOURNAL OF MAMMALOGY, 1959, Vol. 40, pp. 149-150.

TABLE 2.—*Diving rates of Myotis lucifugus*

DATE	MEAN NO. OF DIVES/HR.	RANGE OF DIVES/HR.	NO. OF OBSERVATIONS
30 June	792	540–1,260	10
3 July	726	360*–1,234	6
4 July	634	432–720	5
5 July	1320	960–1,800	4
6 July	1015	720–1,680	5
7 July	1665	540–2,880*	13
16 July	1263	747–1,938	8
18 July	1196	600–2,160	21
19 July	1437	900–2,250	24
31 July	1327	600–1,800	10
6 August	1369	720–2,160	11
$\bar{x} = 1159$		Total = 117	

*Range.

Four big brown bats, *Eptesicus fuscus*, were observed in the same way on the evening of July 10, at another site not far from the swale described above. Fourteen periods of observation were recorded, totaling 7 minutes. The mean number of dives per hour for all observations was 1,283 and the range of rates for each period of observation was 480–1,800 dives per hour.

Even if it were assumed that 50 per cent of the observed dives by *Myotis lucifugus* were *misses*, half of the impressive mean, 1,159 dives per hour (Table 2) would still come very close to the estimate, obtained through stomach analysis, of 500 insects caught per hour. These data seem to support the hypothesis that insectivorous bats capture flying insects by echolocation.

Helpful suggestions and review of the manuscript by Drs. Fred R. Cagle and Donald R. Griffin are deeply appreciated.—EDWIN GOULD, *Dept. of Zoology, Tulane Univ., New Orleans, Louisiana. Received November 14, 1957.*

The Structure of the Flukes in Relation to Laminar Flow in Cetaceans

By P. E. PURVES[1]

Eingang des Ms. 5. 12. 1967

Introduction

In drawing attention to the strong dorsal curvature of the flukes of cetaceans during the downstroke of the tail, FELTS (1966) stated "We have found nothing in fluke anatomy proper which explains this difference in linearity during the powerful fluke beat, but we believe the answer will be found in differential output by dorsal and ventral tail musculature, with variation in movement compensated for by the difference in dorsal and ventral areas of the body and by corrective flipper movements".

However, in a discussion of "Gray's Paradox", PURVES (1963) pointed out that the weight of the epaxial locomotor muscle-mass is approximately double that of the hypaxial mass and that in maintaining power on the upstroke alone, the effective length of the animal, for the purpose of calculating REYNOLD's Number, was reduced below the level at which turbulence was likely to occur. In these circumstances, if flexure of the flukes were due to muscular action, the former would be expected to curve more strongly in a ventral direction, rather than dorsally during the power stroke.

It is the purpose of this paper to demonstrate that the upward curvature of the flukes is not due to differential muscular action but to the anatomy of the flukes themselves, and that their differential flexure is of supreme importance in the maintenance of laminar flow over the body.

The anatomy of the flukes in cetaceans was examined in very great detail by ROUX (1883) and little can be added to his description at the macroscopic level, but a very brief recapitulation is required here. The main body, or central core of the fluke is constituted from a great number of closely packed, anteroposteriorly directed laminae of white-fibrous tissue fig. 1 (B) in which each individual lamina consists of a reticulum of collagen fibres vertically and diagonally orientated, see fig. 1 (C). Overlying these laminae of the dorsal and ventral aspects of the flukes are several layers of radiating collagen fibres fig. 1 (A), and the whole assembly is covered by the black, external epithelium.

The flukes of a living, or recently dead cetacean will bend much more readily in a dorsal direction by manual pressure than in the ventral direction, the difference in flexibility varying between the species. An extreme example of this differential flexibility is to be found in the Long-snouted Dolphin *Stenella longirostris* and the flukes of this species were used in the present investigation. The specimen had been presented deep-frozen by Marineland of the Pacific and was used for casting and anatomical studies. After the black epithelium had been removed, the appearance of the dorsal and ventral surfaces seemed identical, and gross sectioning of one of the flukes in several directions revealed no anatomical reason for the differential flexibility.

However, when the layers of radiating collagen fibres had been removed from the dorsal and ventral surface of the other fluke, the core was found to bend with

---

[1] See D. VAN HEEL, Z. Säugetierkunde, 33 (1968), H. 6, S. 383.

ZEITSCHRIFT FUR SAUGETIERKUNDE, 1969, Vol. 34 pp.1-8.

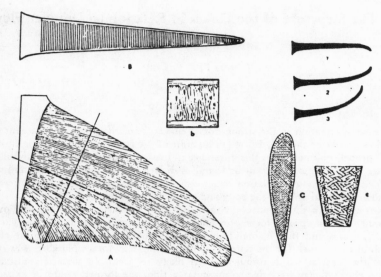

Fig. 1. Diagram showing distribution of collagen fibres in the flukes of a cetacean

A = Shows the surface appearance of radiating collagen fibres on the dorsal and ventral aspects of the flukes after the black epithelium has been removed. B, b = A schematic diagram of a section of the fluke along the indicated macroaxis showing anteroposteriorly directed laminae of white fibrous tissue covered dorsally and ventrally by layers of radiating collagen fibres. C, c = Schematic diagram of a section of the fluke through the indicated transverse axis showing vertically and diagonally orientated collagen fibres.
Diagram (after FELTS) showing the from of the flukes during (1) the upstroke (2) the glide and (3) the downstroke

equal facility in both dorsal and ventral directions. Clearly then, the reason for the differential flexibility resided in the radiating collagen fibres on the surfaces of the flukes and not in the structure of the core.

Teased and sectioned fibres were examined by phase-contrast and electron micros-copy, the photomicrographs being shown in fig. 2 (A–D) and the electronmicrographs in fig. 3 and 4. The original material had been preserved in formalin for about a year. It was dehydrated and embedded in epoxy resin and the sections were stained with uranyl acetate and lead citrate. It will be seen that the collagen fibres of the ventral aspect of the flukes have a strongly pleated appearance whilst those on the dorsal aspect are nearly straight. Indeed in *Stenella longirostris* the dorsal fibres seem actually to be "prestressed" since initially perfectly parallel cross sections of the fresh fluke assume a wedge-shape a short time after sectioning. Examination of foetal material shows that this difference in structure is embryonic in origin and that even the deve-loping fibroblasts of the ventral surface have an undulating distortion.

It can readily be seen that the radiating fibres of the ventral surface are capable of expansion, with the pleats opening out like the bellows of a concertina but of reasser-ting and assuming their original shape when tension is released. This clearly could not happen whith the initially straight fibres of the upper surface, since collagen fibres are known to be virtually inextensible, under normal conditions. These fibres could, of course shorten by being thrown into minute, sinusoidal wrinkles. It is well known that when any flat plate bends, the surface on the convex side of the curvature must expand, whilst that on the concave side must shrink by a corresponding amount. When the fluke is perfectly horizontal, the collagen fibres on the ventral surface are pleated whilst those on the dorsal surface are staight. Under these conditions appreciable bending can only take place in a dorsal direction, and it is noteworthy that when this happens, the external epithelium of the upper surface exhibits minute wrinkles which lie at right angles to the axes of the radiating collagen fibres. Examination of the orientation of the fibres with respect to the total shape of the fluke shows where dorsal flexure can be expected i. e. along the macroaxis of the fluke towards the distal extremity and along the thin, trailing edge, especially in its proximal region. In the ventral direction, the fluke will be much more rigid, since the initially straight fibres of the dorsal surface would have to stretch beyond breaking point to produce any appreciable bending.

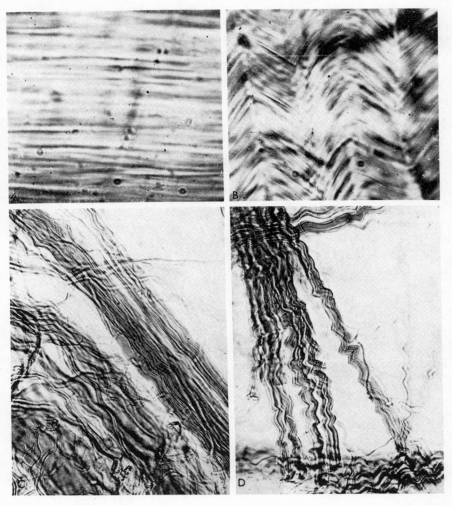

Fig. 2. Phase contrast photomicrographs mag x 300 showing (A) straight layers of collagen fibres on dorsal aspect of flukes (B) pleated layers of collagen fibres on ventral surface (C) teased fibres from dorsal aspect (D) teased fibres from ventral aspect

39

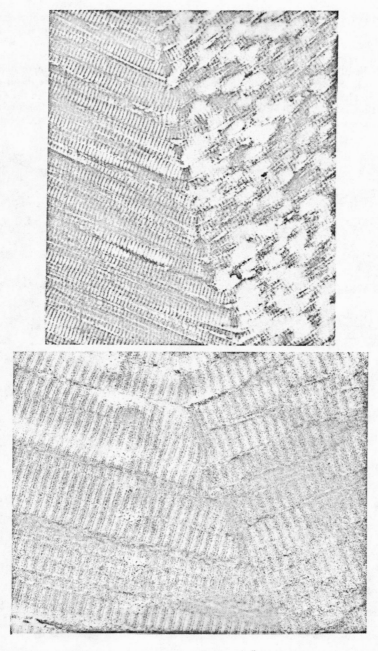

Fig. 3. Electron-micrograph mag x 18,000 of collagen fibrils on ventral aspect of flukes —
Fig. 4. Electron-micrograph mag x 50,000 indicating distortion of collagen molecules on ventral
aspect of flukes

Since the orientation of the radiating fibres varies slightly between the species, dependent upon the overall shape of the flukes, there are slight differences in the distribution of dorsal flexibility.

It should be pointed out that *Stenella longirostris* is a conspicuos example of a cetacean showing differential distortion of the radial collagen fibres — but that all the cetaceans examined demonstrate it to a greater or lesser degree.

A study of the insertions of the tendons of the epaxial and hypaxial muscles of locomotion shows that a large angle of incidence can develop on the upstroke but that this is prevented to some extent during the downstroke. For a demonstration of the reason for this phenomenon it is convenient to describe the epaxial muscles first fig. 5 A. In the caudal segment, the epaxial muscles consist only of two major portions which are prolongations of the spinalis dorsalis (MSD) and the longissimus dorsalis (MDL). In this region, the muscles are heavily developed, but quite discrete, since they must permit of the relative movement which is concomitant of the sinuous, vertical movement of the tail. The spinalis dorsalis has very powerful attachments to the upper half of all the neural spines (NS) and to the dense fibrous tissue which forms the dorsal

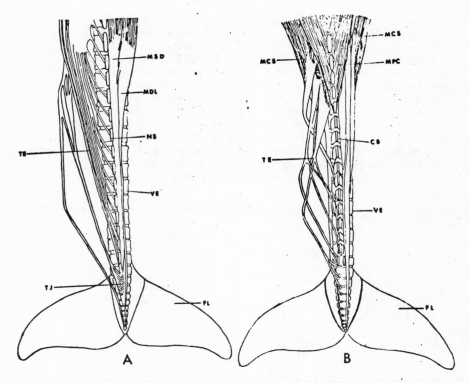

Fig. 5 A. Diagram of the distal end of the epaxial muscles of locomotion in the tail of a Common Porpoise *Phocoena phocoena*. The tendon sheaths have been removed from the muscles of the left side and the individual tendons partially separated to show their insertions on the neural spines — *B.* Diagram of the distal end of the hypaxial muscles of locomotion in the tail of a Common Porpoise *Phocaena phocaena*. The tendon sheaths have been removed from the muscles of the right side and the individual tendons partially separated to show their insertions on the chevron bones

border of the tail. It is important to note that the posterior attachment to the vertebrae ceases at the commencement of the tail flukes (FL) at a point (TJ) where the neural spines are inconspicuous or absent. A single, slender tendon of the longissimus extends to the very end of the tail.

Contraction of the epaxial caudal muscles would therefore act mainly in lifting the tail and the anterior part of the flukes allowing the posterior part of the flukes to lag under water pressure.

Turning now to the hypaxial caudal muscle (fig. 5 B) which consists only of the sacrococcygeus (MCS) it will be seen that its numerous tendons (TE) are inserted into the lateral surfaces of all the chevron bones (CB) which extend to the very end of the tail. Although the sacrococcygeus is a relatively weak muscle compared with the combined spinalis and longissimus dorsi, its contraction would cause uniform flexion of the entire caudal peduncle with no sharp angle at the anterior insertion of the flukes. The pubococcygeus (MPC) takes no part in flexion of the tail and indeed has been referred to as part of the levator ani.

Discussion

The combination of differential angle of incidence of the flukes with reciprocal flexure is such that during rapid acceleration from slow speed, the water is driven posterodorsally on the upstroke but that there is no drive on the downstroke, the water being "spilled" dorsally by the upward curvature of the flukes, and the small angle of incidence. This arrangement ensures that the direction of water-flow relative to the body does not alternate with changes in the direction of the tail-beat, a factor of great importance in the prevention of large turbulences and in the initiation of laminar flow.

In a more comprehensive paper to be published later, it will be demonstrated that the total body contours and the mode of locomotion serve to keep the water flowing in a constant direction relative to the surface of the body. See Fig. 6.

In support of the general theory of locomotion in cetaceans propounded above — a few observations made on living specimens in clear water are noteworthy. In addition to the gross distribution of pigment on the external skin, as depicted in various text

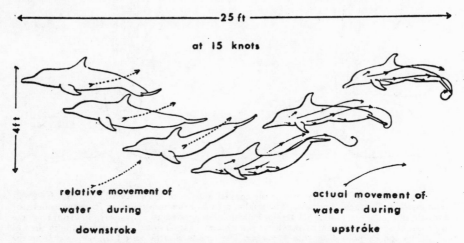

Fig. 6. Diagram showing undulating movement of the body of a cetacean during one complete cycle of the tail and the movement of water relative to the flanks

books there are fine "brush-marks" leading posterodorsally along the entire flank from head to tail. These are particularly conspicuous in the Californian variety of the Bottle-nosed dolphin *Tursiops truncatus* and in the Pacific striped-dolphin *Lagenorhynchus obliquidens*. These "brush-marks" follow the orientation of the dermal ridges beneath the external epithelium, PURVES (1963), and they also indicate the direction of the water flow relative to the body (Fig. 6).

It is also notable than when dolphins "stand on their tails" as they have been trained to do in most "dolphinaria" there is a tendency for the body to oscillate in a vertical direction with the dorsal component of movement occurring during extension of the tail. Since, however, the animals are also able to move backwards during this process, a small amount of thrust during flexion must be involved.

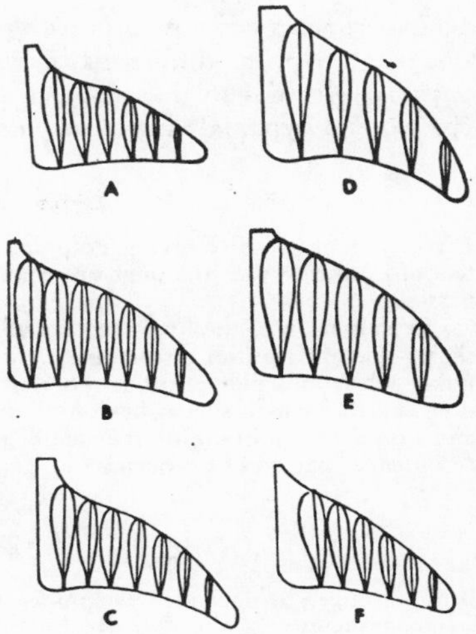

As stated, the strong dorsal flexure of the flukes referred to above, occurs mainly during rapid acceleration from a slow speed, when strong muscular effort is required for flexion of the tail. During sustained, high-speed swimming, both the amplitude of the tail-beat and dorsal flexure of the flukes are very small, extension and flexion of the tail take place extremely rapidly and it is difficult to detect with the unaided eye that the downstroke is the slower one. This can, however, be seen from examination of cinematograph frames, PURVES (1963). In terrestrial mammals, flexion of the

Fig. 7. Diagram showing hydrofoil cross section of the flukes in various species of cetacean. The vertical lines represent the positions of sections of a cast of the flukes, and the curved lines on the right and left side of each vertical line represent the contour of the dorsal and ventral surfaces respectively. A = *Stenella roseiventris* (Gray, 1866), B = *Stenella graffmani* (Lönnberg, 1934), C = *Stenella longirostris* (Gray, 1828), D = *Sousa plumbea* (G. Cuvier, 1829), E = *Lagenorhynchus cruciger* (Quoy and Gaimard, 1824), F = *Neomeris phocaenoides* (G. Cuvier, 1829)

tail is gravity assisted and the hypaxial musculature is therefore greatly reduced. Although due to the relatively large amount of bone and reduced blubber content, the caudal region has a higher specific gravity than other parts of the body, the effect, in water of the downward pull of gravity is to a large extent counteracted by buoyancy so that if muscular effort is to be avoided during flexion of the tail, at high speed, some other mechanism must be invoked to assist in returning the tail to its position before the power stroke.

It is postulated that this assistance is provided by the hydrofoil cross section of the flukes. Fig. 7 (A—F) shows a series of diagrams of the flukes of various species of cetacean with profiles of the cross sections at regular intervals. The profiles are asymmetrical in outline with the side of greatest curvature representing the ventral surface. The arrangement is the reverse of the aerofoil in which "lift" is provided by reduced pressure on the upper surface of the wing. Provided the angle of incidence is kept small, the reduced pressure on the ventral surface draws the flukes rapidly downwards after the forward velocity has been provided by the upstroke. Since the density of water is approximately 1,000 times greater than that of air, the downward pull on the hydrofoil would be an equivalent amount greater than the "lift" on an aerofoil of the same size for any given velocity and angle of incidence. The ventral movement will also be assisted by the extreme dorsal "fairing" on the caudal peduncle.

Experiments are now proceeding at the Delft Hydraulics Laboratory to determine quantitatively, the differential drive on the flukes at various angles of incidence and various velocities so that this can be correlated with the known difference between epaxial and hypaxial muscle weights.

Summary

Direct observations of living dolphins, the study of the locomotor muscles and insertion of tendons indicate that the only upstroke of the tail is a power stroke — the downstroke being passive.

Examination of the fine structure of the horizontal collagen fibres in the flukes of cetaceans shows that differential distortion of the fibrils is correlated with the upward curvature of the flukes when muscular effort is required for flexion of the tail during rapid acceleration from slow speed. At high speed, flexion of the tail is assisted by the hydrofoil section of the flukes, and dorsal streamlining of the caudal peduncle. Both of these phenomena help to reduce the turbulence that would otherwise be generated by alternate movements of the tail.

Zusammenfassung

Beobachtungen an lebenden Delphinen sowie das Studium der Bewegungsmuskulatur und des Sehnenansatzes ergaben, daß der Aufwärtsschlag der Schwanzflosse eine aktive, der Abwärtsschlag eine passive Bewegung darstellen.

Die Untersuchung der Feinstruktur der horizontal verlaufenden Collagenfibrillen in der Schwanzflosse der Cetacea zeigt, daß eine Beziehung zwischen der Verdrehung dieser Fibrillen und dem Aufbiegen der Schwanzflosse besteht, und zwar dann, wenn bei schneller Beschleunigung aus langsamer Bewegung heraus eine starke Muskelbeanspruchung zur Durchbiegung des Schwanzes erforderlich wird. Bei hoher Geschwindigkeit wird die Bewegung des Schwanzes unterstützt durch das strömungstechnisch günstige Profil der Schwanzflosse sowie durch die dorsale Stromlinienführung des Rumpfhecks (n. CASSELL's: Blumenstiel).

Beide Phänomene helfen mit, die Turbulenz zu verringern, die sonst durch die beidseitige Bewegung des Schwanzes entstehen würde.

Acknowledgements

Acknowledgements are due to Mr. J. V. BROWN for phase-contrast photomicrography and to Miss D. PARRY for the electron-micrographs. I also wish to thank the Director, Mr. E. F. DEN HERDER, of the Dolphinarium, Harderwijk, Netherlands, and the Curator, Dr. W. H. DUDOK VAN HEEL for the opportunity to study live cetaceans at close-quarters.

Bibliography

FELTS, W. J. L. (1966): Some Functional and Structural Characteristics of Cetacean Flippers and Flukes: in Whales, Dolphins and Porpoises. Edit. NORRIS, K. S., Univ. Calif. Press, 255—276.

PURVES, P. E. (1963): Locomotion in Whales. Nature 197, 334—337.

ROUX, W. (1883): Beiträge zur Morphologie der functionellen Anpassung. I. Structure eines hoch differenzierten bindegewebigen Organs (der Schwanzflosse des Delphins). Arch Anat. Entw., 4, 76—162.

Address of the author: Dr. P. E. PURVES, British Museum (Natural History), Cromwell Road, London S. W. 7, Great Britain

THE ENERGETICS OF HARBOR SEALS IN AIR AND IN WATER WITH SPECIAL CONSIDERATION OF SEASONAL CHANGES[1]

J. S. HART AND L. IRVING[2]
With the assistance of B. MACKENZIE

Abstract

The energetics of six harbor seals in air at temperatures from 25° C to −20° C and in water from 25° C to 0° C was studied in animals acclimatized to summer conditions at Woods Hole, Mass. Over the above temperature range, the temperature of skin of the back cooled from about 35° to 1° with lowering temperature of the medium. Temperatures of the flippers were less dependent upon the surroundings than those of the body skin. The dependence of metabolism upon temperature was operative below 2° C in air and below 20° C in water (the critical temperatures), but the body skin temperature at these critical temperatures was the same, viz. 21° C. Metabolism in air and in water was the same over the range of comparable skin temperatures. Body insulation was equal in air and in water at the respective critical temperatures. The insulation index of the air was approximately 20 times that of the water. Heat conductivity of living blubber to water averaged 2.5 cal/cm²/hr/°C, which exceeded that reported for dead blubber by about 50%.

When compared with seals tested at St. Andrews during December, summer seals had a higher critical temperature, a lower body insulation index at the critical temperature, and a warmer body skin temperature for the same metabolic rate. No seasonal changes were found in thermoneutral metabolic rate, and no discernible changes in skin temperatures or in thermal gradients in the blubber.

Introduction

The phenotypic modifications of mammals following changes in climate fall into two general categories, metabolic and insulative (4). In the former, cold is met by the development of an enhanced ability to produce heat, while in the latter it is met by reducing heat loss either by greater pelage insulation or greater cooling of peripheral tissues. Natural metabolic acclimatization, which has been observed by Hart in deer mice (5), may occur in species of small body size. In animals such as the fox and porcupine with thick fur, Irving and co-workers (9) have found that there was a marked restriction of the emission of heat associated with the thicker fur during winter. Their findings complemented the observations of Scholander et al. (10) on the importance of fur for the low critical temperatures of arctic animals during winter, and those of Hart (3) on the greater winter pelage insulation of the larger mammals.

In "bare skinned" animals such as pigs (6), and seals (7), fur has little or no protective value and the skin surface assumes a dominant role in the loss of heat. Any modifications to suit low winter air or water temperatures must therefore be brought about either by greater heat production or by reduction

[1]Manuscript received April 22, 1959.
Contribution from the Division of Applied Biology, N.R.C., Ottawa. The research was aided by a grant from the National Science Foundation to the Woods Hole Oceanographic Institution where the work was carried out. W.H.O.I. Contribution No. 1030.
Issued as N.R.C. No. 5259.
[2]Present address: Arctic Health Research Center, Anchorage, Alaska.

CANADIAN JOURNAL OF ZOOLOGY, 1959, Vol. 37, pp. 447-457.

of heat loss through greater cooling of the living peripheral tissues. The remarkable capability of seals to show surface cooling in cold environments has already been demonstrated by Irving and Hart (7). The close correlation between the degree of cooling and the metabolic response in different individuals suggested the direction for further study of seasonal changes.

In the present investigation, the results obtained on a sample of harbor seals during December 1955 are compared with those obtained on a sample of the same population during the summer of 1956. With these additional data it has been possible to give a more detailed account of the energetics of seals in air and in water than was possible during the winter of 1955.

Experimental Animals

Six harbor seals, *Phoca vitulina concolor*, captured at Boothbay Harbour, Maine, in May 1956 were shipped to Woods Hole, Mass., during July 1956. They were held in a large pound and fed frozen fish during the period of captivity from July to September. Observations on the animals were made in August and September, during which period water temperature varied from 20 to 22° C. The animals were presumably from the same population as those studied during the winter of 1955 (7). The similarity of the animals and methods of testing facilitate direct comparison of the 1955 and 1956 results.

Methods

The test methods used were identical with those reported earlier (7) except for the automatic instead of manual recording of temperature gradients. The availability of a cold room also made it possible to utilize a greater range of air temperatures than was possible in 1955. In brief, the procedure consisted in the testing of one animal per day at three or four different temperature conditions in air and in water. Surface temperatures were measured on a potentiometer indicator and tissue temperatures at various depths were recorded at 16 points in each 4 minutes by means of gradient needles (7) prepared by L. J. Peyton.

After thermal balance was obtained in approximately 1 hour, three or four 10–15 minute samples of expired air were obtained for the measurement of oxygen consumption during the second hour, as previously described (see Fig. 3).

In addition to these measurements, a few observations were made on the heat flow from the seal's surface to water of various temperatures to correlate heat flow with the observed thermal gradients measured close to the same site. For this purpose the rise of temperature of the water in a small Dewar flask held against the seal's side was measured with a calibrated thermocouple and a sensitive Leeds and Northrup d-c. amplifier. The calorimeter, which was previously calibrated by producing heat electrically, had a precision of approximately ±5%.

46

Results

Resting Metabolism

The metabolism of seals during the summer was dependent on environmental temperature below about 20° C in water and 2° C in air. The resting metabolism of all the seals in air and water warmer than these critical temperatures is shown in Table I together with body weights and respiratory quotients. The mean resting metabolism (18.3 ml/min/kg$^{3/4}$) did not differ significantly from that found for winter animals (Table I).

TABLE I

Average metabolism of seals at Woods Hole in **air above 0° C**
and in water above 20° C

Seal No.	Weight, kg	O$_2$ consumption		R.Q.	No. of tests
		ml/min	ml/min/kg$^{3/4}$		
1	32.8	237	17.4	.76	13
2	31.7	219	16.3	.76	7
3	25.1	207	18.4	.69	7
4	24.4	217	19.8	.74	5
5	22.8	208	18.9	.71	7
6	27.4	213	18.1	.70	7
Mean summer	27.4		18.3±.38		
Mean winter*	33.7		19.3±.55		

*Excluding "runt" seal.

Owing to insufficient data in winter, it was not possible to compare the metabolic rates of summer and winter seals in air below the critical temperature but the comparisons for animals tested in water (Fig. 1) illustrate some appreciable differences. At subcritical temperatures, summer seals at Woods Hole had higher metabolic rates than winter seals at St. Andrews. The difference was reflected in a higher critical temperature in water in summer than in winter animals. In spite of the seasonal trends it may be seen that the exceptionally high metabolism of the "runt" seal tested during the winter was still greater than that found for any of the seals during the summer. The individual variability was also exemplified by summer seal No. 2 (◒), which had a much lower metabolism than any of the winter seals and which did not maintain a constant deep body temperature. The data on these exceptional seals have not been included in the subsequent results.

Skin Temperatures in Air and in Water

The data shown in Fig. 2 indicate that skin temperature on the surface of the back and on the flippers is closely dependendent on air or water temperature. In air, skin temperatures on the back fell markedly with lowering of the ambient temperature. The difference in temperature between skin and ambient increased with lowering tempeararture even in the thermoneutral range (above 2° C). There were no discernible seasonal differences in skin temperatures, but insufficient data were obtained in air below the thermoneutral range for an adequate comparison.

47

The temperatures of the flippers in air, while following the general trend of temperatures of skin of the back, were more variable and this implies separate control of heat flow through these appendages as noted in our earlier study (7).

In water, skin surface temperatures showed a small increase above water temperatures as the latter fell from 26° to 0° C. As previously shown (7), differences in temperature between skin and water were small, the greatest

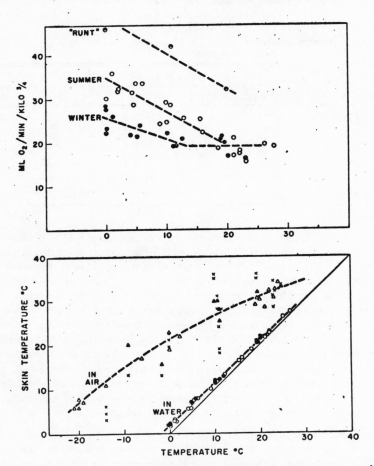

FIG. 1. Oxygen consumption of harbor seals during winter (●) and summer (○) in water. Large variation is illustrated by exceptionally high metabolism of "runt" (◐) seal (winter) and low metabolism of seal No. 2 (◑, summer).

FIG. 2. Body skin temperature of seals during winter (▲ ●) and summer (△ ○) are shown as a function of air (▲ △) and water (● ○) temperature. Each point is average of 3–5 measurements. Flipper temperatures (✕) as a function of air temperature are more variable than those of body skin. Solid line indicates equality of skin and environmental temperature, broken lines indicate skin temperature trends. Difference between skin temperature and ambient is given by broken line minus solid line.

48

difference (2° C) occurring at 0° C. In water, no discernible seasonal differences in skin temperatures were evident but the accuracy of thermocouple measurements was probably insufficient for their detection.

Temperature Gradients and Heat Flow

Temperature gradients in the seal's tissues represent one parameter effecting heat flow which becomes meaningful when the conductivity of the tissues is known. Winter gradient curves, obtained from temperature measurements at various depths, have been previously reported (7). Figure 3 shows temperature contours for a summer seal under five different thermal conditions. The rapid attainment of thermal equilibrium within about 30 minutes indicates active regulation, which is also manifested in ice water by synchronous oscillations of 1 to 2° C in temperature of the subcutaneous tissues to a depth of 23 mm. In many such tests the flippers showed a marked tendency for independence in regulation, differing by 5 to 10° C from the temperature of the body surface.

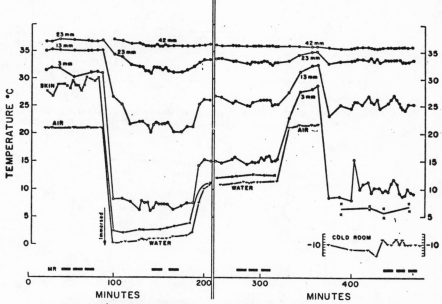

FIG. 3. Temperature measurements at various depths in a seal in air at 21° C, in water at 0–2° C, in water at 10–12° C, in air at 22° C, and in air at −10° C. Air temperatures, mean of five points within 25 cm of seal, agreeing within 1.5°. Water temperatures, mean of eight points in tank, agreeing within 0.1°. Skin temperature mean of two points on back just posterior to axilla and differing less than 0.5°. Horizontal bars marked "MR" show when gas samples taken.

In Fig. 4 are shown simultaneous records during 9 hours of two gradient needles inserted into the back 16 cm apart. The general similarity in response at the two locations and the speed of attainment of thermal balance is demonstrated. Plotting the simultaneously recorded gradients of the two positions

49

at time 560 (Fig. 5) showed that around 5 to 20 mm in depth the two curves differed by 2° to 3° C. Owing to the shifting of the needles by 1 to 3 mm during the 9 hours of recording, the difference of 2° to 3° C represented the error to be expected when the gradient is steep. In water at 5° C (Fig. 5) the base of the blubber was 3° C cooler than the maximum recorded temperature of the deep musculature. Thus the temperature gradient is not confined to blubber and may at times involve only part of it.

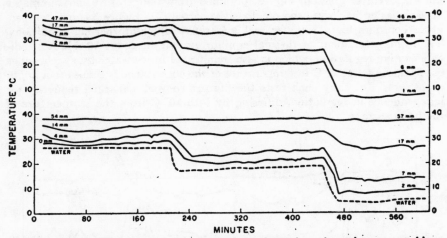

FIG. 4. Simultaneous records of temperature gradients of a seal at points separated by 16 cm on back over thorax. Upper record, point embedded in rib; lower, point intercostal.

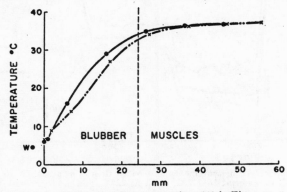

FIG. 5. Simultaneous recorded gradients from time 560 in Fig. 4.

To compare the temperature gradients during summer and winter, the temperature difference from skin to 37° C has been correlated with the depth of tissue corresponding to that difference (gradient length) shown in Fig. 6. Whether tested in air or water, summer or winter, the temperature–depth patterns were sensibly the same. The individual variability was marked and exceeded the errors in measurement.

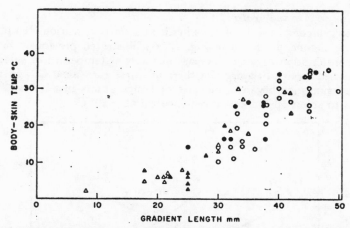

FIG. 6. Length of gradient as a function of the difference in temperature between deep body and skin surface for summer (△ ○) and winter (▲ ○) in air (▲ △) and in water (● ○)

Heat flow from the seal to water was measured on four animals at two or three temperatures (Table II). The heat flow increased with increasing gradient and decreasing temperature of the water. Conductivity values showed considerable variability between animals and temperatures. The average value of 2.5 cal/cm²/hr/°C is about 50% greater than the 1.6 cal/cm²/hr/°C measured by Scholander *et al.* (12) for dead blubber. The greater conductivity is attributable to the circulation of the living blubber.

Two seals (Nos. 1 and 3) were tested at temperatures well above the critical level (20° C). It is interesting to note that in warm water the conductivity of the blubber was not greater than that found at temperatures lower than the critical temperature.

TABLE II

Thermal characteristics of living seal blubber

Seal No.	Water temp., °C	Heat flow, cal/cm²/hr	Gradient,* °C/cm	Conductivity, cal/cm²/hr/°C
1	27.0	9.2	4.2	2.2
	18.0	15.8	7.0	2.3
	4.5	29.8	11.0	2.8
2	23.0	8.4	4.5	1.9
	11.0	12.1	6.5	1.9
3	26.0	11.2	4.0	2.8
	12.5	20.7	6.5	3.2
	2.0	31.6	9.5	3.3
6	22.0	13.9	6.0	2.3
	9.2	18.6	8.0	2.1
	0.0	29.8	11.7	2.5

*Measured in outer 10 mm of tissue.

51

Metabolism in Air and Water

The oxygen consumption of seals in air and water of various temperatures during the summer is shown in Fig. 7. As illustrated previously in Fig. 1, oxygen consumption began to increase in water at temperatures below 20° C and increased to nearly twice the thermoneutral rate at 0°C. In air, the oxygen consumption began to increase at temperatures just below 2° C and increased to about 50% above thermoneutral at −20° C.

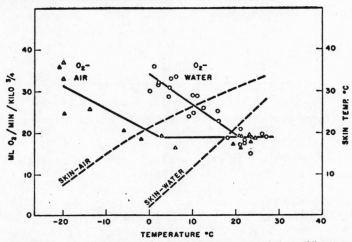

FIG. 7. Oxygen consumption of seals in air (△) and in water (○) at different temperatures during the summer. Body skin temperatures as a function of temperature of medium are also shown.

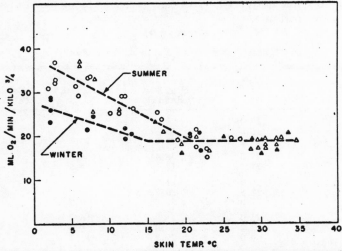

FIG. 8. Oxygen consumption as a function of body skin temperature for seals during winter and summer. Symbols same as for Fig. 2.

The broken lines in Fig. 7 give the average temperatures of skin of the back as a function of air or water temperature previously illustrated in detail in Fig. 2. A comparison of metabolism and skin temperatures brings out the fact that for a given skin temperature in air or water the metabolism is nearly the same. Thus, the critical temperature occurs at a skin temperature of approximately 21° C in water and in air. For an oxygen consumption rate of 30 ml/min/kg$^{3/4}$ the skin temperature is about 6° C in water, 8° C in air. These comparisons illustrate the general correspondence between metabolism and skin temperature in air and water.

The correspondence shown in Fig. 7 leads to the correlation between metabolism and skin temperature shown in Fig. 8, which combines results obtained both in air and in water into a composite description of seasonal changes. It is apparent that the principal differences between results obtained during the winter and those obtained during the summer is that in the latter metabolism began to increase at a higher skin temperature and was maintained at a higher level for the same skin temperature.

Insulation of Body and Medium

From the heat production, body, skin, and ambient temperatures, the insulation index (including evaporative heat loss) may be derived (Table III). Comparisons are made at the critical temperatures at which total body insulation is theoretically maximal (10). Insulation indices of body, medium, and total (body + medium) are calculated for summer and winter seals in water and for summer seals in air and in water.

The estimations show that the insulation index of the medium is some 20 times greater for air than for water but the errors in the measurements of small temperature differences in water renders the quantitative comparisons uncertain. In spite of the large difference in the cooling effects of air and water the total insulation in air is only about double that in water because the

TABLE III

Thermal properties of seals at critical temperature

(T = temperature, °C; MR = mean standard metabolism; I = insulation index)

	In water, winter	In water, summer	In air, summer
T, medium	13	20	2°
T, skin	14.5	21.0	21.0
T, body	37.0	37.0	37.0
MR, Cal/kg$^{3/4}$/min	.909	.862	.862
I, medium = $\dfrac{T(\text{skin}-\text{medium})}{MR}$	1.2	1.2	22.1
I, body = $\dfrac{T(\text{body}-\text{skin})}{MR}$	24.8	18.6	18.6
I, total = $\dfrac{T(\text{body}-\text{medium})}{MR}$	26.4	19.8	40.7

insulation index of the body is about equal in air and water at the respective critical temperatures. Finally, the insulation index of the seals' body in water appears to have been approximately 30% greater during the winter of 1955 than during the summer of 1956. The lower insulation in summer follows from the higher critical temperature and metabolic rate below the critical level observed in the seals during the summer.

Discussion

The study of the energetics of harbor seals in air and in water during winter and summer has revealed two principal new findings. The first was that increase of metabolism by cold during the summer was closely dependent upon the degree of body-skin cooling whether the medium was air or water (Fig. 7). The metabolic rates were approximately the same at comparable skin temperatures in water or in air with 20 times the cooling effect as water. It was also shown in summer that the body insulation index was the same in air or water at the critical temperature (skin temperature about 21° C). The metabolic rates could not be correlated with temperatures of the extremities, which showed a much less regular dependence on ambient temperature.

The second new finding was that, apart from two exceptional seals, the seasonal changes paralleled in direction the seasonal insulative acclimatization seen in certain land mammals with thick fur (9), i.e. the critical temperature was higher and over-all insulation was lower during the summer, and the heat production was greater over most of the temperature range. Unlike the land mammals, the seasonal change in energetics of harbor seals cannot be associated primarily with changes in insulation of the fur but with physiological adjustments in the living tissues themselves. The greater heat production at comparable cool temperatures during the summer suggests higher skin temperatures and an altered distribution of temperatures within the blubber. Yet, no seasonal differences in skin temperatures or in temperature gradients were observed, owing, presumably, to insufficient data for seals in air and to insufficient sensitivity of thermocouple measurements for seals in water. It may be appreciated that with the existing small temperature differences between skin and water (maximum 2° C), more sensitive methods would be required for the detection of seasonal changes, which might be no more than 1/2° C.

A puzzling outcome of this study was the seasonal shift in metabolic response to cold corresponding to the same skin temperature. So far as we are aware, this adjustment has not been previously reported. It is apparent that the same skin temperature corresponded to a greater heat flow in the summer than in the winter animals, and that compensatory shifts must have occurred in the avenues of heat loss. One possibility is that the temperature of the body surface was not changed, but more heat was lost from the appendages during the summer, through some modification in operation of the heat-exchanger system characteristic of aquatic mammals (11). Another possibility is that more heat was lost by evaporative cooling during the summer, but when the seal was in water this would have to be entirely from the lungs.

The seasonal changes suggested above can be regarded as extensions of the immediate compensations to changes in ambient temperature. As the body skin temperature increased, above critical temperature, heat loss from the body surface apparently decreased while heat loss through other channels (appendages and possibly evaporation) must have increased. This can be deduced from the fact that metabolism (and total heat loss) was independent of ambient temperature at skin temperatures above about 21° C (Fig. 8), yet the temperature difference between skin and ambient (and hence heat flow) decreased as the skin temperature increased above 21° C (Fig. 2). Direct measurements of heat flow from the body surface in water also suggest decreasing flow through that surface with increasing temperature in the thermoneutral zone, but the data were insufficient for final decision.

The central importance of skin temperatures in the metabolic responses of seals raises important problems concerning the stimulation of metabolism through peripheral nervous impulses. The approximate equality of metabolism in air and water at equal skin temperatures conforms with the view (1, 2) that thermogenesis is determined by peripheral impulses that are dependent on temperature in the skin. The seasonal shift in metabolic response for the same skin temperature implies a shift in nervous impulses with greater peripheral stimulation of metabolism in summer animals. It is unfortunate that integrative methods do not exist for assessing peripheral nervous stimulation, for very large species differences must exist, particularly between well-furred species with regularly warm skin and "bare skinned" species with variably cold skin.

Acknowledgment

We are grateful to L. W. Scattergood, U.S. Fisheries, Wildlife Service, Boothbay Harbor, for advising us of the steps necessary to assure the capture of seals.

References

1. BAZETT, H. C. Theory of reflex controls to explain regulation of body temperature at rest and during exercise. J. Appl. Physiol. 4, 245–262 (1951).
2. CARLSON, L. D. Man in cold environment. Arctic Aeromed. Lab. Monog. 77–79 (1954).
3. HART, J. S. Seasonal changes in insulation of the fur. Can. J. Zool. 34, 53–57 (1956).
4. HART, J. S. Climatic and temperature induced changes in the energetics of homeotherms. Rev. can. biol. 16, 133–174 (1957).
5. HART, J. S. and HEROUX, O. A comparison of some seasonal and temperature changes in Peromyscus; cold resistance, metabolism, and pelage insulation. Can. J. Zool. 31, 528 (1953).
6. IRVING, L. Physiological insulation of swine as bare-skinned mammals. J. Appl. Physiol. 9, 414–420 (1956).
7. IRVING, L. and HART, J. S. The metabolism and insulation of seals as bare-skinned mammals in cold water. Can. J. Zool. 35, 497–511 (1957).
8. IRVING, L. and KROG, J. Temperature of skin in the arctic as a regulator of heat. J. Appl. Physiol. 7, 355–365 (1955).
9. IRVING, L., KROG, J., and MONSON, M. The metabolism of some Alaskan animals in winter and summer. Physiol. Zool. 88, 173 (1935).
10. SCHOLANDER, P. F., HOCK, R., WALTERS, V., JOHNSON, F., and IRVING, L. Heat regulation in some arctic and tropical mammals and birds. Biol. Bull. 99, 237–258 (1950).
11. SCHOLANDER, P. F. and SCHEVILL, W. E. Countercurrent vascular heat exchange in the fins of whales. J. Appl. Physiol. 8, 279–282 (1955).
12. SCHOLANDER, P. F., WALTERS, V., HOCK, R., and IRVING, L. Body insulation of some arctic and tropical mammals and birds. Biol. Bull. 99, 225–236 (1950).

55

SIZE–FECUNDITY RELATIONSHIPS AND THEIR EVOLUTIONARY IMPLICATIONS IN FIVE DESMOGNATHINE SALAMANDERS

Stephen G. Tilley

Museum of Zoology, University of Michigan, Ann Arbor

Received June 5, 1968

The plethodontid salamander genus *Desmognathus* comprises seven species according to current taxonomy, of which six occur in, and four are endemic to the Appalachian Mountain system of eastern North America. Over most of the southern Blue Ridge Physiographic Province several of these forms may exist sympatrically. An apparent maximum of sympatry occurs in the Balsam Mountains of southwestern Virginia, where five species, *D. quadramaculatus, D. monticola, D. fuscus, D. ochrophaeus,* and *D. wrighti* occur in abundance.

Organ (1961) studied the ecological relationships and population dynamics of these species at Whitetop Mountain and Mt. Rogers in the Balsam Mountains. Hairston (1949) compared the ecologies of *D. quadramaculatus, D. monticola, D. ochrophaeus,* and *D. wrighti* in the Black Mountains of North Carolina where those four forms occur sympatrically. Both authors found that, in the order given above, these species form a series in which decreasing size is paralleled by an increasing tendency toward terrestrial habits. Organ further found that the trend is also paralleled by increasing juvenile survivorship. He concluded that heavier juvenile mortality is associated with aquatic sites, and that *D. quadramaculatus, D. monticola, D. fuscus, D. ochrophaeus,* and *D. wrighti* represent an evolutionary trend in which selection has favored progressively more terrestrial habits.

Size and egg production are positively correlated in the genus *Desmognathus,* as they are in many animals. Organ (1961) also emphasized that the larger species lay larger clutches than the smaller ones, and that the evolutionary trend within the

genus has been "the gradual transformation of a population with a high egg production and low survival into a population with low egg production and a high survival to maturity." He found no differences in number of clutches per year or age at maturity that might compensate for differences in clutch size.

This paper attempts to further explore and compare the relationships between size and fecundity among the five sympatric species of *Desmognathus* and to elaborate on the hypotheses drawn by Organ relative to evolutionary trends in reproductive habits. In particular I have sought to determine whether fecundity differences among the five species are explained simply by differences in their sizes, or whether size–fecundity relationships are more complex.

MATERIALS AND METHODS

This study is based mainly on Organ's series of *Desmognathus* from the Balsam Mountains. With regard to the species *wrighti* and *quadramaculatus,* I restricted this study to these series. I have included specimens of *D. monticola* from western North Carolina in addition to specimens from the Balsam Mountains in an attempt to include more of the total snout–vent length range for that species. Data on series of *D. ochrophaeus* from the vicinity of Highlands, North Carolina and *D. fuscus* from Licking County, Ohio are included where comparisons with Balsam Mountain material of those two species are appropriate.

Whenever possible, only females with eggs greater than 1 mm in diameter were examined. Otherwise it was difficult to distinguish smaller eggs from those to be deposited the following year, since in the

EVOLUTION, 1968, Vol. 22, pp. 806-816.

early stages of yolk deposition egg sizes are so variable as to obscure the differences between the clutches of successive years.

Snout–vent length measures the distance from the tip of the snout to the posterior angle of the vent. The method of covariance analysis was utilized to compare the slopes and elevations of the regression lines for the five species, using the methods and forms of calculations given in Snedecor (1956). The squared deviations and cross products of deviations were calculated from computer calculated raw sums, sums of squares, and sums of cross products. In the case of *D. quadramaculatus* rounding error prevented the use of computer calculated raw sums, and hand-calculated sums were used instead.

SUMMARY OF HABITS AND LIFE HISTORIES

The following accounts are based primarily on the studies of Hairston and Organ, supplemented in certain cases by my own observations.

Female Reproductive Cycles

Organ concluded that all five of the species deposit eggs biennially, but Martof and Rose (1963) found evidence for annual egg laying in *D. ochrophaeus* in the southern Appalachians. Tilley and Tinkle (1968) have presented evidence for an annual or possibly even biannual cycle in *D. ochrophaeus* in the vicinity of Mt. Mitchell and in the Balsam Mountains. Spight (1967) concluded that *D. fuscus* deposits eggs annually in eastern North Carolina and Harrison (1967) found that a sixth species, *D. aeneus*, also lays annually. Martof (1962) found evidence for biennial reproduction in another desmognathine, *Leurognathus marmoratus*.

The same weaknesses which Tilley and Tinkle found in the arguments for biennial egg laying in ⁻*D. ochrophaeus* probably apply as well to *D. wrighti, D. fuscus, D. monticola*, and *D. quadramaculatus*. Spight's study bears this out for *D. fuscus*.

Harrison's work indicates that annual egg laying may occur in *D. aeneus*. The evidence for bienniality in *Leurognathus* is not, in my opinion, compelling. In view of these arguments it would seem dangerous to assume bienniality in *D. wrighti, D. monticola*, and *D. quadramaculatus*. While more data on this point are sorely needed, I shall assume all five species dealt with here to be annual reproducers.

Nesting Habits

All five species exhibit parental care, in which the females remain with the eggs until hatching. Pope (1924) found that females of *D. monticola* and *D. quadramaculatus* attach each egg individually to the roof of the nesting cavity so that the eggs form a flat mass one or two eggs thick, whereas *D. fuscus, D. ochrophaeus*, and *D. wrighti* (information on the latter species from Organ, 1961) generally deposit their eggs in spherical clusters with only a few actually attached to the roof of the nesting cavity.

Females of the five species utilize somewhat different sites for egg deposition. *D. quadramaculatus* utilizes the most aquatic sites, depositing eggs on the undersides of rocks in the beds of streams and beneath small waterfalls. *D. monticola, D. ochrophaeus*, and *D. wrighti* deposit eggs in less aquatic sites than *D. quadramaculatus*, beneath stream banks and, in the case of *D. ochrophaeus*, beneath moss on rocks and logs in seepage areas. *D. fuscus* appears to lay eggs in situations intermediate between those utilized by *D. quadramaculatus* and those used by the other species.

Length of the Larval Period

The length of the larval period varies greatly among the five species, and reflects the aquatic to terrestrial trend discussed above. In the terrestrial *D. wrighti* metamorphosis occurs prior to hatching (one wonders, therefore, why it deposits its eggs in aquatic sites). Organ gave estimates of 26–28 months for *D. quadramaculatus*, 12–

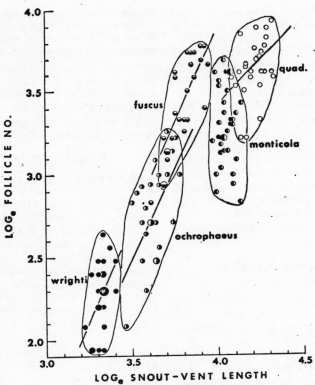

Fig. 1. Relationships between size and fecundity in five species of *Desmognathus*. Lines represent least squares regression lines of log. follicle number on log. snout–vent length.

13 months for *D. monticola*, 13–16 months for *D. fuscus*, and 10–11 months for *D. ochrophaeus*. The estimate for *D. ochrophaeus* is in error (Tilley and Tinkle, 1968); the larval period of that species is from 4 to 6 months at Mt. Mitchell, North Carolina.

Age at Maturity

Organ estimated that males of all five species matured at 3.5 years of age, while Spight (1967) estimated 3 years for males of *D. fuscus*. Both authors concluded that females require an additional year to produce their first clutch of eggs.

Habitats

D. quadramaculatus occurs chiefly in larger and faster streams, while *D. monti-*

cola prefers the banks of streams, as does *D. fuscus*. Organ found that both *D. ochrophaeus* and *D. wrighti* occur in terrestrial situations. Males of both species are largely terrestrial during the summer months, moving to aquatic sites such as seepage areas and spring heads during the winter. His data, as well as Hairston's and my own observations, indicate that of the two, *D. wrighti* is the more terrestrial. The aquatic sites preferred by *D. ochrophaeus* are of the seepage area–spring head variety, rather than the stream or stream side habitats occupied by *D. quadramaculatus* and *D. monticola*.

The species are also segregated altitudinally to a certain degree. *D. ochrophaeus* occurs from the lowest to the highest avail-

TABLE 1. *Summary of regression data.* n = *sample size,* r = *correlation coefficient. Equations and correlation coefficients are for regressions' of log. follicle number on log. snout–vent length.* v = *Balsam Mountains (Virginia),* o = *Ohio.*

Species	n	r	Significance level	Regression equation
D. wrighti	23	0.458	0.050	$Y = 2.4130X - 5.7235$
D. ochrophaeus	25	0.598	0.010	$Y = 2.1773X - 5.1407$
D. fuscus (v)	26	0.837	0.001	$Y = 2.2845X - 5.2727$
D. fuscus (o)	18	0.687	0.010	$Y = 1.7484X - 3.3944$
D. monticola	35	−0.163	< 0.100	–
D. quadramac.	26	0.390	0.050	$Y = 1.0700X - 0.8825$

able habitats in the Appalachians. In the Balsam Mountains *D. fuscus* has a similar distribution, but does not extend as high as does *D. ochrophaeus*, while *D. quadramaculatus* and *D. monticola* occur from the lowest elevations in the Balsam Mountains to just above 5000 feet. Organ found that *D. fuscus* and *D. monticola* have mutually exclusive distributions, with *D. fuscus* occupying the banks of the headwaters of streams at high elevations and *D. monticola* occupying the banks of streams at lower elevations. *D. wrighti* is essentially a high elevation species, whose populations reach their maximum densities in the spruce–fir forests of the southern Appalachians. However, it extends to as low as 3000 feet near Mt. Mitchell (personal observation and Hairston, 1949) and Organ found it as low as 3500 feet in the Balsam Mountains.

RESULTS

Figure 1 shows the relationship between snout–vent length and follicle number in the five species studied. Plots of the untransformed data were curvilinear, presumably because follicle number is a function of body volume rather than body length. Furthermore, the variance in follicle number was positively correlated with snout–vent length. For these reasons both variables were converted to their natural logarithms, which are plotted in Figure 1. All of the statistics discussed below are based on the natural logarithms of the data.

The log.–log. transformation succeeded in making the variances along the regression lines relatively homogeneous, but not in removing all of the curvilinearity. *D. wrighti* appears to have somewhat higher log. follicle number values than might have been expected from extrapolation from the regression for *D. ochrophaeus*. *D. quadramaculatus*, on the other hand, appears to have slightly lower values. Table 1 gives the correlation coefficients and regression equations for the five species, Table 2 the results of the covariance analyses in which the regression for *D. ochrophaeus* was compared with those for the other four species. Whereas there is a suggestion of curvilinearity when all the species are graphed together, the regressions for *D. wrighti* and *D. quadramaculatus* do not differ significantly from that for *D. ochrophaeus* at the five percent level, neither with respect to the slopes nor to the elevations of the regression lines (Tables 2 and 3). The analysis suggests, rather, that the relationship between snout–vent length and fecundity is identical in the species *wrighti*, *ochrophaeus*, and *quadramaculatus*.

Since the correlation coefficient for *D. monticola* is insignificant (in fact, negative) at the five percent level, that species was excluded from the covariance analysis. The hypothesis that *D. monticola* lies on the regression line common to *D. wrighti*, *D. ochrophaeus*, and *D. quadramaculatus* was tested as follows: A single regression line was calculated for the three species, having the equation $Y = 1.5027X - 2.7020$. From this equation the mean log. follicle number corresponding to the mean log. snout–vent length was calculated (3.3931). This value

TABLE 2. *Summary of covariance analyses. F tests for similarity of slopes and elevations constructed as in Snedecor, 1956. Subscripts as in Table 1. Based on log.-log. transform.*

Test	Slopes		Elevations		Conclusions	
	F	Significance level	F	Significance level	Slopes	Elevations
Overall (less *monticola*)	1.100	< 0.05	27.235	0.01	equal	different
ochrophaeus vs. *wrighti*	0.040	< 0.05	1.754	< 0.05	equal	equal
ochrophaeus vs. *fuscus* (v)	0.024	< 0.05	10.273	0.01	equal	different
ochrophaeus vs. *fuscus* (o)	0.282	< 0.05	4.495	0.05	equal	different
ochrophaeus vs. *quadramac.*	1.821	< 0.05	0.349	< 0.05	equal	equal
fuscus (v) vs. *fuscus* (o)	0.786	< 0.05	5.373	0.05	equal	different

was compared with the actual value for *D. monticola* (3.3001) by means of a *t*-test. The resultant $t = 2.1577$, df $= 33$ is significant at the five percent level. Thus *D. monticola* appears to lay somewhat fewer than the expected number of eggs.

In order to further test the hypothesis that the relationship between clutch size and body size is the same in both *D. wrighti* and *D. ochrophaeus*, the clutch sizes of female *D. wrighti* were compared with those of very small female *D. ochrophaeus* from the southwestern portion of the latter's range near Highlands, North Carolina. These data were not analyzed statistically but, as shown in Figure 2, female *D. ochrophaeus* of the same size range as *D. wrighti* lay approximately the same number of eggs.

The overall covariance analysis (excluding *D. monticola*) shown in Tables 2 and 3 indicates that all five species lie on lines with the same slope, but that the hypothesis that all lie on a single line is rejected at the one percent level. Comparison of *D. ochrophaeus* with the other species has shown that it lies on the same regression line as *D. wrighti* and *D. quadramaculatus* but on a different line from *D. fuscus*. At any given size then, *D. fuscus* lays more eggs than *D. ochrophaeus* whereas the increase in fecundity per unit increase in size is the same for all the species. The mean number of eggs carried by females of *D. fuscus* examined (31.4), in fact, exceeded the mean number contained in females of *D. monticola* (28.1), although the difference

is not significant at the five percent level ($t = 1.0057$, $.4 > P > .3$). Thus *D. fuscus*, for its size, has a higher fecundity than any of the other species.

The Balsam Mountain region is one of the few areas in the Blue Ridge Physiographic Province where *D. fuscus* occurs, and is perhaps the only part of its extensive range where it is sympatric with as many other species of *Desmognathus*. It seemed possible, therefore, that the reproductive properties of the species in the Balsams might differ from those in other parts of its range. In order to test for such differences, the regression in the Balsam Mountain material was compared with that in a series of 19 females from Licking County, Ohio (UMMZ 125516–17). One of the latter was discarded from the analysis because she contained abnormally few follicles. The regressions are superimposed in Figure 3, and the results of the covariance analysis comparing them are given in Tables 2 and 3. The difference between the slopes is not significant at the five percent level but that between the elevations of the regression lines is, the elevation for the Balsam Mountain series being higher. Furthermore, the Balsam Mountain specimens are larger. Both of these factors would appear to indicate that *D. fuscus* in that region are considerably more fecund than at least those from the Ohio population.

The covariance analysis also indicates that Ohio specimens differ significantly from *D. ochrophaeus*, although less than Balsam Mountain *D. fuscus* do.

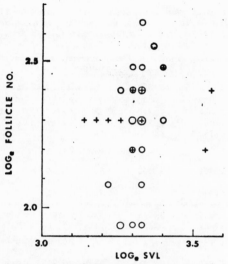

FIG. 2. Relationships between size and fecundity in *Desmognathus wrighti* (circles) from the Balsam Mountains and *D. ochrophaeus* (crosses) from Cullasaja Gorge near Highlands, North Carolina. Regression lines and transformations as in Fig. 1.

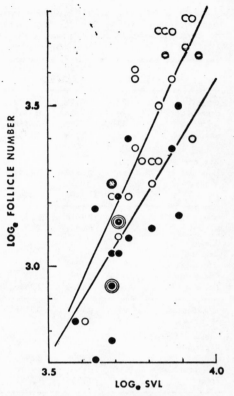

FIG. 3. Relationships between size and fecundity in *D. fuscus* from the Balsam Mountains (hollow circles) and Ohio (solid circles). Regression lines and transformations as in Fig. 1.

Assuming a constant egg volume–body volume relationship in the five species, the regression of clutch size on body length would appear to indicate that a reasonably constant relationship is maintained between clutch volume and body volume, at least among the species *wrighti*, *ochrophaeus*, and *quadramaculatus*. From the comparison of regressions one might expect that the ratio of clutch volume to body volume is higher in *D. fuscus* and lower in *D. monticola*. Ratios were calculated for the specimens examined, and their means among the five species are compared in Figure 4. The clutch volumes were based on the diameters of the largest eggs found in each of the species. These were: *D. wrighti*, 2.5 mm; *D. ochrophaeus*, 3.0 mm; *D. fuscus*, 3.0 mm; *D. monticola*, 4.0 mm; and *D. quadramaculatus*, 4.0 mm. Body volumes were calculated as perfect cylinders using snout–vent length as length and width at the axilla as diameter. The ratios of axillary width to snout–vent length were

compared among the five species. Those species between which the ratios did not differ significantly at the five percent level were all assigned the ratios' mean value for those species. Trunk-length to body-length ratios were also compared and found not to differ significantly at the five percent level among the five species. Thus snout–vent length could be used to compute body volumes. Body volumes were then calculated as the following functions of snout–vent lengths: *D. wrighti*, *D. ochrophaeus*, and *D. fuscus*, $V = .0142(SVL^3)$; *D. monticola*, $V = .0191(SVL^3)$; and *D. quadramaculatus*, $V = .0172(SVL^3)$.

TABLE 3. *Details of individual covariance analyses, constructed after Snedecor, 1956.* f = *degrees of freedom;* x = *deviations from log. mean snout-vent lengths,* y = *deviations from log. mean follicle numbers,* b = *slopes,* SS = *sum of squared deviations from regression line,* MS = *mean squared deviations from regression line (residual variances).*

Source	f	Deviations from means			b	Deviations from reg.		
		Σx²	Σxy	Σy²		f	SS	MS
wrighti	22	0.0414	0.0999	0.9482	2.4130	21	0.7071	0.0336
ochrophaeus	24	0.1618	0.3523	2.1465	2.1773	23	1.3795	0.0599
fuscus	˙25	0.2390	0.5460	2.0302	2.2845	24	0.7829	0.0326
quadramac.	25	0.1128	0.1207	0.8542	1.0700	24	0.7251	0.0302
Pooled						92	3.5946	0.0390
Reg. coef.						3	0.1288	0.0429
Common		0.5550	1.1189	5.9791	2.0160	95	3.7234	0.0391
Adj. means						3	3.1948	1.0649
Total		11.1105	17.3461	33.9995		98	6.9182	
ochrophaeus	24	0.1618	0.3523	2.1465	2.1773	23	1.3795	0.0599
wrighti	22	0.0414	0.0999	0.9482	2.4130	21	0.7071	0.0336
Pooled						44	2.0866	0.0474
Reg. coef.						1	0.0019	0.0019
Common		0.2032	0.4522	3.0947	2.2253	45	2.0885	0.0464
Adj. means						1	0.0814	0.0814
Total		1.3800	2.2639	5.8838		46	2.1699	
ochrophaeus	24	0.1618	0.3523	2.1465	2.1773	23	1.3795	0.0599
fuscus (v)	25	0.2390	0.5460	2.0302	2.2845	24	0.7829	0.0326
Pooled						47	2.1624	0.0460
Reg. coef.						1	0.0011	0.0011
Common		0.4008	0.8983	4.1767	2.2412	48	2.1635	0.0450
Adj. means						1	0.4623	0.4623
Total		0.7731	2.3092	9.5231		49	2.6258	
ochrophaeus	24	0.1618	0.3523	2.1465	2.1773	23	1.3795	0.0599
quadramac.	25	0.1128	0.1207	0.8542	1.0700	24	0.7251	0.0302
Pooled						47	2.1046	0.0447
Reg. coef.						1	0.0814	0.0814
Common		0.2746	0.4730	3.0007	1.7225	48	2.1860	0.0455
Adj. means						1	0.0159	0.0159
Total		4.7530	7.0763	12.7371		49	2.2019	
fuscus (v)	25	0.2390	0.5460	2.0302	2.2845	24	0.7829	0.0326
fuscus (o)	17	0.1276	0.2231	0.8261	1.7484	16	0.4360	0.0256
Pooled						40	1.2189	0.0304
Reg. coef.						1	0.0239	0.0239
Common		0.3666	0.7691	2.8563	2.0979	41	1.2428	0.0303
Adj. means						1	0.1628	0.1628
Total		0.4247	0.9956	3.7394		42	1.4056	
ochrophaeus	24	0.1618	0.3523	2.1465	2.1773	23	1.3795	0.0599
fuscus (o)	17	0.1276	0.2231	0.8261	1.7484	16	0.4360	0.0256
Pooled						39	1.8155	0.0465
Reg. coef.						1	0.0131	0.0131
Common		0.2894	0.5754	2.9726	1.9882	40	1.8286	0.0457
Adj. means						1	0.2162	0.2162
Total		0.3878	0.9404	4.3253		41	2.0448	

The ratios for the five species are graphed in Figure 4. Non-overlap of the black boxes, representing twice the standard error on either side of the means, indicates mean differences significant at approximately the five percent level. As expected from the covariance analysis, *D. fuscus* is characterized by the highest ratios of the five species, and differs significantly from all but *D. ochrophaeus*. The mean ratio for *D. ochrophaeus* is significantly higher than those for *D. wrighti* and *D. quadramaculatus*. No significant differences occur among the latter three species. Thus, while *D. wrighti*, *D. ochrophaeus*, and *D. quadramaculatus* lie on the same regression line when follicle number is plotted against snout–vent length, this regression does not maintain a constant clutch volume–body volume ratio among the three species using the criteria for calculating clutch and body volumes given above.

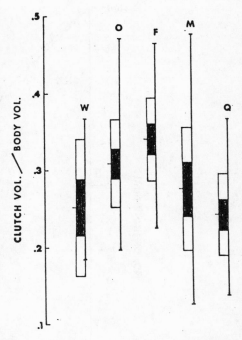

FIG. 4. Comparison of clutch volume–body volume ratios among the five species of *Desmognathus*. Solid boxes represent twice the standard error, hollow boxes one standard deviation on either side of each mean.

DISCUSSION

Fecundity is only one of many variables subject to adjustment by natural selection in the maximization of individual fitness. In the genus *Desmognathus* fecundity is intimately related to body size, both within and between species. At the interspecific level, however, this relationship is not perfect. Considering the variety of habitats exploited by the species dealt with here, perhaps it is closer than one would intuitively expect, particularly among the series *wrighti*, *ochrophaeus*, and *quadramaculatus*. Any theory concerned with the evolutionary modification of demographic parameters in the genus *Desmognathus* must somehow explain both the overall closeness of this relationship and its imperfections.

One means of reconciling the similarity of the relationship in these species with the diversity of their habitats would be to conclude that selection is able to increase fecundity only by increasing body size, and that high fecundities are selectively advantageous in aquatic habitats. This would ignore the imperfections of the relationship between size and fecundity and, more seriously, leaves unanswered the question of the selective advantage of high fecundity in aquatic habitats. Organ's (1961) data show mortality to be heavier in such situations, but to hypothesize that this results in selection for increased fecundity violates the arguments of Lack (1954), who pointed out that high mortality rates result from high fecundities.

Assuming, as most authors have, that aquatic situations are the ancestral habitat of the genus *Desmognathus* (Dunn, 1926; Wake, 1966), and that body size differences were established in advance of terrestrial tendencies in the smaller forms, selection operating whenever the various species came into contact might have re-

63

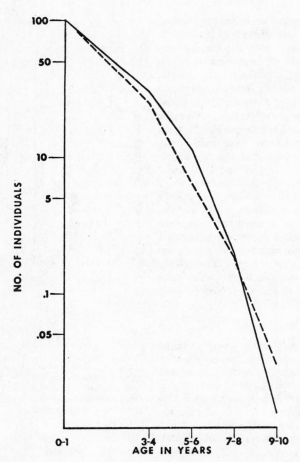

Fig. 5. Survivorship curves for males of *D. fuscus* (solid line) and *D. monticola* (broken line) from the Balsam Mountains. Data on numbers of individuals in successive year classes from Organ, 1961. See text for additional explanation.

sulted in their displacement into different habitats. Terrestrial tendencies would have been most strongly favored in the smaller forms, since these were (and still are) subject to predation by larger salamanders. The latter, by virtue of their size, would have been able to remain in the ancestral habitat.

The data presented in this paper indicate that positive size–fecundity correlations are evident both within and between the species examined. It seems reasonable to assume that such correlations also held among the ancestors of the present forms, so that the larger forms were also the most fecund, just as they are today. This, in turn, would have led to the higher juvenile mortality rates among aquatic species that Organ observed in his data.

The data on clutch volume–body volume ratios suggest that egg size, as well as clutch size has been altered in the evolution of the reproductive rates of the forms studied. Thus *D. ochrophaeus*, while it lies on the same size–fecundity regression line as *D. wrighti* and *D. quadramaculatus*, is characterized by a higher clutch volume–body volume ratio than either of those two species. *D. monticola*, on the other hand, lays fewer eggs than expected from the *wrighti–ochrophaeus–quadramaculatus* regression, but evidently amasses the same relative volume of yolk per clutch.

Clutch volume–body volume ratios are probably more meaningful indications of the actual amount of effort expended at each reproduction than are clutch sizes alone, and do not appear to correlate at all closely with the aquatic to terrestrial trend. *D. fuscus* is particularly discrepant in this regard (Fig. 4), as well as in its average clutch size (Fig. 1). Of the five species considered here, *D. fuscus* is the only one in which the adults have not evolved some means of minimizing predation by larger salamanders in aquatic habitats. *D. quadramaculatus* and *D. monticola* share the advantage of large size. Mature males of *D. ochrophaeus* and both sexes of *D. wrighti* are largely terrestrial during most of the year. The fact that brooding females of both *D. ochrophaeus* and *D. fuscus* are probably subjected to heavier mortality than the other species should cause selection to favor greater reproductive efforts per season (Williams, 1966). Figure 5 compares the survivorship curves for males of *D. fuscus* and *D. monticola*, based on Organ's data for numbers of males in different year classes and mine on fecundities (Organ assumed a larger clutch size in *D. monticola*, based on clutches of the two species that he found in the field). The curves, similar as they are, do indicate slightly lower adult survivorship in *D. fuscus*. Since in these two species both sexes occupy similar habitats, female survivorship curves of the two should exhibit a similar relationship to one another. Organ estimated the mean annual survival rate of brooding females of *D. fuscus* to be the lowest of the five species. However, since he concluded that the species had a biennial laying cycle he also assumed that he could distinguish between females that had brooded during the previous year and those which would produce eggs during the current year, and used this information to calculate the mean annual survival rate for brooding females. Since Martof and Rose (1963) and Tilley and Tinkle (1968) have presented reasons for doubting the presence of a biennial laying cycle, the groups of animals that Organ compared probably did not represent groups of females that were depositing eggs in successive years. Thus, with our present inability to age female salamanders, it is extremely doubtful whether survivorship curves can be constructed for that sex.

If the shorter adult life expectancy of *D. fuscus* is in fact attributable to predation by large aquatic *Desmognathus*, one might expect the reproductive effort per season of individuals free of that source of mortality to be lower. Figure 3 indicates that this may in fact be the case. Female *D. fuscus* from the Balsam Mountains do lay more eggs than those from the Licking County, Ohio population. This is attributable both to their larger size and to a different size–fecundity relationship, whereby for any given size, females of the Balsam Mountain population lay more eggs than females from Ohio. Perhaps their larger size is also an adaptation directed toward increased fecundity.

The fact that *D. fuscus* combines relatively small size and aquatic habits may account for its absence throughout most of the southern Blue Ridge Physiographic Province, in which its preferred habitats are occupied by larger salamanders. As suggested by Dunn (1926) and Organ (1961), competition with *D. monticola*, as well as predation by it and other large salamanders, may be important in determining the distribution of *D. fuscus*.

SUMMARY

Size and fecundity are positively correlated in four of the five species of *Desmog-*

65

nathus inhabiting the Balsam Mountains of southwestern Virginia. This correlation is manifest both inter- and intraspecifically.

Size–fecundity relationships are identical in *D. wrighti, D. ochrophaeus,* and *D. quadramaculatus,* while *D. fuscus* has a higher and *D. monticola* a lower fecundity than expected by extrapolation of the common regression for the other three species. *D. fuscus* and *D. ochrophaeus* both exhibit higher clutch volume–body volume ratios than do the other species.

It is hypothesized that selection has favored terrestrial tendencies in the smaller species because of their vulnerability to predation by larger aquatic salamanders. The fact that the smaller species are necessarily less fecund has resulted in their exhibiting lower mortality rates. The relatively high reproductive efforts of *D. fuscus* and *D. ochrophaeus* may result from their combining relatively small size with aquatic habits.

Acknowledgments

I wish to thank Dr. Donald W. Tinkle, Dr. Charles F. Walker, Dr. Richard C. Bruce, and Kraig Adler for their criticisms of the manuscript, Dr. Tinkle and Dr. James A. Organ for the numerous discussions that led to its inception, and my wife, Mary for her assistance in its preparation. This research was supported by National Science Foundation Grant GB-6230 to the University of Michigan, for research in systematic and evolutionary biology.

Literature Cited

Hairston, N. G. 1949. The local distribution and ecology of the plethodontid salamanders of the southern Appalachians. Ecol. Monog. 19:47–73.

Harrison, J. R. 1967. Observations on the life history, ecology and distribution of *Desmognathus aeneus aeneus* Brown and Bishop. Amer. Mid. Natur. 77(2):356–370.

Lack, D. 1954. The evolution of reproductive rates. *In* J. S. Huxley, A. C. Hardy, E. B. Ford (eds.), Evolution as a process. Allen and Unwin, London.

Martof, B. S. 1962. Some aspects of the life history and ecology of the salamander *Leurognathus.* Amer. Mid. Natur. 67(1):1–35.

Martof, B. S., and F. L. Rose. 1963. Geographic variation in southern populations of *Desmognathus ochrophaeus.* Amer. Mid. Natur. 69(2):376–425.

Organ, J. A. 1961. Studies of the local distribution, life history, and population dynamics of the salamander genus *Desmognathus* in Virginia. Ecol. Monog. 31:189–220.

Pope, C. H. 1924. Notes on North Carolina salamanders, with especial reference to the egg-laying habits of *Leurognathus* and *Desmognathus.* Amer. Mus. Nov. 306:1–19.

Snedecor, G. W. 1956. Statistical methods. Iowa State Univ. Press, Ames.

Spight, T. M. 1967. Population structure and biomass production by a stream salamander. Amer. Mid. Natur. 78(2):437–447.

Tilley, S. G., and D. W. Tinkle. 1968. A reinterpretation of the reproductive cycle and demography of the salamander *Desmognathus ochrophaeus.* Copeia 1968(2):299–303.

Wake, D. B. 1966. Comparative osteology and evolution of the lungless salamanders, family Plethodontidae. Mem. S. California Acad. Sci. 4:1–111.

Williams, G. C. 1966. Natural selection, the costs of reproduction, and a refinement of Lack's principle. Amer. Natur. 100(916):687–690.

A Field Study of Temperature Relations in the Galápagos Marine Iguana

George A. Bartholomew

When marine iguanas are on shore, their preferred body temperature lies between 35 and 37° C, and this is 10° C (or more depending on the season) above the body temperature at which they operate while feeding at sea. They appear to be behaviorally normal with body temperatures as high as 40° C and as low as 25° C. Marine iguanas spend most of their time on shore. At Punta Espinosa on Isla Fernandina where the largest known population of the species occurs, thousands of animals haul out on the bare lava flows and remain exposed to the intense radiation of the equatorial sun throughout the day. Black bulb temperatures may exceed 50° C, but these lizards, without resorting to shade, are able to keep their body temperatures below 40° C by making postural adjustments which minimize the area of body surface exposed to the sun, and allow a maximum exposure to the relatively cool trade winds. If marine iguanas are tethered so that they cannot employ this postural thermoregulation, they soon overheat and die when exposed to the full sun.

The reluctance of marine iguanas to escape into the sea when disturbed, which has been so often commented on since the time of Darwin, appears to be related to a reluctance to cool off rather than to an avoidance of the sea.

The cooling rates in water and the heating rates in air of marine iguanas are inversely related to body size. The relatively slow rate of cooling in water suggests the existence of cardiovascular adjustments for reducing heat loss when in the water.

Introduction

THE marine iguana of the Galápagos Islands, *Amblyrhynchus cristatus*, is unique among lizards in its behavioral and physiological adjustments to the marine littoral habitat. It feeds in intertidal and subtidal areas on marine algae, spends the night and much of the day on rocks immediately adjacent to the surf zone, and lays its eggs in holes in the sand above the high tide line. In appropriate situations it is extremely abundant. Local populations often include hundreds of animals, and in some areas aggregations of more than a thousand occur. Punta Espinosa on Isla Fernandina (Narborough), where most of the present study was made, probably supports a greater biomass of lizards than any other place in the world.

The present study, carried out during January and February 1963, undertakes to examine the behavioral responses of these remarkable animals to their unique thermal environment; barren lava flows whose surface temperatures often exceed 50° C on the one hand, and, on the other, the sea with a temperature ranging from 22 to 27° C depending on the season.

Marine iguanas share, with many of the other vertebrates which live on oceanic islands, a remarkable tameness which makes them almost as easy for an investigator to work with as domestic animals. However, despite their large size, abundance, and tameness, they have been studied little. The remoteness of the islands where they live and the difficulty of maintaining them in captivity (Eibl-Eibesfeldt, 1963) have kept all but the most general aspects of their adjustments to the physical environment unknown. Much of what has been published on marine iguanas is based on the observations which Darwin made over 100 years ago, or on general observations by visitors to the Galápagos Islands concerned primarily with other matters. Information on their physiology is extremely limited. Schmidt-Nielsen and Fange (1958) have reported briefly on the salt gland. Dowling (1962) presented a semipopular account of aspects

COPEIA, 1966, Vol.2, pp. 241-250.

	$\overline{X}$	Max	Min	N	s
A. 2 to 2.5 hr after sunset.					
Deep body	26.6	27.3	25.2	13	0.6
Rock surface	26.1	27.0	25.2	13	0.5
Air	25.8	26.0	25.5	13	0.1

B. After 1 hr in "elevated basking posture."
Measurements made in full sun on bare lava,
between 1000 and 1500 hr.

	$\overline{X}$	Max	Min	N	s
Deep body	37.9	40.0	36.2	18	1.4
Skin on back	37.3	39.0	35.0	15	1.0
Lava surface	43.1	46.2	39.0	14	1.6
Air	30.4	32.0	28.1	18	1.7
Black-bulb	41.3	44.1	39.0	16	2.2

C. In "prostrate basking posture." Measurements
made between 0900 and 1620 hr; sky with
light to heavy overcast.

	$\overline{X}$	Max	Min	N	s
Deep body	32.5	37.5	26.7	24	2.8
Air	28.7	30.5	27.8	24	1.2

D. Females digging nest holes.

	$\overline{X}$	Max	Min	N	s
Deep body	33.8	38.4	25.8	18	3.1
Air	27.8	28.8	25.0	16	1.2
Sand surface	39.0	45.6	26.0	16	6.3

of their biology, including a general survey
of the daily cycle of body temperature, and
Mackay (1964) recently reported some tele-
metered data on body temperature.

METHODS

Except for the determinations of body
temperatures of egg-laying females which
were made with a quick-acting mercury
thermometer, all temperatures were measured with thermister probes accurate to
0.1° C. Body temperatures were measured
rectally with a minimum insertion of eight
cm. Surface temperatures of both animals
and substratum were determined with a
shielded "banjo-tipped" probe. Air temperature was measured in the shade above
ground occupied by the lizard being observed. Water temperatures were taken with
the same probe used for body temperatures.
When possible, the sex of the animals being
measured was determined, and in all cases
snout–vent length was measured.

Air velocities were measured in the areas
actually occupied by the lizards with a Biram
type anemometer and a stopwatch.

RESULTS

Free-Ranging Animals

Except during the breeding season, the
daily activity cycle of the marine iguana has
three sharply separate components, sleeping,
feeding, and basking, each of which is characterized by a particular pattern of body
temperatures.

The animals sleep at night either in crevices in the lava flows and rocky shores or
completely exposed on the surface of the
rocks. The adult lizards have no important
predators on land, but, at least on Punta
Espinosa, individuals a year or less old are
occasionally preyed upon by the Galápagos
hawk, *Buteo galapagoensis*. These young animals are much more wary than the adults
during the daytime, and appear always to
spend the night in cracks and crevices.

At night, the animals' temperatures fall to
that of the environment and by two to three
hr after sunset the body temperatures of the
lizards, the surface temperature of the rocks,
and the air temperature are virtually the
same (Table 1A).

The course of body temperature after sunrise depends on whether the sky is overcast
or clear, and also upon the state of the tide,
which in the Galápagos Islands has a total
excursion of almost two m. If the tide is at
or near its low point at dawn, many of the
lizards enter the water to feed shortly after
sunrise without any prior warming up. Thus,
they embark on what is by far their most
vigorous and dangerous activity with a body
temperature no higher than 26° C. In my
experience, the animals appear superficially
to be as responsive and as rapid in their
movements with a body temperature of 25–
27° C as they are with a body temperature
of 35–37° C. Indeed, animals which have
been at sea feeding, and return to shore with
body temperatures the same as that of the
sea (25–26° C), are much more alert and
difficult to capture than animals with body
temperatures 10–12° C higher which are
basking on the rocks (see DISCUSSION).

Judging from two all-day watches I maintained at Punta Espinosa, only about a third
to a half of the animals went to sea on any
given day. The others remained ashore all
day. Although feeding is more intense at low
tide than at other times, presumably because
the algae-covered rocks are then closest to
the surface, animals can be seen in the sea,
diving to feed at any stage of the tide and

it any daylight hour. However, feeding is minimal in the late afternoon. At Punta Espinosa, individuals commonly swim 500 to 800 m offshore and have been seen feeding on the bottom at a depth of at least 12 m (Hobson, 1965).

A salient feature of their activity, is that marine iguanids frequently feed at low body temperatures, 26° C or less depending on the season, whereas the activity temperatures in most other iguanids are in the middle thirties.

Postural thermoregulation.—Aside from occasional flurries of aggressive behavior, the marine iguanas usually spend their time ashore basking. Individual animals may remain for an entire day within an area of one m² completely unshaded from the intense equatorial sun. They have an interesting series of behavioral responses related to body temperature, which in turn is related to, but not strictly dependent on, the intensity of solar radiation.

There are two primary postures which the

marine iguanas assume, depending on time of day, intensity of solar radiation, and on body temperature. These postures show no apparent relation to size or to sex and their significance appears to be entirely thermoregulatory. The animals assume a "prostrate basking posture" early in the morning on either sunny or overcast days and at any time of the day when the sky is cloudy. Animals which have just returned from the sea usually assume this posture regardless of the time of day or the conditions of solar radiation. Animals in the "prostrate basking posture" lie flat on their bellies with their heads and necks on the substratum and their legs sprawled flat and approximately at right angles to the body (Fig. 1A). Their direction of orientation varies with the time of day and the intensity of solar radiation.

On Punta Espinosa, the large population of marine iguanas occupied the various tongues of a flow of pahoehoe lava. Each of these tongues is convex in cross section and each has a deep fissure running along its midline. At or shortly after sunrise (about 6:15 AM local time), the animals, approximately three-quarters of which had spent the night in the central fissure, would move to the east-facing slopes of the lava tongues (regardless of whether this was on the landward or seaward side) and assume the "prostrate basking posture." Most of the animals lay with their heads pointing uphill and thus oriented their bodies as nearly as possible at right angles to the rays of the sun so that they intercepted a maximum amount of solar radiation. This orientation was not adventitious. Frequent readjustments of position were required for its maintenance because of the comings and goings of animals to feed, and because of the intermittent displacements of individuals by those dominant to them.

Since Punta Espinosa is only about 20 km south of the equator, the sun is directly overhead during the middle of the day. During the midday hours, animals which had just returned from the sea typically assumed the "prostrate basking posture," but oriented themselves randomly with regard to direction.

When conditions of air movement and solar radiation are such that the body temperatures of the basking lizards are likely to rise above the limit which they comfortably tolerate (39–40° C), they assume a charac-

teristic and highly stereotyped "elevated basking posture" (Fig. 1B), in which the head and neck are high in the air and the front legs are extended so that the forequarters are held well clear of the substratum. This posture is similar to that assumed by some desert lizards during periods of heavy heat load (Cowles and Bogert, 1944). Animals in the "elevated basking posture" show an extremely consistent pattern of orientation at all times except for a couple of hours around noon. Under conditions of bright sunshine, almost all animals in a given group will orient the long axes of their bodies so that they head directly into the sun. With this orientation much of the back and the hindquarters are shaded by the head, neck, and shoulders. Consequently, a minimum of solar radiation is intercepted and a maximum of body surface is exposed to the relatively cool trade winds, the temperature of which rarely exceeds 30° C. The effectiveness of this posture in reducing heat input is often enhanced by the fact that the lizards take advantage of irregularities in the terrain and face uphill when orienting toward the sun. This allows them to keep their long axes parallel to the rays of the sun even when it is high in the sky.

So consistent is this orientation on the lava flows at Punta Espinosa where many hundreds of marine lizards aggregate in dense herds, that virtually every animal will be in the same posture and virtually all will have their bodies parallel so that the whole group appears to be mechanically aimed at the sun.

The body temperatures of 18 adult lizards which had held the "elevated basking posture" for at least one hr were determined (Table 1B). Body temperatures extended from 40.0 to 36.2° C, a range which overlaps the higher body temperatures of the animals in the "prostrate basking posture." Although the two ranges of temperature overlap slightly, their means differ markedly and they represent very different situations biologically; in the elevated posture the animals are staying as cool as they can, while in the prostrate posture they are obtaining as much heat from the environment as they can.

The range of body temperatures over which animals employ the "prostrate basking posture" extends at least from 26.7 to 37.5° C (Table 1C). At body temperatures below 34–35° C, body temperature *per se* appears to be the factor causing these lizards to assume the "prostrate basking posture," but the assumption of the "elevated basking posture" and the abandonment of the prostrate posture appears to depend not only on body temperature but also on the intensity of solar radiation. In open shade or under conditions of thin overcast, animals on numerous occasions were seen sprawled flat on their bellies, although not with legs outspread, with body temperatures as high as 38.4° C. Under these conditions the maintenance of a suitable body temperature was completely passive and required no behavioral regulation.

Preferred body temperature.—It is possible to obtain a reasonably precise estimate of the preferred temperature of the marine iguana by comparing the ranges of body temperatures characteristic of the prostrate and elevated postures (Tables 1B and 1C). At body temperatures of 35° C or less, the lizards assume the prostrate posture and at body temperatures above 37° C, they usually assume the elevated posture (if exposed to the sun). It thus appears that when they are at a temperature below 35° C they try to warm up and when they are at a temperature above 37° C they attempt to cool off or at least to avoid getting hotter. It is reasonable, therefore, to infer that their preferred temperature lies between 35° and 37° C, although they appear to behave in a normal manner with body temperatures as low as 25° C and as high as 40° C.

Effects of rain.—During the afternoon of 26 January it rained briskly from 3:40 to 5:00. Prior to the rain, the animals had been in the "elevated basking posture" and so presumably had body temperatures in excess of 37° C. All animals remained in the open exposed to the rain. The body temperatures of six were measured between 4:05 and 4:33. Their body temperatures ranged from 26.7 to 30.3° C and the mean was 27.1 (± 1.7)° C.

Body temperatures during egg laying.—The mating and copulation of the marine iguanas at Punta Espinosa occurred prior to our arrival. During our stay, egg laying began and reached its full peak with dozens of females often on the beach at the same time, digging nest holes and fighting among themselves.

Female marine iguanas lay their eggs in holes which they dig to a depth of about 15 inches in the moist sand on beaches at or above high tide line. The making of the nest hole involves a great expenditure of energy. Not only do the females dig a deep and commodious hole, but they fight incessantly among themselves for possession of the holes. Often a female will dig several holes before she completes one, enters it, and lays her two large eggs.

There was no single body temperature characteristic of the strenuous and critical activity of nest hole digging and egg laying. As shown in Table 1D, body temperatures during these activities sometimes were less than 26° and sometimes were more than 38° C. Moreover, the body temperature of a given female could change markedly during the activities associated with egg laying. If the female wandered around a long time over the hot sand she would, of course, warm up. If she spent a long period in the moist, cool sand of the burrow she would cool off. There was no overt difference between the behavior of females with markedly different body tempreatures, either in intensity or persistence of nest hole digging. However, the time the nest digging started appeared to depend on thermal conditions. Groups of lizards consisting only of gravid females congregated on the edges of the lava flows adjacent to the beach. On clear, sunny mornings the first females came out on the beach as much as two hr earlier than on overcast mornings. On the overcast morning of 3 February, for example, the females remained in aggregations on the lava adjacent to the nesting beach until 9:05 while on the sunny morning of 4 February, they began to dig nest holes at 7:45. However, once nest digging began, it continued independent of weather conditions. Occasional individuals even engaged in nest digging at night. In one instance, a solitary female was found laying her eggs at 2:00 AM with a body temperature of 26° C.

Incubation temperatures.—After the females lay their two eggs, which weigh between 80 and 120 g each, in a nest chamber at the bottom of the hole, they fill in the hole and cover over the entrance. An estimate of typical incubation temperatures of the eggs was obtained by placing a thermister in a nest chamber and recording its temperature at intervals during a three-day period. A maximum–minimum thermometer also was buried at a depth of 15 inches (the usual depth of

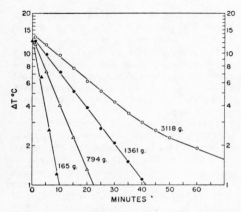

Fig. 2. The relation of the difference between deep body temperature and water temperature (ΔT) in marine iguanas being cooled from a body temperature of approximately 40° C in water with a temperature of 27 to 28° C.

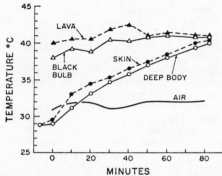

Fig. 3. The relation of skin and deep body temperature to environmental temperatures in a female marine iguana weighing 1,470 g tethered in a prostrate posture on bare lava at Punta Espinosa. Animal was placed in the sun at 10:00 AM (minute zero). Sky with thin overcast, but sun visible. Air movements at the site of the animal varied between zero and 75 cm/sec (mean 45 cm/sec).

the nest chamber) in an area where nest holes were common and left in place for three days. The maximum–minimum · thermometer showed a range of temperatures from 27.7 to 29.8° C and the thermister readings ranged from 29.4 to 30.0° C. On the basis of these measurements, it seems reasonable to assume that the development of the embryos takes place at temperatures in the vicinity of 28 to 30° C.

Experimental Studies

Cooling rates.—Although marine iguanas often enter the sea to feed when their body temperatures are in the middle twenties, they more often enter the water after a period of basking with body temperatures above 35° C. In neither situation do they pause at the water's edge nor show hesitation about

TABLE 2. THE RELATION OF SIZE OF MARINE IGUANAS TO COOLING RATE IN WATER WHEN DIFFERENCE BETWEEN BODY AND WATER TEMPERATURE IS 10° C.

Weight (g)	Cooling Rate °C/Min
165	2.53
794	1.14
1,361	0.63
1,490	0.64
3,118	0.39

entering the sea. The animals we were able to capture immediately upon their return from feeding had temperatures that did not differ significantly from that of the sea. It thus becomes a matter of both physiological and ecological interest to determine the rates of cooling of marine iguanas in water, because this determines the body temperature when they are in the water, swimming, and feeding.

The cooling rates in seawater of marine iguanas of different sizes were measured. A vinyl-sheathed thermister probe was inserted through the cloaca into the large intestine to a depth sufficient to place the thermister in the center of the abdomen. The thermister leads were then secured to the tail with adhesive tape. The iguana was placed in the sun and allowed to warm up until its deep body temperature reached 40° C; it was then secured to a wooden pole with light line so that it could move its head and legs but would not be able to swim away. The lizard was then immersed up to its nostrils in a large tide pool that had a free exchange of water with the open sea. Ripples and small waves sometimes covered the head completely with water. Body temperature and water temperature were measured at regular intervals until the former fell to within approximately 1° C of the latter. In no case did water temperature vary more than 0.5° C during an experiment, and in all cases water temperature was between 27 and 28° C (1 to 2° C higher than the open sea).

The iguanas were docile and virtually motionless during the periods of measurement. The curves in Fig. 2, which show the rates of cooling, are measures of the difference between the rates of heat loss by conduction to the water and the rates of heat production by metabolism. The curves for the three small individuals can be fitted by a straight line when plotted semilogarithmically, but the slope of the cooling curve for the largest animal decreased markedly as body temperature approached water temperature. The inverse relation of cooling rate to body weight may be seen clearly. Since the rate of cooling changed continuously as body temperature decreased, to relate the rates of cooling of the various animals to their weights it is instructive to examine the rate of change in body temperature at a given temperature difference between body and water (ΔT). The cooling rate at $\Delta T = 10°$ C can be determined from the slope of a semilogarithmic plot of the difference between body and water temperatures against time such as used in Fig. 2. The cooling rate at $\Delta T = 10°$ C decreased with increasing size, and the smallest animal had a cooling rate approximately 6.5 times that of the largest (Table 2).

Heating rates.—Measurements of rates of heating were obtained by tethering animals in the sun in areas near and similar to those in which they ordinarily basked. The lizards were captured at sunrise and placed in the shade so they would remain at air temperature. Between 10:00 and 10:30 AM, they were tethered in the full sun with their legs tied out laterally so that they could not avoid remaining in an approximation of the previously described "prostrate basking posture," although they were free to raise the head and neck. A thermister was inserted into the large intestine and its leads secured to the tail as in the cooling experiments. Core body temperature, skin temperature on the back, air temperature, substratum temperature, black-bulb temperature, and air velocity were measured at regular intervals. The course of body temperature was followed to 40° C in four animals and to heat death in one. A typical record is shown in Fig. 3. The radiant energy from the sun and the heat gained by conduction from the

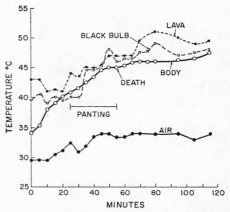

Fig. 4. The relation of deep body temperature to environmental temperatures of a female marine iguana weighing 1,418 g and tethered in a "prostrate basking posture" on a lava flow at Punta Espinosa. Animal placed in sun at 9:00 AM (minute zero). Air movement at site of the animal varied from zero to 40 cm/sec. Sun obscured by thin cloud cover starting at minute 80.

substratum caused the core body temperature to rise rapidly above air temperature and to approach black-bulb temperature. Since skin and core temperatures closely approximated each other, they offer no evidence to suggest major peripheral vasomotor responses for controlling the rate of heating over the range of temperatures tested.

The tethered animals could not effectively use behavioral or postural thermoregulation. One animal allowed to continue to heat up after its temperature reached 40° C died at a body temperature of 46° C. Its body temperature eventually rose to 47° C and in time might have risen even higher (Fig. 4).

To obtain an indication of the relation of size to heating rates, two animals, one weighing 794 g and the other weighing 3,118 g, were cooled to air temperature by placing them in the shade and then tethering them side by side on a sandy area in the full sun. The course of their body temperatures was followed to 40° C (Fig. 5). The small animal heated about twice as fast as the large one, a relative difference much less than that of the cooling rates in water. The heating rates, unlike the cooling rates, are not exponential curves and are the result of many factors, of which solar radiation, conduction from the sand, metabolic heat production, and heat loss to the air are the more obvious.

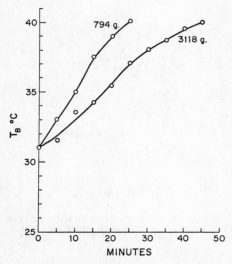

Fig. 5. The increase in body temperature of two male iguanas tethered in the "prostrate basking posture" side by side in the full sun in a sheltered area near the Darwin Biological Station on Isla Santa Cruz starting at 1:10 PM. Black-bulb temperature varied between 48 and 52° C; air temperature 33–36° C.

DISCUSSION

Among the lizards of which the temperature responses have been studied, marine iguanas are unique in two respects: (1) they are able to depend exclusively on postural changes for their behavioral regulation of body temperature, and (2) their preferred body temperature is at least 10° C above the body temperature at which they operate while feeding.

Postural thermoregulation.—Although many lizards control their body temperature in part by adjustments in posture as pointed out by Cowles and Bogert (1944), virtually all of them place a major dependence for thermoregulation on changes in location; they shuttle back and forth between full sun and shade, move in and out of holes and crevices, or burrow into the loose substratum. The marine iguanas on Punta Espinosa, however, partly because of the equable climate in which they live and partly because of the nature of the lava flows which they occupy, often regulate their body temperature while on land exclusively by postural adjustments without utilizing shade or shelter. As previously described, when the animals are be-low their preferred temperature they assume the "prostrate basking posture," but when environmental conditions are such that their body temperatures will rise above the preferred level they assume the "elevated basking posture." The effectiveness of this elevated posture in holding body temperature to within acceptable limits is demonstrated by the following facts:

1. Black-bulb and substratum temperatures in the lizard rookeries on Punta Espinosa often exceeded 50° C, but the core temperatures of the lizards in the rookeries never exceeded 40° C.

2. If animals were tethered on the lava so that they could not assume the "elevated basking posture" nor aim themselves at the sun, their body temperatures rose sharply. In the one case in which the course of body temperature of a tethered lizard was followed above 40° C, the animal died at a body temperature of 46° C.

The effectiveness of the "elevated basking posture" depends on three main factors: (1) it minimizes the area of the body that intercepts direct solar radiation, (2) it holds much of the body free of the substrate and so minimizes heat conduction from this source (and perhaps allows some heat loss by radiation from the venter to the shaded substratum), and (3) it affords maximum exposure to the relatively cool trade winds which blow regularly in the Galápagos. Air temperature of wind blowing off the sea rarely exceeds 30° C and so allows the lizards to lose to the air the heat they gain from the sun. Where shade is available from rocks or vegetation, some lizards utilize it (Dowling, 1962:172), but they do not have to do so. Thousands of lizards at places such as Punta Espinosa remain in the full heat of the equatorial sun all day long, day after day, adjusting the level of body temperature to varying conditions of heat loss and heat gain by shifts in posture and direction of orientation.

Preferred temperature versus activity temperature.—As shown previously in this paper, the activity of marine iguanas takes place over a range of body temperatures of at least 15° C. The extent of their behavioral independence of body temperature is shown by the fact that they feed in water near 25° C, and the fact that they dig nest holes

74

when their body temperatures are as low as 26° C and as high as 38° C. Nevertheless, these lizards obviously do have a preferred body temperature and when given the option, they keep body temperature between 35° and 37° C. The body temperature of the lizards while feeding in the water of course depends on their temperature when they enter the water, their size, and on how long they stay in the water. Although conclusive documentation is not yet available, on the basis of our observations at Punta Espinosa, the typical feeding pattern appears to involve only a single prolonged trip to sea and these feeding trips are made no oftener than once a day. As shown in Fig. 2, the body temperature of small marine iguanas, which was initially at 40° C, would approximate that of the water in 10 min and the body temperature of even a very large lizard would fall from 40° C to approximately that of the water within an hour. Moreover, if a lizard enters the sea early in the morning, its body temperature is already near 25 or 26° C at the time it starts to feed. Thus, much of the marine iguanas' aquatic activity (the most strenuous and hazardous part of their behavior) takes place at a body temperature which is not only remarkably low for an iguanid, but is also 10–12° C below the preferred temperature of these animals when they are on land. It is apparent that marine iguanas have conspicuous behavioral independence of temperature, and from this one can infer that they also have considerable metabolic scope for activity at low temperatures. (See Bartholomew and Tucker, 1963, 1964, for a discussion of what little is known about metabolic scope in reptiles, and Fry, 1947, for a general consideration of the topic.)

The difference between the water temperature and the preferred temperature of the marine iguana while on land offers an insight into a pattern of behavior which has become firmly established in the literature. Darwin reported (as have many other persons since) that marine iguanas, despite their aquatic habits, are extremely reluctant to enter the water when disturbed by humans. The following passage from the "Voyage of The Beagle" has been frequently quoted:

"I several times caught this same lizard, by driving it down to a point and though possessed of such perfect powers of diving and swimming, nothing would induce it to enter the water; and as often as I threw it in, it returned. . . . Perhaps this singular piece of apparent stupidity may be accounted for by the circumstance, that this reptile has no enemy whatever on shore, whereas at sea it must often fall prey to the numerous sharks. Hence, probably, urged by a fixed hereditary instinct that the shore is its place of safety, whatever the emergency may be, it there takes refuge."

Darwin's observations were accurate. It is, indeed, practically impossible to drive a marine iguana from the land into the sea, but the explanation for this pattern of behavior probably depends on factors quite different from those which Darwin adduced. In my experience, the willingness or the reluctance of this lizard to enter the water is related to its body temperature at the time it is disturbed. As pointed out above, the marine iguana while ashore during the day maintains its temperature at or above 35° C by basking. It is these basking animals with high body temperatures which are reluctant to enter the water. If one waits until he sees a lizard returning from its feeding at sea and then approaches such an animal as it comes ashore, it almost invariably returns immediately to the water and swims rapidly away. So pronounced is this tendency that I found it extremely difficult to obtain body temperatures of animals that had been at sea feeding. When they have just left water and have a body temperature approximating that of the sea, they show absolutely no reluctance to escape by retreating back into the water and swimming away. It thus seems probable that the reluctance of basking marine iguanas to escape into the sea is related to the fact that such an action would decrease body temperature by 10 or 15° C from the level at which they ordinarily maintain themselves while on shore during the daylight hours. Apparently, this preference for body temperatures between 35 and 40° C is so pronounced that they avoid entering the water except for purposes of feeding.

The adaptive significance of the marine iguanas' maintenance of an elevated body temperature of course has not been determined, but two points merit comment: (1) these lizards are highly social and have a well-developed pattern of social dominance; other things being equal a warm animal would have an advantage over a cold one, and (2) a high body temperature should facilitate digestion of seaweed; assuming a Q_{10} of 2, holding body temperature about $10°$ C above that of the sea could double the rate of digestion.

Rates of temperature change.—The field methods improvised for studying cooling rates in the present study allow only a crude estimate of the thermal conductance of marine iguanas in water, and the number and size distribution of the animals measured was too small to allow an adequate quantitative statement of the relation of size to cooling rate. The data (Table 2 and Fig. 2) do, however, afford an instructive comparison of the cooling rates in water of marine iguanas with the cooling rates in air of varanids of the same size. When the difference between body and air temperatures is $10°$ C, the cooling rate in air of a 1,000-g varanid lizard, calculated from the formula (Bartholomew and Tucker, 1964):

$$\log \text{°C/min} = -0.385 \log wt + 0.663$$

is approximately $0.3°$ C/min. This is about one-third the observed cooling rate in water of marine iguanas of the same size range. Considering the difference in the specific heats of water and air, this difference is unexpectedly small. It is, therefore, reasonable to infer that marine iguanas may have cardiovascular mechanisms for minimizing heat loss while in the water. Bartholomew and Lasiewski (1965) have shown this to be the case. However, since cooling rates in at least three other families of lizards are known to be under partial physiological control (Bartholomew and Tucker, 1963, 1964; Bartholomew, Tucker, and Lee, 1965) it is not possible to say at this time if the marine iguana's capacities in this respect are qualitatively unusual.

No data on heating rates of other large lizards directly comparable to those given in the present paper are available. It may be noted, however, that Colbert, Cowles, and Bogert (1946) measured heating rates of alligators tethered in the sun and found that heating rates were inversely related to size as they are in the marine iguana.

This study was carried out as a part of the Galápagos International Scientific Project sponsored by the National Science Foundation (GE-2370) and the University of California in cooperation with the Government of Ecuador and the Charles Darwin Foundation for the Galápagos Islands. I am indebted to Mr. Ross Kiester for enthusiastic and effective assistance in the fieldwork on Isla Fernandina.

LITERATURE CITED

BARTHOLOMEW, G. A. AND R. C. LASIEWSKI. 1965. Heating and cooling rates, heart rate, and simulated diving in the Galapagos marine iguana. Comp. Biochem. Physiol. 16:573–582.

——— AND V. A. TUCKER. 1963. Control of changes in body temperature, metabolism, and circulation by the agamid lizard, *Amphibolurus barbatus.* Physiol. Zool. 36:199–218.

——— AND ———. 1964. Size, body temperature, thermal conductance, oxygen consumption, and heart rate in Australian varanid lizards. *Ibid.* 37:341–354.

———, ———, AND A. K. LEE. 1965. Oxygen consumption, thermal conductance, and heart rate in the Australian skink, *Tiliqua scincoides.* Copeia 1965(2):169–173.

COLBERT, E. H., R. B. COWLES, AND C. M. BOGERT. 1946. Temperature tolerances in the American alligator and their bearing on the habits, evolution, and extinction of the dinosaurs. Bull. Am. Mus. Nat. Hist. 86:333–373.

COWLES, R. B. AND C. M. BOGERT. 1944. A preliminary study of the thermal requirements of desert reptiles. Bull. Am. Mus. Nat. Hist. 83:261–296.

DOWLING, H. G. 1962. Sea dragons of the Galapagos: the marine iguanas. Anim. King. 65:169–174.

EIBL-EIBESFELDT, I. 1963. Meerechsen in Gefangenschaft. Nat. Mus. 93:410–414.

FRY, F. E. J. 1947. Effects of environment on animal activity. Pub. Ont. Fish. Res. Lab. No. 68:1–62.

HOBSON, E. S. 1965. Observations on diving in the Galapagos marine iguana, *Amblyrhynchus cristatus* (Bell). Copeia 1965(2):249–250.

MACKAY, S. 1964. Galapagos tortoise and marine iguana deep body temperatures measured by radio telemetry. Nature 204:355–358.

SCHMIDT-NIELSEN, K. AND R. FANGE. 1958. Salt glands in marine reptiles. Nature 182:783–785.

DEPARTMENT OF ZOOLOGY, UNIVERSITY OF CALIFORNIA, LOS ANGELES 90024.

TERRITORIAL BEHAVIOR: THE MAIN CONTROLLING FACTOR OF A LOCAL SONG SPARROW POPULATION

Frank S. Tompa

It has been shown frequently that territories are compressible. It is also known that the average territory size for a species in a given area may be significantly influenced by local conditions. However, it has been doubted whether territories can ever shrink to a point beyond which they can become no smaller and thus set an upper limit to the numbers of that local population.

This paper describes a situation in which a local passerine population, affected by favorable environmental conditions, could reach high densities for several consecutive years, and in which the upper limit was set by territorial behavior. It throws some light on how territorial behavior, combined with other factors, may regulate a given population. Conclusions are based in part on data already available; nevertheless, references are made to factors—food and nestling mortality—that have not yet been fully investigated.

Song Sparrows (*Melospiza melodia*), the subjects of this study, defend a territory that normally includes mating, nesting, and feeding grounds, and thus falls into the territory category "A" of Nice (1941). This study, undertaken in order to find out the regulatory mechanism in a local Song Sparrow population, was started in the spring of 1960 and is still in progress. Some data concerning this population were also available for the period between 1957 and 1960 (R. Drent and G. van Tets, pers. comm.).

STUDY AREA AND ENVIRONMENT

This study was made on Mandarte Island in the Gulf Islands archipelago, on the southern coast of British Columbia; appropriate additional small-scale habitat and population surveys were carried out also on neighboring islands (Figure 1). Mandarte Island, with an area more than five hectares, rises abruptly from sea level to an average elevation of 15 meters. A longitudinal groove in the limestone block divides the island into a northeastern and southwestern half. The SW half is a grassy plateau, and is bordered by 20- to 25-meter-high cliffs along the shoreline, while the other half slopes gradually from the groove toward three- to five-meter cliffs of the NE shore.

The vegetation of Mandarte can be divided into three main zones: barren rocks and cliffs (including rocky beaches), grassy meadows, and shrubbery. The shrubbery is of primary importance in this study; it follows the longitudinal axis of the island and is supported by the relatively thick soil

THE AUK, 1962, Vol.79, No.4, pp.687-697

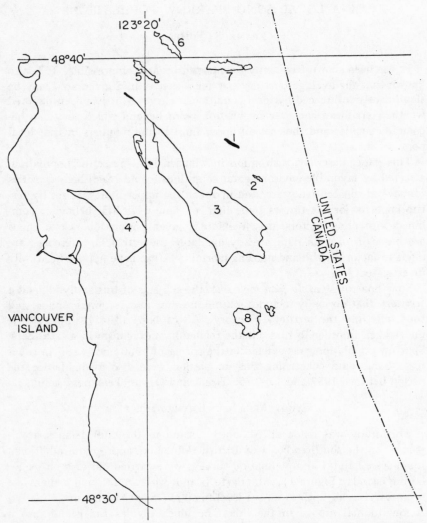

Figure 1. Mandarte Island (in black) and neighboring islands. 1. Mandarte Island; 2. Halibut Island; 3. Sidney Island; 4. James Island; 5. Forrest Island; 6. Damville Island; 7. Gooch Island; 8. D'Arcy Island.

accumulated in the groove. It reaches the NE shore at some points and altogether covers somewhat more than one hectare, while grassland covers more than 50 per cent of the island.

The composition of shrubbery is given in order of abundance: Waxberry (*Symphoricarpos albus*), Wildroses (*Rosa* spp.), Saskatoon berry (*Amelanchier florida*), Blackberries (*Rubus* spp.), Ocean Spray (*Holodiscus dis-*

78

color), and Fireweed (*Epilobium angustifolium*), one or another domi-
nating at different localities. At some places the shrubbery is heavily inter-
woven with stems of Northern Bedstraw (*Galium boreale*). Although a
few small cherry trees (*Prunus virginiana* and *P. emarginata*) are scattered through the shrubbery, taller trees can be found at one point only,
where the groove has expanded and allowed more soil to accumulate. Here
a group of trees—Douglas-fir (*Pseudotsuga menziesii*), Grand Fir (*Abies
grandia*), and Pacific Madrone (*Arbutus menziesii*)—has established itself
over an area of some 500 square meters, together with rich undergrowth
of willows (*Salix* spp.), Ocean Spray (*Holodiscus discolor*), and English
Hawthorn (*Crataegus oxyacantha*). It is important to note that at least
during the last 50 years no substantial change has occurred in the vegetation cover of the island (Anderson, 1916). ·

In the summer, grasslands are occupied by breeding colonies of Glau-
cous-winged Gulls (*Larus glaucescens*). On the steep SW cliffs two species
of cormorants (*Phalacrocorax auritus* and *Ph. pelagicus*) breed regularly,
while crevices along the shoreline offer nest sites to Pigeon guillemots
(*Cepphus columba*). Regular breeders in the shrubbery are the crows
(*Corvus brachyrhynchos*) and Song Sparrows, while Rufous Humming-
birds (*Selasphorus rufus*) are suspected to breed there. The number of
breeding crows was approximately 50 in each of the last four seasons. In
1961 two pairs of Red-winged Blackbirds (*Aegelaius phoeniceus*) raised
single broods after failures in previous years. There are neither amphibians
nor reptiles on Mandarte, and deermice (*Peromyscus maniculatus*) are the
only mammals.

SONG SPARROWS

Dense vegetation cover, absence of predators and nest parasites, sufficient moisture, and favorable climate, as well as other factors, offer exceptionally good conditions to Song Sparrows, when compared with adjacent areas. Because of the usually mild winters in this region, these
birds, belonging to the race *Melospiza melodia morphna* Oberholser, are
residents the year around. The length of the breeding season normally
extends from the second half of March to late July.

Field work was carried out during the last two summers and involved
the color banding of adult and juvenile birds, and recording features of
the breeding season. A total of 401 (93 adults and 308 young) birds were
banded. The sexes of the birds were determined by behavioral characteristics. Population counts were made approximately every fortnight during
the summers, and nearly every month through the winters 1960–1961 and
1961–1962. The number of breeding pairs remained relatively constant
(46–48 in 1960 and 47 in 1961), but the number of nonbreeding adults

79

was unknown for the first summer, because at that time they were not all banded. In 1960 the total adult population was 98–100. In 1961, 47 pairs of Song Sparrows started breeding on Mandarte. Five additional territories were occupied by unmated males throughout the season, while two unmated males composed the floating population. Thus the total number of adults at the onset of breeding was 101.

Survey of territories. Every available place in the shrubbery was utilized by Song Sparrows during the course of the study. Helped by obvious perching trees and singing posts, territory-owner males kept sharply defined boundaries throughout the breeding seasons, although the aggressiveness of the birds gradually decreased toward the end of the summers. Territorial activity reached its minimum in late July and early August, when adults entered their postnuptial molt. Suthers (1960) distinguished between utilized area and maximum territory occupied by Song Sparrows inhabiting a lakeshore environment; on Mandarte territories in the shrubbery were too small and tightly packed for this distinction to be made.

When they were feeding nestlings, adults mainly searched for food in the shrubbery. However, when foraging for themselves, they frequently entered the grassland adjacent to their territories, and occasionally the tidal zone also—the latter, to a certain extent, serving as a common feeding ground. It was only at the end of the breeding season, when caterpillars became scarce, that parents collected food items, mainly lacewings and other insects, from the grassland.

Territory boundaries in the meadows, unlike those in the shrubbery, were difficult to define. Areas in the former used by adults often overlapped; occasional fights occurred, although never with such vigor as in the shrubbery. These observations, and the obvious insignificance of the area of utilized grassland compared with the area of shrubbery defended by a pair (as will be shown later), suggest that these grassy areas should not be considered as part of territories, but rather as a constituent of home ranges.

In 1961, before the territories were measured, daily observations were made throughout the season to determine the boundaries. During that period the size of individual territories proved to be constant. Measurements were made with a 33-meter (100-foot) tape. Certain errors are due to the very irregular shape of some territories, especially at places where the dense vegetation precluded accurate measurements. However, estimations showed that these errors were not more than 5 per cent. Measurements of grassy areas for the calculating of home ranges were rather approximate, because the boundaries here were not sharply defined, there were no obvious landmarks, and the ranges overlapped.

Territory and home range measurements are shown on Table 1. Considering the shrubbery part of home range as real territory, the average

80

TABLE 1
TERRITORY AND HOME RANGE MEASUREMENTS FOR BREEDING AND
UNMATED MALES IN 1961
(Measurements given in square meters)

Status of males	Number	Area of territories			Area of home ranges		
		Min.	Max.	Av.	Min.	Max.	Av.
Breeding	47	110	400	288	167	822	473
Unmated	5	65	105	82	(98	135	120)[1]

[1] Home range measurements for four unmated males. The fifth, which possessed 65 m^2 of shrubbery, utilized some 300 m^2 of grassland. However, the home range boundaries were too loose to take accurate measurements.

territory size for 47 breeding pairs was one tenth of the minimum for Ohio as reported by Nice (1943). Including grassy areas, the average home range size was still one fifth of the size of the Ohio minimum. Territories of the five unmated males were without exception smaller than the minimum for breeding pairs. Four of these males defended their territories throughout the season; in fact, they were still singing in late June and early July, when breeding males were very rarely heard. However, the fifth male did not show any sign of aggressiveness toward neighboring males. Two additional males were unable to establish territories; they stayed in the same general area of the island throughout the summer, apparently tolerated by territory-owning males.

As mentioned before, there was no correlation between the area of utilized grassland and that of defended shrubbery. Even when the latter was well below average, breeding pairs were able to rear two or three broods without any sizable grassland. On the other hand, one male was unable to obtain a mate with only 65 square meters of shrubbery, even though he also used more than 300 square meters of grassland with a home range area of ca. 365–375 square meters. Although features of the shrubbery might influence the size of individual breeding territories, the five unmated males, each defending an area of shrubbery of 105 square meters or less, possessed territories distributed over the island in a way that covered the range of all vegetation types. This suggests that the determining factor of successful mating was the amount of shrubbery defended by a male rather than the total area utilized.

· *Site tenacity and emigration.* During the first summer 55 adult birds were banded—somewhat more than 50 per cent of the total adult population. Of these birds 29 survived the winter and started to breed in 1961. With one exception they all kept their old territories, apart from minor changes in boundary lines. One male, which stayed unmated through the summer of 1960, in the next summer moved to a neighboring territory where the owner had perished during the winter.

81

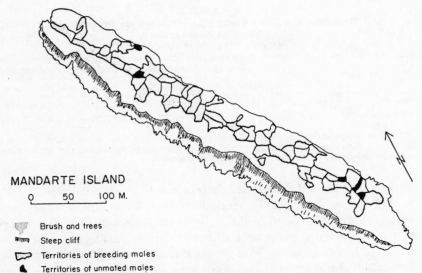

MANDARTE ISLAND

0   50   100 M.

🌿 Brush and trees

🐚 Steep cliff

☐ Territories of breeding males

♠ Territories of unmated males

Figure 2. Map shows the arrangement of Song Sparrow territories.

Of the 113 young banded in 1960, 21 were recovered in 1961. Nineteen of these stayed on Mandarte Island, while two had emigrated to adjacent islands. Those young that stayed can be further divided in the following way: six breeding males, 11 breeding females, and two unmated males. All of them occupied places left vacant through adult mortality. In one area of the island, following a heavy loss of adults and their replacement by yearlings in 1961, the territories were completely rearranged, although the number of territories for this area remained unchanged. (Figure 2 shows the subdivision of shrubbery into individual territories in 1961.)

During the summer of 1961 there was only one example of territory desertion by a female, whose mate had disappeared in July. This female settled down in September on a territory ca. 150 meters away, where the owner had lost his mate in August. From the beginning of breeding in 1961 to the end of January 1962, the loss in adult population was 22 per cent. Vacant places caused by adult mortality during the summer were filled by young birds in the fall, which once their postjuvenile molt had been completed, showed signs of territoriality.

Emigration of young birds first occurred in late summer and lasted until October. In late August two Mandarte young, both from the first brood, were observed on Halibut Island, ca. 1,300 meters to the south. They showed definite signs of territoriality. These birds were followed shortly by one young from the second and three from the third brood, which also established themselves on Halibut Island. The males obtained territories, and stayed there through the winter. One young of unknown sex from the second brood was recovered on 1 September six km to the west of Mandarte on James Island. Both of these islands are forested and support local Song Sparrow populations with lower densities when compared with Mandarte Island.

This first phase of emigration was markedly correlated with the revival of territoriality in autumn. It affected those young that already showed signs of increasing aggressiveness, even though they were unable to establish themselves on Mandarte, since previously vacant places had been filled by other young males. Following this period, territoriality gradually decreased, reaching its minimum during November and December. During this time territory owners, both old and young, usually stayed on their home ranges, although the surplus young population gathered in loose feeding groups of 5–10, frequenting the meadows and the abandoned nesting grounds of cormorants.

At the end of January 1962 definite signs of the revival of territoriality were observed. Singing was often heard, and frequent chasing occurred. Vacant places caused by winter mortality were already filled by first-year birds. There had been no further sign of emigration since the fall. There were approximately 55 young in excess, when compared with the breeding population in 1960 and 1961. As indicated by data from 1961, the second phase of emigration occurs in February and mainly in March, which is the period of spring territorialism and includes the final spacing and mating, before the onset of breeding. This spring emigration concerns young males left without a territory, as well as first-year females that could not settle down on an already established territory. It is worthwhile to note that there was no detectable immigration of Song Sparrows to Mandarte Island during 1961, and no indication that this had happened in 1960.

Discussion and Conclusions

Howard's original theory of the functions of territory has been continuously argued and modified since 1920, partly because of different ways of interpreting it, partly because of the very complex nature of territorialism. The object of territory defense—nest site, mating and feeding ground, etc.—varies from species to species, and even within a given species it is under the influence of seasonal changes and features of the habitat. Nevertheless, most contemporary authors agree on two main functions of the territory, *i.e.*, behavioral and ecological. The former mainly concerns pair formation and maintenance of a pair, while the latter may include the assurance of adequate food supply during certain parts of the annual cycle and/or the regulation of population densities. However, the behavioral and ecological functions are often so closely related that distinction between the two becomes very difficult.

83

Based upon these considerations the following questions suggest themselves:

1. Does territorial behavior play any significant role in the control of the Mandarte Island Song Sparrow population?
2. If so, is the minimum required territory size for successful mating and/or breeding determined by:
   a. the amount of food available;
   b. other features of the habitat, such as type and density of the vegetation, number of perching posts, exposure to prevailing wind, etc.
3. Or is the regulation mainly behavioral, the size of the territories depending upon the aggressiveness or tolerance of the individuals, thus assuring the owners of permanent mates, sufficient nesting sites, and the avoidance of interference during the breeding season.

On Mandarte Island the Song Sparrow population has remained at a high density for at least the last two years, presumably as a result of the suitable habitat, and the absence of severe mortality factors during the annual cycle, especially in the breeding season. Although quantitative data are not available for the years previous to 1960, observations carried out by other students do not indicate any significant changes in the population since 1957 (Drent and van Tets, pers. comm.). The unchanged environmental conditions on the island during the past 50 years would also favor relative stability in population numbers.

The territories, as shown above, have been remarkably smaller than those reported for this species on the continent. The fledging success during the last two years was higher (more than 60 per cent of the eggs laid) than in Ohio (ca. 36 per cent, Nice, 1937) and San Francisco Bay (49.3 per cent, Johnston, 1956). Nest destruction, nest parasitism, and predation did not play any important role in nestling mortality. The abundance and availability of food might be influenced by the vegetation, which varies from one territory to another; thorough investigation is necessary to find out whether starvation plays any substantial role in the less than 40 per cent egg and nestling losses, especially as the numbers of caterpillars, the main food item of nestling Song Sparrows, show a gradual decrease toward the end of the breeding season. Although there is no indication that the size of breeding territories is affected directly by the availability of food supply, the data are not quantitative enough to support final conclusions on the food value of territories on Mandarte Island.

On the other hand, observations, population counts, and the survey of territories suggest that territorial behavior plays an important, if not the main, role in the control of this local population. Under different conditions this function of the territory is not always obvious enough to be recognized. In an area with yearly changing physical and biological conditions, with less suitable habitat, and with a significant annual immigration, the fluctuations in the breeding population may be substantial. In one year, because of favorable conditions, the habitat may become overcrowded, the territories will be relatively small and tightly packed, and hostility of the individuals will increase. On the other hand, following a bad year with low reproductive success, heavy mortality, and/or decreased rate of immigration, the population will be scarce, the territories loosely attached to each other with vacant places in the habitat, and the chance for encounter between neighboring birds relatively low.

Very rarely are conditions favorable for a length of time in one area for the same species, thus permitting high numbers for consecutive years with little fluctuations. But when this happens, the so far latent or less obvious function of territorial behavior in population control becomes operative. Where the suitability of habitats has been artificially raised, e.g., by the provision of nest boxes, significant increase in breeding populations has occurred. This phenomenon was well demonstrated by experiments of Kluyver and Tinbergen (1953) in European titmice, and of von Haartman (1956) in Pied Flycatchers (*Muscicapa hypoleuca*). However, such an increase cannot be indefinite. With higher densities, under favorable conditions, the size of territories will decrease. This shrinkage in size is accompanied by an increasing resistance on the part of individuals, which in time will reach a point, beyond which no further decrease in territory size can occur. This procedure has been described in detail by Tinbergen (1957) in his discussion of the role of hostility (including both aggressiveness and avoidance) in the mechanism of dispersion.

That the same phenomenon can occur also under natural circumstances was shown again by Kluyver and Tinbergen (1953). In their study of titmice they found differential regulation of densities in neighboring, but basically different, habitats. In mixed woods, described as desirable for titmice, territories were relatively small, boundaries well defended, and the population showed small-scale yearly fluctuations. On the other hand, in adjacent, less favorable pine woods, territories were larger, with loose boundaries and less fighting, and the number of breeding birds changed significantly from one year to the other. Also, there was a detectable emigration from the mixed woods to the less favorable habitats with lower densities.

A similar situation due to habitat selection was described by Glass (1960) in the European Chaffinch (*Fringilla coelebs*). In this study, the difference in population densities between the stable populations in desirable habitats and the unstable ones exhibiting yearly fluctuations in less favorable habitats (and one-way emigration as a result of population

85

pressure) was still more pronounced than in the study of Kluyver and Tinbergen.

Apparently the same is true on Mandarte Island, where favorable conditions allowed a stable population with high density during at least the last two but presumably five or more years. The territories have become extremely small. They are tightly packed, and all available space in the shrubbery is being utilized. Because of the increased pressure, the yearly population surplus emigrates to adjacent islands with less desirable habitats for Song Sparrows, in a manner similar to that shown with the titmice and chaffinch. The emigration of Song Sparrows occurs in two steps as shown by population surveys and field observations. The first phase begins in late summer and reaches its peak during the autumnal territoriality. This involves mainly young males, which already show signs of territorality, and cannot settle down since places vacant as a result of adult mortality have been filled. The second phase of emigration occurs during late winter and early spring, when territory establishment and mating takes place prior to the onset of breeding, and affects those yearlings that are still in excess and have a lower tolerance threshold toward crowdedness than the others. Similar two-phase emigration is characteristic of several territorial passerine species (Kalela, 1958).

This emigration of yearly surplus from Mandarte into less suitable habitats, with no detectable immigration from those areas, reveals the real importance of territorial behavior in the mechanism of population control at high density levels. While the size of individual territories is determined by the aggressiveness and tolerance of the neighboring males, and to a certain extent is under the influence of the vegetation cover, the success of obtaining a mate for the breeding season is dependent upon the amount of shrubbery defended by a male. Thereby the females, when rejecting or accepting a particular part of the habitat, may also play an important role in population control. By the acceptance of an appropriate amount of vegetation cover, the chance for successful breeding is increased, by preventing interference and possibly by assuring shelter and adequate food supply for the young. However, the role of the food on Mandarte Island is still to be investigated.

Acknowledgments

I am indebted to Drs. J. F. Bendell, D. H. Chitty, I. McT. Cowan, and M. D. F. Udvardy for advice and criticism throughout the course of the study, as well as to Messrs. R. Drent, P. R. Grant, and K. Vermeer for their friendly help in the field.

Summary

In 1960 a study was undertaken to reveal the controlling mechanism of

86

a local Song Sparrow population on Mandarte Island, British Columbia. The present paper discusses the role of territorial behavior in the regulation of breeding numbers.

This population is at a high density, and has showed relative stability over the past years. The survey of territories, observations on behavioral aspects, population counts, and the emigration of yearly surplus into neighboring, less attractive habitats indicate that territorial behavior plays the most important role in the regulation of Song Sparrows on this island. It has been concluded that the size of individual territories is determined by the aggressiveness and tolerance of the individuals, while the chance for successful mating is apparently dependent upon the size of shrubby area defended by a male.

LITERATURE CITED

ANDERSON, W. B. 1916. Bare Island Indian Reserve. B.C. Proc. Mus. Nat. Hist. Annual Reports, 1915. Pp. 14–16.

GLASS, P. 1960. Factors governing density in the chaffinch (Fringilla coelebs) in different types of wood. Arch. neerl. Zool., 13: 466–472.

HAARTMAN, L. VON. 1956. Territory in the Pied Flycatcher Muscicapa hypoleuca. Ibis, 98: 460–475.

JOHNSTON, R. F. 1956. Population structure in salt marsh inhabiting Song Sparrows. Part II. Density, age structure, and maintenance. Condor, 58: 254–272.

KALELA, O. 1958. Über ausserbrutzeitliches Territorialverhalten bei Vögeln. Ann. Acad. Sci. Fenn. Ser. A. IV. Biol., 42: 42 pp.

KLUYVER, H. N., and L. TINBERGEN. 1953. Territory and the regulation of density in titmice. Arch. neerl. Zool., 10: 265–289.

NICE, M. M. 1937. Studies in the life history of the Song Sparrow I. Trans. Linn. Soc. N.Y., IV. 247 pp.

NICE, M. M. 1941. The role of territory in bird life. Amer. Midl. Nat., 26: 441–487.

NICE, M. M. 1943. Studies in the life history of the Song Sparrow II. Trans. Linn. Soc. N.Y., VI. 329 pp.

SUTHERS, R. A. 1960. Measurements of some lake-shore territories of the Song Sparrow. Wils. Bull., 72: 232–237.

TINBERGEN, N. 1957. The functions of territory. Bird Study, 4: 14–27.

Department of Zoology, University of British Columbia, Vancouver, B.C., Canada.

EFFECT OF SIZE OF MATE ON COURTSHIP IN A CICHLID FISH, ETROPLUS MACULATUS

George W. Barlow

Department of Zoology
and
Museum of Vertebrate Zoology
University of California
Berkeley, California 94720

ABSTRACT

The first goal of this investigation was to test the prediction that orange chromides (Etroplus maculatus; Pisces: Cichlidae) will court more before mates larger than them, and less before those who are smaller. This prediction was based on two premises: (1) When a fish is the smaller of two it is in greater danger of attack than when it is the larger. (2) Courtship behavior lowers the chance of being attacked. In most situations the prediction was borne out.

A central fish, the rover, was given the choice of two screened-off chamber fish of the opposite sex, one larger and one smaller than the rover.

Unlike normal, unrestrained fish, exclusive pairs failed to form. The males visited back and forth interacting well with both chamber females; the same held for females visiting males. The screen precluded complete attack and apparently obviated the necessity of forming the 'peace treaty' that is the hallmark of pair bonding.

Males and females of these cichlids express the same action patterns. Sexual differences are quantitative. The males tended to court more, and also attacked more, than did the females. However both relative size and whether the fish is in a chamber or is the rover, altered the amount of behavior shown.

Males attacked more when interacting with the larger females, and females attacked more when interacting with the smaller males. This may explain the species-typical relation of normal pairs in which the male is larger than his mate.

INTRODUCTION

It is commonly held that courtship displays stimulate the reproductive physiology of the opposite sex. I will call this the arousal hypothesis. Tinbergen (1959a, 1959b) has argued, however, that many of these displays might also, or instead, be interpreted as appeasement behavior, signals reducing the probability of attack. While this idea has gained general

COMMUNICATIONS IN BEHAVIORAL BIOLOGY, 1968, Vol. A-2, pp. 149-160.

acceptance, there have been no experiments to test its validity. Most of the evidence remains anecdotal. The chief purpose of this investigation was to test the appeasement hypothesis of courtship behavior in a cichlid fish.

In cichlid fishes there is first a brief period of pair formation followed by a much longer courtship phase (Baerends and Baerends-van Roon, 1950). Most of the aggressive behavior occurs during pair formation. During the courtship phase, overt attack is reduced, and the action patterns typical of courtship prevail.

Some attacking does occur during courtship, nevertheless. It is often incomplete, consisting of intention movements. Some of these may be detected by the observer, but many may be perceived only by the fish. This points to a major difficulty in the analysis of appeasement behavior during courtship. Those signals that effect appeasement doubtless act as negative feedback, keeping the behavior of the mate in check before the level of actual attack is reached. It is quite possible that a fish may even send out appeasement signals prior to any indication of attack by its mate. The approach followed here, therefore, was to manipulate the potential for attack through the relative size of the mate. (Direct observations have confirmed the general conclusion that the large fish dominate the smaller.)

There is a complication, however, and one that seems at first to present a paradox. In Etroplus maculatus, the orange chromide, the male of a pair typically is larger than the female. The argument that potential for attack is proportional to size would predict that the female should court more than the male if courtship is appeasing. In fact, she does not: The male does. This means that courtship plays some role other than appeasement, such as arousal. But it does not rule out appeasement.

The appeasement hypothesis that was tested explicitly stated the following: If a male is tested against two females, one of them larger than he and the other smaller, more courtship will be shown in the presence of the larger; the corollary is that of the two females presented to the male, the smaller female should court more in the presence of the relatively larger male. The same argument applies to a female exposed to two males.

A second problem approached in this work is that of sexual differences. Aronson (1949) drew attention to the remarkable behavioral 'isoethism' in many of the cichlid fishes: The males and the females express the same action patterns; the differences in sexual behavior are only quantitative. These differences in the orange chromide are examined here, but now considering both relative size and context.

It is not always clear just what should be considered as uniquely courtship behavior. The policy here is to speak of action patterns that occur only during the courtship phase as being central. These would be quivering, nipping and skimming. But other action patterns may play an important role, such as digging, tail beating, and charging (or biting) in the social interactions of courtship. Even apparently nonsignal movements such as yawning, chafing and foraging might reflect the behavioral adjustments caused by differences in sex and size.

MATERIALS AND METHODS

Fish:

These orange chromides, one to two years old, were second to third generation descendants of fish originally imported from Ceylon. All were reproductively experienced, and of proved sexual identification. Sexes were isolated for several months prior to the experiments.

Arena:

The physical conditions were as follows. Water: tap, plus 5 grams marine salt per liter; pH 7.5 to 8.3; temperature 28 +/- 0.25; continuous filtration through gravel bottom.

Illumination: warm, white florescent tubes; 250 f.c. at water surface; on at 0700 and off at 2000, preceded and followed by half-hour of simulated twilight. All but the front side of each of the two identical aquaria was closed off. No viewing port was used; the observer simply sat quietly before the aquarium.

Each aquarium was divided into three compartments (dimensions in Figure 1) using two pervious transparent screens (Saran Ms-907); thus the fish could interact in every way except for actual contact. An opaque plastic fence 10 cm. high was placed behind each flower pot (the spawning site) causing the fish to come forward to interact in the view of the observer. Finally, a central dividing line drawn on the back and front wall was used to determine whether the fish was in the right or left half of the aquarium.

Procedure:

Exploratory studies proved the difficulty of using unrestrained subjects. The pairs became increasingly more difficult to form as the size relationship departed from the norm. Pilot experiments on size preference established the practicality of offering one fish a choice of two other fish in chambers behind screens. Remarkably, the typical pair bond did not then form. Rather, the fish in the middle, the rover, visited back and forth. This was an ideal situation for testing the differential effects of size on both the central fish, hereafter called the rover, and the chamber fish. To ascertain the feasibility of further studies, the test was purposely made difficult by using size differences smaller than typical.

Between the hours of 1400 and 1600, in the experiment reported here, two rover fish were selected of the same sex and size. I then picked two sets of two fish of the opposite sex, one five per cent longer (about 10 per cent heavier) and the other five per cent shorter (about 10 per cent lighter) than the rover, thus just perceptibly larger and smaller. These chamber fish were placed left or right at random.

Recording started the following day. The fish were fed between 0830 and 0900. Three 10-minute observations were made on each group, at about 1000, 1230 and 1500. These were summed to provide 30 minutes of observation for each of the two combinations of rover plus two chamber fish.

After the last observation, the rovers were removed from the aquaria and exchanged. This provided two new combinations of rover and chamber fish, using the same animals.

The next day the same observational procedure was followed. After the last recording all fish were removed, weighed and measured. They were not used again.

This trial, consisting of four 30-minute observations, was repeated five times, yielding 20 samples for analysis. There was one such set of 20 samples for rover males with chamber females, and one such set for rover females with chamber males.

The time spent by the rover with the larger or the smaller chamber fish plus nine action patterns, were recorded using a manually operated keyboard connected to a 20-channel Esterline-Angus event recorder. This produced a continuous record of the behavior of the rover. The behavior of the large or the small chamber fish was recorded only when the rover was in its half of the tank.

Behavioral measures:

Most of the action patterns have been described by Baerends and Baerends-van Roon (1950) in sufficiently general fashion to apply here. Where differences are appreciable, a fuller account is given. And when a different name is used, that employed by Baerends and Baerends-van Roon is given in parentheses.

Frequency measures were employed in most cases. The exceptions, quivering, skimming and 'time' were measured to the nearest second.

TIME — The number of seconds spent with a particular category of chamber fish. Scoring occurred when the entire body and tail passed across the center dividing line.

YAWN — The fish opens and extends its mouth into an O-shape while abducting the median and pelvic fins. It pauses, then snaps the mouth shut (see also Barlow, 1961).

FORAGE — Two different types of foraging were seen but scored as the same. One is a biting movement at the substrate, whether horizontal or vertical, without conspicuous rebound. The other is simply sucking in floating objects.

CHAFE — An accelerating swim toward an object. The fish strikes some part of itself on the object and rebounds away in a decelerating glide.

CHARGE — An accelerating swim directed at the other fish, approaching to within one body length. In the experiment it commonly resulted in bouncing off the screen, followed by biting at the screen and forceful swimming into it. Each rebounding surge was tallied as a separate charge.

TAIL BEAT — During courtship, tail beating is often reduced to an incomplete, seemingly arrested lateral beat of the tail toward another fish. Wide tail beating and all intermediates occur on a continuum; I have not distinguished between them.

DIG — The fish tilts down anteriorly and takes gravel into the mouth but does not chew it. It tilts up slightly, or as much as to the horizontal, and expels the gravel in a single puff, or swims one to two body lengths before ejecting it. Usually the fish returns to the same spot for the next one to several digs.

QUIVER — The fish seems to shiver, starting at the head, while passing lateral waves back along the body; these die as they are propagated to the rear. The head is swung sideways and symmetrically about five cycles per second, and at a low amplitude of about five to 10 degrees. The quivering is sustained variously one to several seconds, commonly being interrupted by brief pauses. If a pause was less than one second, it was included in the duration of the quivering. As an aid to the reader unfamiliar with this behavior, it has many of the attributes of 'greeting ceremonies' in higher vertebrates.

NIP (NIP OFF) — The fish fixes on some upright surface, such as a flower pot, from a distance of about one head length. It then moves forward smartly, contacting the wall with the mouth fully open and usually O-shaped. At once it bites the wall and rebounds. This movement is commonly repeated several times in rapid succession. It is thought to clean the substrate in preparation for the eggs (Baerends and Baerends-van Roon, 1950).

SKIM — The fish swings its ventral surface into contact with the vertical or even overhanging wall. Then it moves in a slow meandering path along it. This is the spawning movement, but no sexual products are released.

RESULTS

Parametric tests:

Ethologists often worry whether their data are normally distributed. A standard statistical analysis for this would be to test for skewness (g-1) and kurtosis (g-2) (Fisher, Sect. 19, 1954). It involves laborious comparisons of the expected and the realized values of the third and fourth moment generating functions. Prior to the general availability of high-speed computers, investigators attempted to cope with the problem of non-normality by short-cut procedures, such as a square-root transformation checked against a plot of the data on probability paper (Aronson, 1949). More generally, they have avoided the issue through the use of nonparametric analyses. Even today, skewness and kurtosis are not tested. And the assumption all too often is that the data are not normally distributed.

91

The data reported here were originally analyzed through covariance techniques. Prior to that analysis, skewness and kurtosis were tested using the untransformed data, log (x+1), square root of x, and x divided by time (time corrected).

The remarkable outcome was that the assumption of normality could not be rejected for either log or square-root transformations nor, with a few exceptions, for the raw data. But significant differences (p = .05) from zero for either kurtosis or skewness were found for most of the action patterns that were time-corrected.

The reader may well ask then why the remainder of the paper is devoted to nonparametric tests when a more powerful parametric analysis is warranted. The disappointing result of the analysis of covariance was that in no instance could it be stated that there were significant differences in the action patterns. Most of the error, not surprisingly, was contributed by the individual fish.

The situation was one of consistent trends, but with considerable differences between individuals. But if there was no effect of size on the responses, then the fact that the small males quivered more before the large females in 18 out of 20 comparisons is highly improbable. A nonparametric approach seemed appropriate.

Nonparametric tests:

The data were ideally suited for the Wilcoxon matched-pairs sign-ranks test (summarized in Tables 1 and 2, related in turn to Figures 2, 3 and 4). A two-tails critical region was employed in most cases. But a one-tail test was used for quiver, nip and skim (Table 1) because an increase was predicted.

Visiting the chamber fish by the rover fish:

Prior to examining the data, it was difficult to detect a difference in the behavior of the rovers, males or females, related to the size of the chamber fish. The rovers visited back and forth, interacting well with both chamber fish.

Both the male and the female rovers spent slightly more of their time, about 55 per cent in each case, with the larger chamber fish. This difference only approached significance in the males (Table 1).

The appeasement hypothesis:

The hypothesis would be accepted (not proved) if the fish courted more in the presence of larger fish of the ooposite sex. This prediction was made explicitly for those action patterns that occur exclusively during the courtship phase, to wit, quivering, nipping and skimming. It can be tested by looking at the pattern of differences within a given category, such as either sex as a rover, or as two chamber fish (Table 1, Figures 2, 3, 4).

The rover fish, male and female, and the chamber males behaved most in accord with the prediction. The differences in quivering were significant for all three. Skimming, however, was significantly greater in the presence of larger fish only in the chamber males (Table 1).

Equally notable was the similar effect of larger size on nearly all the action patterns, not just quivering, nipping and skimming, for the rovers and for the chamber males (Figures 2-4). The larger chamber males performed more behavior than the smaller only in the cases of foraging (p = .01) and chafing (not sig.).

Looking only at the rovers, male and female, 17 out of 18 comparisons revealed that more of a given behavior was shown in the presence of the larger chamber animal. The one exception, charging by rover females (p = .02), is noteworthy; it is also consistent with other work in preparation. While rover females charged more at smaller males, the males showed just the opposite relationship, charging more at the larger chamber females.

TABLE 1

Differences within sexes.
Significant p values from Wilcoxon matched-pairs signed-ranks test.

	Time	Yawn	Forage	Chafe	Tail Beat	Charge	Dig	Quiver	Nip	Skim
Rover Males	(.10)	.05		(.10)	.01		.05	.01		
Rover Females						.02		.05		
Chamber Males	−		.01					.05	(.10)	·.05
Chamber Females	−									

TABLE 2

Differences between sexes.
Significant p values from Wilcoxon matched-pairs Signed-ranks test.

	Yawn	Forage	Chafe	Tail Beat	Charge	Dig	Quiver	Nip	Skim
Rover Male Large Female	.05				.01	.01	.01		.01
Rover Male Small Female				.05	.02				.01
Large Male Rover Female	(.10)	.01	(.10)	.01	.01	.05	.01	.01	
Small Male Rover Female	-	.01	(.10)	.01	.01	.01	.01		

93

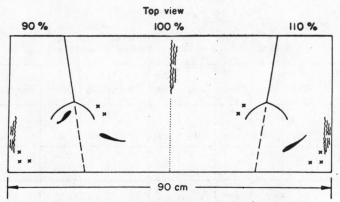

Top view

90 %   100 %   110 %

|← —————————————— 90 cm —————————————— →|

Figure 1. Scale plan of the experimental arena, 30 cm. deep. The x's and
wavy lines indicate plastic plants. Solid lines are opaque walls, except for the
lowest line which is the glass front of the aquarium. The dashed line is for the
screen; the dotted line locates the center of the aquarium. The fish (not to
scale) to the left is within a halved flower pot.

The chamber females stand in contrast to the foregoing. First, no significant differences
whatsoever were found between the large and the small females. Second, if there was any trend,
it was for the large females to exceed the small. The differences were often small, and of about
the magnitude predicted from the larger females being visited about 55 per cent of the time by
the rover males as against 45 per cent for the smaller females.

Differences between the sexes:

In general the males performed the action patterns more frequently than did the females
(Table 2, Figures 2-4). When significant differences occur in the data, the males usually exceed
the females (13 of 20, Table 2). And these differences occur most frequently in action patterns
involved in social interactions, for example, quivering, digging, charging and tail beating.

The females surpassed males significantly in foraging, a trend repeated in many studies,
and in skimming, which is also confirmed in other work in progress. Moreover, the rover females
charged more than the chamber males. (Charging by the rover fish, irrespective of sex, exceeded
that of the chamber fish it visited. The reciprocal relationship held for tail beating, the chamber
fish surpassing the rover, regardless of sex.)

DISCUSSION

Failure to form pair bonds:

One of the most remarkable results of this study was the failure of the fish to form
exclusive pairs. Pilot experiments showed, however, that when a chamber female spawned, the
male fertilized the eggs through the screen, and they became mates; he then ceased courting the
female in the opposite chamber and attacked her. Otherwise rovers courted freely with both
chamber fish.

Evidently either of the sexes is able to court with at least two other fish of the opposite
sex. Ordinarily this is precluded by aggressive behavior. The sign of pair formation, in a
community with other fish, is the directing outwardly of the aggressive behavior of the male and
the female. The male fights mostly with the male of the other pair, and the females
predominantly between themselves. Yet pairs form with no difficulty even when isolated from

94

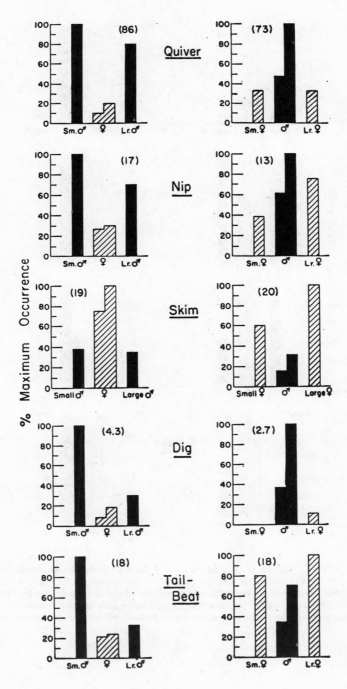

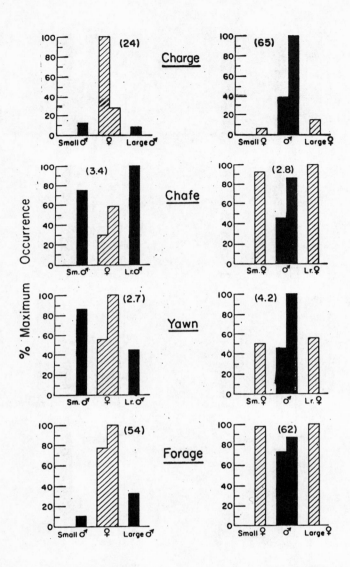

Figures 2,3,4. The average behavior per hour of the chamber fish is represented by the two single bars, to the left for the smaller fish and to the right for the larger. The average behavior per hour of the rover is depicted by the center fused pair of bars; the bar to the right shows the response to the large chamber fish, to the left the response to the smaller. Black indicates male while oblique lines indicate female. The number in parentheses refers to the largest of the average occurrences per hour, which corresponds here to 100 per cent.

96

other fish. Hence, directing attack at other fish is not necessary for pair formation, but it is a reliable indicator of pairing in a group.

The essential point is that pair formation involves a 'peace treaty' between the male and the female. A screen between the fish obviates the necessity for this adjustment. Were it not for the greater difficulty of establishing a 'treaty' between fish of the same sex, either sex would be able to mate simultaneously with more than one fish of the opposite, or of the same sex. In fact, females kept without males commonly formed isosexual pairs and occasionally even 'troikas', three females mated together. Males never formed such isosexual pairs, a striking difference between the sexes.

Appeasement hypothesis:

The hypothesis was borne out by the results. The central courtship activities of quivering, nipping and skimming were expressed more often in the presence of the larger fish. (Chamber females, however, showed no significant differences or meaningful trends.)

The findings could satisfy other hypotheses as well. Larger fish might be more stimulating in the sense of sexual arousal, or by virtue of being behaviorally more 'vigorous'. But the absolutely larger fish were the less active courters. And simply saying larger fish are more stimulating adds no information unless you can say why that should be. The appeasement hypothesis meets that requirement.

An unexpected result was the general trend for most of the action patterns to occur more frequently in the presence of the larger fish (chamber females excepted). The simplest conclusion, in keeping with the formulation of the problem, is that a stronger general activation of most of the action patterns, not just those central to courtship, occurs when an orange chromide is presented with a larger fish of the opposite sex. Furthermore, an increase in all of these action patterns may cause a reduction in the probability of attack in the receiver of these signals.

This effect is not so general as to apply to all action patterns, however. Importantly, charging is influenced in the opposite direction in females. And charging is the clearest index of attack in this study.

Appeasement appears to occur in another way. Direct observation has shown that the most immediate response to being charged at is to turn away, hold ground and tail beat; this has many of the attributes of appeasement signals in other animals (Tinbergen, 1959a,b). This interaction of charge and tail beat is revealed in Figure 3 and Table 2. For example, rover females charge more than do chamber males, while the males tail beat more than the females. The same applies to charging by rover males and tail beating by chamber females.

Appeasement during courtship, then, operates in two ways. During overt attack the recipient responds by turning away and tail beating. When aggression occurs in a milder form such as intention movements, or not at all, the typical courtship behaviors are brought into play. In this study, charging and tail beating occurred mostly at the beginning of each visit by the rover. The tail-beat type of appeasement is more characteristic of pair formation under normal conditions, while the main courtship movements prevail after the pair has formed.

Tail beating is usually categorized as aggressive behavior in fishes, although on a lower level than such actions as charging and biting (Baerends and Baerends-van Roon, 1950; Barlow, 1962). Its effect as an appeasement behavior most likely stems from its role as a low-level threat; this would cause some fear in the aggressor, blocking overt attack (Dunham, et al., 1968), but not enough to result in fleeing. Tail beating, then, should be an especially appropriate response during pair formation when the probability of damaging attack is greatest. But since fear might interfere with arousal, natural selection would have favored the use during courtship of appeasement signals that do not cause fear.

97

Why such actions as quivering should lessen the probability of attack remains an open question. Part of the explanation may be that such courtship actions are appeasing because they evoke sexual responses that are incompatible with attacking.

This dichotomous view of appeasement has both general explanatory and predictive power. It explains the ubiquitous response of the male, among lower vertebrates, of showing aggressive behavior to an intruder approaching his territory. These responses are characterized by the frequent occurrence of lateral displays and tail beats. The male communicates that he is ready to attack, but only if he must. Such displays should lower the readiness to attack in the intruder, male or female. If the intruder is a male, he may still withdraw without fighting. If a female, she may hold position while establishing her sexual identity.

The prediction that follows is that tail beating and lateral display will become the important parts of the male-female interaction leading to spawning in those species where the female visits the male in his territory and quickly spawns and leaves. Good examples are the mouthbreeding cichlid Tilapia mossambica (pers. observ.) and a leaf fish, Polycentrus schomburgkii (Barlow, 1967). In comparing cichlid species, those displays that are basically aggressive in origin should become most frequent in the early pair-formation stage as the pairing becomes more enduring and prolonged.

Differences in behavior between sexes:

In general, males showed more of a given action pattern than did the females (see also Ohm, 1958-1959; Greenberg et al., 1965). But context can sometimes reverse a given relationship (see below).

There are only two action patterns which the females performed significantly more frequently than did the males, irrespective of context. These are foraging and skimming. That the females eat more is to be expected because they need more food to produce eggs. Skimming, the ritualized act of spawning, is also performed more by the females at the time of spawning. These findings support Aronson's (1948, 1949) major thesis stemming from his study of Tilapia macrocephala (= T. melanotheron) the blackchin mouthbreeder. He concluded that the essential differences between males and females lie in the amount of courtship behavior performed, not in any qualitative differences.

The females in Aronson's study were the more active courters. There might be a number of reasons why our studies produced opposite results on this point. For one, he measured the behavior immediately prior to, and just following, spawning. This work on the orange chromide deals with courtship just after what would normally correspond to pair formation. Nevertheless, the few data Aronson presented from pairs early in courtship also indicated that the female was the more active courter.

Another important consideration is that the male may actually play the female role in the blackchin mouthbreeder. In nearly all of the cichlid mouthbreeders in which only one sex picks up the eggs, it is done by the female, not the male. But in the blackchin mouthbreeder the male is the 'mother'.

s Finally, Aronson did not take relative size into consideration. And the blackchin mouthbreeder modulates its courtship behavior greatly depending on the relative size of the mate (Barlow and Green, in preparation).

A more interesting and specific difference between the sexes in the orange chromide is that charging was oppositely influenced by relative size. The males charged more when relatively small. But one anticipates that a fish should attack more when relatively larger than its opponent. This is indeed what the females did.

Of course context plays a role. The rovers, irrespective of sex, charged more than the chamber fish. This charging was most frequent when the rover swam from one fish to the other.

The combination of swimming at the chamber fish, plus approaching a now slightly less familiar fish, seemed to trigger the accelerating swim of charging.

In short, the main sexual differences as revealed by these limited measures is that the males tend to court more than do the females, with the exception that the females skim more often than do the males. Also, males tend to charge more at females who are larger than them, whereas females charge more at males who are smaller than them. This doubtless accounts in large measure for the species-typical arrangement in which a male is mated with a small female who elicits little attack from him. In turn, the female is less likely to attack her larger mate. But none of these data shed light on the ease with which females form isosexual pairs while males never do.

BIBLIOGRAPHY

Aronson, L.A. Problems in the behavior and physiology of a species of African mouthbreeding fish. Trans. N.Y. Acad. Sci., Ser. 2, 2: 33-42, 1948.

Aronson, L.A. An analysis of reproductive behavior in the mouthbreeding fish, Tilapia macrocephala (Bleeker). Zoologica, 34: 133-158, 1949.

Baerends, G.P. and J.M. Baerends-van Roon. An introduction to the ethology of cichlid fishes. Behaviour, Suppl. 1: 1-242, 1950.

Barlow, G.W. Ethology of the Asian teleost Badis badis. I. Locomotion, maintenance, aggregation and fright. Trans. Illinois St. Acad. Sci., 54: 175-188, 1961.

Barlow, G.W. Ethology of the Asian teleost Badis badis. III. Aggressive behavior. Z. Tierpsychol., 19: 29-55, 1962.

Barlow, G.W. Social behavior of a South American leaf fish, Polycentrus schomburgkii, with an account of recurring pseudofemale behavior. Amer. Midl. Nat., 78: 215-234, 1967.

Dunham, D.W., K. Kortmulder and J.J.A. van Iersel. Threat and appeasement in Barbus stoliczkanus (Cyprinidae). Behaviour, 30: 15-26, 1968.

Fisher, R.A. Statistical methods for research workers. 12th. edition. N.Y., Hafner, 356 pp., 1954.

Greenberg, B., J.J. Zijlstra and G.P. Baerends. A quantitative description of the behavior changes during the reproductive cycle of the cichlid fish Aequidens portalegrensis Hensel. Proc. Koninkl. Nederl. Akad. v. Wetenschappen – Amsterdam, Ser. C., 68: 135-149, 1965.

Ohm, D. Vergleichende Beobachtungen am Balzverhalten von Aequidens (Cichlidae). Wis. Z. Humboldt-Univ. Berlin, Math - Nat. R., 8: 357-404, 1958-1959.

Tinbergen, N. Comparative studies of the behaviour of gulls (Laridae): a progress report. Behaviour, 15: 1-70, 1959a. „   "

Tinbergen, N. Einige Gedanken uber "Beschwichtigungsgebarden." Z. Tierpsychol., 16, 651-665, 1959b.

ACKNOWLEDGEMENTS

Supported by N.S.F. Grants GB 5314 and GB 6604. For their helpful comments on the manuscript, I am grateful to C. Richard Dawkins, Richard Green and David L.G. Noakes. Thanks are also due Professor Horace Norton, University of Illinois, who supervised the parametric analyses.

99

IRRUPTIONS OF THE CLARK NUTCRACKER IN CALIFORNIA

By JOHN DAVIS and LAIDLAW WILLIAMS

The Clark Nutcracker (*Nucifraga columbiana*) is usually restricted in California to the higher mountains, where it occupies "typically, upper forest belt . . . Prime dependence of this bird is upon the seeds of various conifers . . ." (Grinnell and Miller, 1944: 299). The winter range of the nutcracker in California is poorly understood, as few observations have been made of this species in winter. The available evidence suggests that at this season the population is scattered between the breeding range at the higher elevations and the upper-middle and middle altitudes. L. M. Lofberg, who lived at Florence Lake, 7640 feet, Fresno County, from 1926 to 1934, states (written communication) that nutcrackers were present at this locality every winter and that the dominant conifer there is the ponderosa pine (*Pinus ponderosa*). In many winters "there are frequent though irregular wanderings which carry individual birds or small companies in late summer and autumn far and wide, to lowest altitudes and farthest confines of State" (Grinnell and Miller, *loc. cit.*). In addition, in some years relatively large numbers of nutcrackers appear at low elevations, reaching the coastal and desert regions at widely separated points. The frequency of records and the numbers of birds involved indicate that in those years substantial segments of the montane populations have moved from the normal winter range to seek winter quarters elsewhere.

Invasions since 1898.—Since 1898, sight records and specimens in museum collections indicate that five major invasions of nutcrackers have occurred in the fall and winter into the Californian lowlands. In the fall and winter of 1898–1899, six were collected near Santa Cruz, Santa Cruz County (specimens, Museum of Vertebrate Zoology), and a single bird was seen near Riverside, about 35 miles west of the Colorado Desert (Willett, 1912:69).

A second invasion occurred in the fall of 1919, with numbers of nutcrackers remaining at some lowland localities well into 1920. The species was reported from Waddell Creek, Santa Cruz County (specimen, Stanford Museum of Natural History); on the Monterey Peninsula (Fisher, 1920:36; Schlesinger, 1920:41; Mailliard, 1920:161); in and near Santa Barbara (Dawson, 1923:24, 26); on Santa Cruz Island (Hoffmann, 1920:188; Dickey and van Rossem, 1923:127, five specimens, Dickey Collection); on shipboard off Los Angeles (Ferris, 1920:39); on the Colorado Desert near Indio (Esterly, 1920:40); and in the Laguna Mountains, San Diego County (Fortiner, 1920:190).

In 1935, nutcrackers appeared at Santa Cruz (six specimens, Museum of Vertebrate Zoology); on the Monterey Peninsula (L. Williams, MS); at Point Lobos, Monterey County (Grinnell and Linsdale, 1936:90); near Pinnacles, San Benito County (Unglish, 1937:39); near Coalinga, Fresno County (Arnold, 1937:33); near Santa Barbara (Rett, 1938:125); near the mouth of the Santa Clara River, Ventura County (Rett, *loc. cit.*); on the Colorado Desert near Indio (Clary and Clary, 1936:119); and at various localities in San Diego County, with flocks of 50 to 60 reported from the Cuyamaca region (San Diego Soc. Nat. Hist., Nat. Hist. Mus. Bull No. 108, 1935:[1]).

In the fall and winter of 1950–51, reports came from Santa Cruz County (Condor, 53, 1951:104, "Cooper Club Meetings"); from Hastings Reservation, Carmel, and Fremont Peak State Park, all in Monterey County (Audubon Field Notes, 5, 1951:38, 225); the Sierra Nevada foothills near O'Neals, Fresno County (Childs and Howard, 1955:16); near Lompoc, Santa Barbara County (Ken Legg, written communication); Beverly Hills, Los Angeles County (Audubon Field Notes, 5, 1951:40); and South Cuyamaca Peak, San Diego County (Brattstrom and Sams, 1951:204–205).

THE CONDOR, 1957, Vol. 59, pp. 297-307.

The latest irruption occurred in the fall of 1955, with records from Prairie Creek, Humboldt County (Ken Legg, written communication); from Marin County, where 30 were seen on March 30, 1956 (H. Cogswell, oral communication); near Santa Cruz (The Sanderling, 12(8), 1956:4); near Watsonville, Santa Cruz County (W. J. Moffat, written communication); Mount Hermon, Santa Cruz County, and the Mount Hamilton Range, east of Gilroy, Santa Clara County (L. R. Mewaldt, written communication); near Jamesburg, Monterey County (specimen, Museum of Vertebrate Zoology); the northern Santa Lucia Mountains, Monterey County; the Monterey Peninsula (unpublished records, several observers); near Fillmore, Ventura County (Condor, 58, 1956:80, "Cooper Society Meetings"); and at various coastal and desert localities in southern California (Audubon Field Notes, 10:59).

In all these irruptions, reports came from southern California as well as from the central part of the state. The record of 1956 from Prairie Creek is the only report from northern California.

Age of invading birds.—Lack (1954:235), summarizing information on irruptions of *Nucifraga caryocatactes* in Europe, states that there is a remarkably high proportion of juveniles in such irruptions. Museum specimens indicate that such may not be the case in California. Of the total of 21 specimens examined by us, 11 were of adults and ten were birds of the year. However, during the 1955–56 invasion of the Monterey Peninsula, we trapped and banded three first-year birds from a small flock observed on a number of occasions. At no time did we observe more than one adult in this flock. Our impression was that most of the birds that we saw on the Peninsula were first-year individuals. Mewaldt (written communication) noted a single first-year bird at Mount Hermon in January, 1956. The evidence from all sources suggests that adults are not rare in groups of nutcrackers invading the lowlands of California and that birds of both age groups take part in such invasions.

The invasion of the Monterey Peninsula Region, 1955–56.—The first indication of a coastward movement in central California in the fall of 1955 came from southern Santa Cruz County. Eight nutcrackers were seen near Watsonville on October 7, and they remained there for almost a month. Inland records for Monterey County are all for October from various stations in the Santa Lucia Mountains (Palo Corona Peak, one seen, October 13; Sid Ormsby Fire Look-out, one seen, October 15; Chew's Ridge, 12 seen, October 23; near Jamesburg, one collected, October 26).

On the Monterey Peninsula, nutcrackers were first recorded (two birds seen) on October 9 in the Rancho Aguajito subdivision, an area heavily wooded with Monterey pine (*Pinus radiata*). On October 13 one was seen at Pacific Grove. Throughout the rest of the fall and winter, 32 persons reported seeing this species at various places in and near Monterey, Pacific Grove, and Carmel. The stations of occurrence are separated by as much as nine and one-half miles (Carmel Highlands to the tip of Point Pinos). At several feeding stations the birds were seen almost daily for a period of several months. Except at two localities, there were no reports of nutcrackers after the end of March, 1956.

Many of the reports came from feeding stations, and when two or more such reports came from stations in the same neighborhood, it is probable that such records referred to the same individuals. Eliminating such duplicating records, 11 separate localities, both feeding stations and natural foraging areas, remain. Nevertheless, because of the probable wandering of nutcrackers from one locality to another, it would be impossible to state the total number of nutcrackers on the Monterey Peninsula during the winter of 1955–56. The maximum number reliably reported from one place at one time is ten.

One of the two places at which nutcrackers were seen after March, 1956, was at

Carmel Woods, near the north boundary of Carmel, where the records centered around one or two feeding stations. The other was at Grove Highlands, two and one-half miles north of Carmel Woods, at the southern boundary of Pacific Grove. The first reports for the Carmel Woods area were for late November, or early December. Almost daily occurrence at the S. R. Turner feeding station in Carmel Woods started on February 15, 1956. According to Mr. Turner, not more than two birds came to his station at one time during the spring of 1956. The last record was for May 26, when one bird was seen. Williams visited this station on February 16, March 15, and May 24. On each visit only one bird could be seen well enough to judge age by plumage characters, and in each case it was a first-year bird. The first record for the Grove Highlands area occurred on October 24, 1955. Some birds persisted in this area until July 8, 1956.

The principal source of information from the Grove Highlands area came from a feeding station maintained by Mr. and Mrs. Fred E. Zimmerman. Suet was put out from November, 1955, until about July 22, 1956, except for an occasional interruption of a few days. This food seemed to be the principal attraction for the birds. Starting on February 13, 1956, Mrs. Zimmerman kept a daily record of the presence or absence of nutcrackers, the maximum seen at one time, and notes on certain aspects of behavior. Such records were maintained until August 20, 1956.

These records show that nutcrackers were present on each day through July 8, 1956, with the exception of May 21 and June 19, and one period of seven days, June 25 to July 1, when suet was not provided. Mrs. Zimmerman was absent from March 24 to 28, but the birds were not entirely absent during this period; they were seen by a neighbor, and Williams noted them at the station on March 28. The numbers of birds seen at the station at one time ranged from one to nine; the average number seen per observation day from February 13 to July 8 was 2.8.

The apparent departure of the nutcrackers after July 8 was abrupt, as from one to four had been seen on each of seven preceding days, but none was seen from July 9 on, although suet was provided for about two weeks more.

At least one adult frequented the Zimmerman station. A single adult was noted by Mrs. Zimmerman on six days, and her diagnosis of age was corroborated by Williams on three other days, and by both of us on one other day. The last day that an adult appeared was on June 17, according to Mrs. Zimmerman.

Behavior of invading birds.—Fisher (1920:36) stated that nutcrackers at Pacific Grove, during the invasion of 1919–20, "seemed to take kindly to the cones of the Monterey pine." Mailliard (1920:160), observing nutcrackers at Pacific Grove in March, 1920, noted that "while they fed to some extent on the Monterey pines, apparently more intent upon the tips of young buds than upon the contents of the cones, they picked also a good many scraps and bits of grain or crumbs in the streets . . . ." During the 1935–36 invasion of the Monterey Peninsula, a nutcracker was seen by Williams pecking into the cones of the Monterey pine. On April 19, 1956, Williams observed first one, then another nutcracker hacking at a cone in a Monterey pine. Although the cone could not be examined closely, it appeared to be unopened save for one crack between two rows of scales. It was into this crack that both birds pecked, but it could not be seen what food, if any, was obtained. Mrs. Zimmerman also noted nutcrackers working on Monterey pine cones near her feeding station. One was noted feeding on the nuts of "Himalaya pine" (= *Cedrus-deodara*?) in Santa Cruz in November, 1955 (Anna Gayton, oral communication), and one was noted hammering on a cone in a Canary Island pine (*Pinus canariensis*) in Santa Monica, Los Angeles County, on April 23, 1956 (G. T. Hastings, written communication).

Mewaldt (written communication) stated that "a lone, first-year Clark Nutcracker was approached to within eight feet as it fed, or searched for food in litter on the ground in an open stand of *Pinus ponderosa*" at Mount Hermon, Santa Cruz County, on January 8, 1956. "The bird was apparently in poor condition as judged from the untidy condition of the plumage. What few seeds remained from the pines in the 1955 crop were insect damaged."

It has been observed twice that invading nutcrackers may forage by turning over pieces of dry cow dung and taking objects, either from the under side of the dung or from the ground beneath. Dr. William Graf (*in* Mewaldt, written communication) noted two nutcrackers in the Mount Hamilton Range on February 12, 1956, flipping over dung and taking exposed insects "which were found to be quite abundant." Similar foraging behavior by a single nutcracker was noted at Point Lobos on October 12, 1935 (Grinnell and Linsdale, 1936:90).

A nutcracker collected near Jamesburg on October 26, 1955, had been feeding on yellowjackets. The stomach was crammed with the remains of these insects; other remains were scattered along the small intestine, and a whole yellowjacket, recently swallowed, lay in the esophagus.

On April 14, 1956, Mrs. Zimmerman recorded a nutcracker storing a piece of suet in the garden of her home. She reported having seen both the burying and retrieving of cached pieces of suet on numerous occasions for several weeks thereafter, but the habit did not persist over the entire stay of the flock at her feeding station. The procedure for storing was as follows: retaining a piece of suet between the mandibles, the bird made sidewise motions with the bill, thus making a hole in the soft earth. The suet was then dropped in the hole and pushed farther down with the bill. Then, again with sidewise motions of the bill, earth was replaced over the hole. When exhuming the food the same sidewise motions of the bill were used and the item seized and pulled out. In some cases, at least, the retrieving of buried stores did not seem to Mrs. Zimmerman to come about by random searching, but it appeared that the bird went directly to a particular spot to unearth food. In some instances this direct approach was to sites at which it was known to the observer that a cache had been deposited previously, but it was not known in such cases whether the depositor or some other bird was removing the food. Several times a second bird was seen to rob a cache immediately after it had been made. Even though the bird which had stored the food might still be close by, no obvious attempt was made to defend its store.

On February 28, Mrs. Zimmerman reported that she had witnessed courtship feeding at her station. She stated that one bird, in a begging posture, fluttered its wings and gaped at a second nutcracker which was feeding on suet. At first the feeding bird made aggressive pecking motions at the begging bird but finally came near it and put bits of suet in the latter's mouth. On the afternoon of the same day, Mrs. Zimmerman and Williams observed similar begging actions but at that time the bird at the suet reacted only aggressively to the begging bird. In the latter instance at least, both birds involved were in first-year plumage. Begging behavior was reported by Mrs. Zimmerman on February 24, and it was witnessed by Williams on May 8, but no delivery of food from one bird to another occurred at these times. Courtship feeding by the Clark Nutcracker in Montana has been reported by Mewaldt (1956:7).

An instance of abortive breeding behavior in an invading bird was recorded by Mailliard (1920:160–161). It was reported to him that on March 20, 1920, a nutcracker seen near Pacific Grove gathered "sticks and other nest-building material" and flew with them to a stand of pines. No nest or further nest-building activities were seen by Mailliard at the same location on the following day.

Possible causes of invasion.—In seeking for possible causes for the sporadic irrup-

103

tions of nutcrackers in California, the most probable cause seemed to us a shortage of the normal winter food supply. Such a shortage could be caused by a failure of the food supply, or by the build-up of the population to a level so high that a normal food supply would not be adequate, or by a combination of both circumstances.

The winter food of the Clark Nutcracker is not well known. These birds are nearly omnivorous and have been reported to eat insects, acorns, juniper berries, other types of berries, carcasses of animals, and grain of various sorts. Near human habitation they will eat a variety of unnatural foods offered them. However, observations made from the spring through the fall, both in California and in other parts of the range, indicate that nutcrackers depend mainly on the seeds of various conifers. During the winter, on the normal montane range, there would be little else for nutcrackers to eat except conifer seed. The ground in the mountains of California is covered by a heavy snowpack during the winter, and the soil and forest litter would be accessible in only a relatively few protected sites. The insect population would have largely disappeared, and nearly all of the small diurnal rodents, which might furnish some food, would be underground by the time of the first heavy snowfall.

On the west slope of the Sierra Nevada, whence most of the nutcrackers invading the coastal regions of north-central California are probably derived, the main winter diet would probably be the seeds of the white-bark and Jeffrey pines (*Pinus albicaulis* and *P. jeffreyi*) for those birds remaining at high elevations and the seeds of the ponderosa pine for those birds wintering at lower elevations. In addition, the sugar pine (*P. lambertiana*) and the white fir (*Abies concolor*) are widely distributed throughout the middle and upper-middle elevations of the western Sierra Nevada and would probably be of some importance in providing seed for wintering nutcrackers. The most important sources of seed would be those remaining in the cones during the winter period (Fowells and Schubert, 1956:35) and those stored by the birds in advance of severe winter conditions. The storing of seeds and nuts for winter use has been reported by a number of ornithologists for the genus *Nucifraga*. Two observations in particular suggest that Clark Nutcrackers store seed in sites which would be accessible during the period of heavy winter snowfall. French (1955:61) noted a bird storing objects, presumably seeds, on a ledge on the face of a cliff, a site which this observer stated would have been accessible to the bird throughout the winter. Farner (1952:86) noted a nutcracker storing peanuts offered by humans; these were being stored in a hole in a nearby white-bark pine. Although the height of the hole was not noted, it may have been above the normal winter snow line.

Some evidence is available for annual cone production by the ponderosa and sugar pines and the white fir on the west slope of the Sierra Nevada. Fowells and Schubert (1956:19–21) reported on annual cone counts of these three species made on a series of experimental plots totaling 46.8 acres in the Stanislaus Experimental Forest. This station is in the western Sierra Nevada, due east of the northern part of San Francisco Bay, at 6000 feet altitude. Counts were made from 1933 to 1942, and from 1948 to 1953, in the late summer of each year shortly before the seeds were shed. Cone counts for ponderosa and sugar pines and white fir made on the experimental plots in 1954 were forwarded by G. H. Schubert. For 1955, cone crop estimates for these species, plus Jeffrey pine, on the entire west slope of the Sierra Nevada have been published by Schubert (1955:1–3). The irruptions of 1935, 1950, and 1955 are thus included in the periods for which some information on cone crops is available.

Up to 1953, two types of cone counts were made in the Stanislaus Experimental Forest: cones produced per acre (table 1), and cones produced per dominant tree (Fowells and Schubert, 1956:21). Dominant trees are those with a diameter at breast height of

Table 1

Cone Counts per Acre, Stanislaus Experimental Forest (from Fowells and Schubert, 1956)

Year	Ponderosa pine	Sugar pine	White fir
1933	237	65	24
1934	203	90	685
1935	0	2	5
1936	338	158	67
1937	12	13	54
1938	18	52	38
1939	5	0	5
1940	72	2	296
1941	166	138	36
1942	7	1	38
1948	105	113	1622
1949	154	4	33
1950	7	0	0
1951	0	0	466
1952	291	267	6
1953	169	4	0

over 19.5 inches. For 1954, only the latter type of count is at hand. Each crop was rated by Fowells and Schubert (op. cit.:20) as none, light, medium, heavy, or very heavy, according to the production of cones per dominant tree. This information is contained in table 2.

Information for the cone crops of 1955 is presented in table 3. The estimates are for the west slope of the Sierra Nevada, which was divided into four zones for purposes of seed collection. Zones II and III are for the west slope of the northern Sierra Nevada, and Zones IV and V are for the west slope of the southern Sierra Nevada. Estimated crops were rated none, very poor, poor, fair, and good. Obviously such ratings as "None to good" are too general to be of use in this study.

In 1935, when there was an invasion of nutcrackers, a virtual failure in the cone crops of all three species occurred in the Stanislaus Experimental Forest (tables 1 and 2).

Table 2

Crop Ratings, Stanislaus Experimental Forest (after Fowells and Schubert, 1956)

Year	Ponderosa pine	Sugar pine	White fir
1933	Very heavy	Medium	Light
1934	Heavy	Heavy	Very heavy
1935	None	Light	Light
1936	Very heavy	Heavy	Light
1937	Light	Light	Light
1938	Light	Medium	Light
1939	Light	None	Light
1940	Medium	Light	Medium
1941	Heavy	Heavy	Light
1942	Light	Light	Light
1948	Medium	Heavy	Very heavy
1949	Heavy	Light	Light
1950	Light	None	None
1951	None	None	Heavy
1952	Very heavy	Very heavy	Light
1953	Heavy	Light	Light
1954	Medium	Medium to heavy	Very heavy

105

However, during the preceding two years, at least one of the species produced a crop rated as either heavy or very heavy. A similar pattern is evident for the invasion years of 1950 and 1955, with very poor crops in those years but one or more heavy or very heavy crops in 1948 and 1949, and from 1951 through 1954 (tables 1, 2, and 3). It appears from the data gathered by Fowells and Schubert that when two or more years of high cone production by at least one of the three species studied by them was followed by a sharp decline in the cone crops of all three, an invasion occurred. Single years of high cone production followed by sharp cone crop decline, such as 1936–37, and 1941–42, did not result in an invasion.

Table 3

Cone-crop Estimates, Sierra Nevada, West Side, 1955 (from Schubert, 1955)

Zone	Ponderosa pine	Sugar pine	Jeffrey pine	White fir
II	None to poor	Very poor to poor	None to poor	Poor
III	....	Very poor to poor	None to poor	Poor
IV	None to poor	None to good	None to poor	None to good
V	None	Poor	None to poor	None

It seems possible that a relative abundance of winter food might lead to a build-up in the population of nutcrackers in the western Sierra Nevada, since the survival of over-wintering birds might be well above average with a good supply of food on the winter range. However, two or more years of good winter food supply might be needed to build the general nutcracker population to such a high level that a poor cone year would lead to substantial numbers of birds leaving the usual winter range. A pronounced build-up of the breeding population would undoubtedly take at least two years, as Clark Nut-crackers do not breed at the end of their first year, but must be at least two years old in order to breed (Mewaldt, 1952:361). Two or more years of successful overwintering might well build up the numbers of two-year old potential breeding birds, thus causing a definite increase in the general breeding population. Although no information is available on the incidence of breeding or on nesting success in any one year, a large potential breeding population in the Sierra Nevada in the spring of 1935, 1950, and 1955 might well have set the stage for a heavy concentration of nutcrackers in the fall of those years, when the pronounced decline in cone crops would be evident. Invasions of nutcrackers into the lowlands presumably occurred, then, as a result of preceding build-up of the general nutcracker population, and particularly of the breeding population, just prior to failure of the winter food supply.

Field observations reported by Dixon (1956:386) tend to support the view that the breeding population of nutcrackers in the Sierra Nevada was unusually high in the spring of 1935. Although the observations were made at Gull Lake, Mono County, on the east slope of the Sierra Nevada, they may be indicative of conditions on the west slope as well. On April 19, Dixon noted adult nutcrackers at one nest feeding their young pieces of flesh torn from the carcasses of Belding ground squirrels (Citellus beldingi) which they had killed. This is a most unusual food for nestling nutcrackers, which are fed mainly shelled pine seeds, with some insect material as well. Twice Dixon noted nut-crackers attacking chipmunks (Eutamias sp.). In one instance, the chipmunk escaped, but in the other, the chipmunk was killed and eaten by the attacking bird. He stated that in 26 years spent in the Mono Basin region (1930–1955, J. B. Dixon, written communication), this was the only season in which he had seen such behavior in nutcrackers, and further, that "in 1935 there was an unusually large number of nesting nutcrackers" in the area. The nesting population was apparently so high that some adults were forced to give their young a highly unusual type of food, and the usual sources of food for full-

106

grown nutcrackers had evidently been so nearly depleted that some individuals were turning to chipmunks to eke out their own diets. Mr. Dixon also writes us that in 1950 he noted "an unusual number of nutcrackers nesting near June Lake [Mono Basin] but no indications of their preying upon small mammals."

In the invasion of 1935, nutcrackers were recorded in the lowlands in September and early October, and in 1955 they had reached the coast near Watsonville, Santa Cruz County, as early as October 7 (eight seen), and they were on the Monterey Peninsula as early as October 9 (two seen). This suggests that some birds start leaving the mountains by the first week in October at the latest. Records for 1935 and 1955 from six weather stations in the Sierra Nevada indicate that some nutcrackers were far from the usual winter range well in advance of any severe drop in temperature and before the first heavy snowfall of the year. Thus, unseasonal onset of severe weather does not appear to be the primary stimulus initiating movement from the winter range; such movement is apparently started in response to the shortage of cones.

It seems likely that storing of seeds starts in September and October, the months during which the cones of most Sierran conifers open and shed seed. Grinnell, Dixon, and Linsdale (1930:304) noted several nutcrackers in the Lassen Peak region of California on October 19, apparently carrying off and storing the seeds of ponderosa pine. A bird that was collected had 34 seeds in its mouth and throat. Grinnell and Storer (1924:395) collected two nutcrackers on the east slope of the Sierra Nevada on September 22 and 25; their throats held 72 seeds of the pinyon (*Pinus monophylla*) and 65 seeds of the white-bark pine, respectively. Farner (1952:85) noted that in the fall at Crater Lake, Oregon, nutcrackers "instinctively" stored peanuts given them by humans. It seems probable that the appearance of storing behavior in the nutcracker coincides with the time of cone opening and seed fall, when extraction of seeds from the open cones would be relatively easy and fallen seed could be harvested readily. Thus, invasions may get under way at the time when many birds start to make their winter stores, but when they fail to find adequate supplies of seeds. The search for seeds might lead nutcrackers to lower altitudes, but in years of severe cone crop decline, many birds apparently fail to find adequate supplies at these low elevations. Further wandering would lead them out of the mountains and eventually to the coastal or desert regions.

The survival value of irruptions of nutcrackers is evident, since the continuance of an unusually large population on the normal winter range despite a very low food supply could bring about depletion of all available food by early or mid-winter, thus jeopardizing the entire population. The situation described by Dixon at Gull Lake in 1935 suggests what might happen when a large nutcracker population is faced by a short food supply, and such a situation would be far worse in winter, when small diurnal rodents would be underground. Storing behavior may perhaps be of survival value in two different ways, primarily in getting the average nutcracker through the average winter, and secondarily in stimulating irruptions in years of high population and low food supply.

It is of significance that in 1935 and 1955 nutcrackers invaded widely separated areas in the southwestern United States. Gilman (1936:41) noted single birds in Death Valley, California, on September 11 and October 11, 1935. These individuals probably came from the Panamint Mountains bordering Death Valley on the west. In these mountains, the conifers are entirely different from those on the west slope of the Sierra Nevada; the genus *Abies* is absent, and the only pines present are the pinyon, the limber pine (*Pinus flexilis*), and the bristle-cone pine (*P. aristata*). Nonetheless, Gilman stated that "this season the nutcrackers were extremely numerous in the Panamint Mountains, as many as forty being in sight at once," again suggestive of a population build-up prior to irruption.

Taylor and Vorhies (1936:42) noted single nutcrackers on the desert in extreme southwestern Arizona on October 22 and 23, 1935. One bird was described as "young." They note that the nearest mountains whence the birds could have come are at least 100 miles away. Presnall (1936:36–37) described a notable invasion of nutcrackers in southwestern Utah between August 15 and October 1, 1935. Again, large numbers of birds were involved, indicative of an abnormally high population on the move. One observer estimated a flock of 200 individuals in one area. Another flock of "over 100" was noted. An apparent invasion of nutcrackers occurred in northeastern Arizona in the fall of 1935. Woodbury and Russell (1945:90–91) reported that either an invasion had occurred in this area, or that the population resident in nearby high mountain country, but normally ranging to lower elevations in search of food and water, was unusually high. Phillips (*in* Woodbury and Russell, *op. cit.*:90) and Wetherill and Phillips (1949: 101) were of the opinion that a true invasion had occurred, with numbers of birds appearing at localities outside the normal range. In 1955, a notable influx of nutcrackers was reported from the Salt Lake City region, Utah. D. W. McCullough (written communication) noted nutcrackers in Salt Lake City, and at Ophir and Jordan Narrows, on nine dates between November 15, 1955, and June 10, 1956. The greatest number seen at one time was nine. The suggestion of population build-up prior to the occurrence of some of these unusual winter records is evident.

Lack (1954:236), discussing the irruptions of certain European birds, including *Nucifraga caryocatactes*, states that the proximate factor stimulating large scale irruptions appears to be overcrowding, but that if we are to assume that irruptions have survival value, then food shortage may still be the ultimate factor involved. Irruptions of nutcrackers in California usually occur in September and October at the earliest, judging by the time of reports of nutcrackers outside the usual winter range, and there is only one record of a nutcracker at an unusual station as early as August, a single bird found dead at Encinitas, San Diego County, on August 24, 1955 (Audubon Field Notes, 9:404). In other words, the invasions do not start before a scarcity of cones is evident, since mature cones are readily visible in August, and it is during this month that foresters actually make cone counts and crop estimates. In the irruption reported in 1935 in southwestern Utah by Presnall (1936:36), the records for August and early September are actually for unusually large numbers of birds moving about within the normal range of the species, and it was not until later in September that records of nutcrackers outside the normal range were reported.

It would appear, then, that irruptions of nutcrackers in the southwestern United States, exclusive of western California, are correlated with unusually large populations, but such irruptions occur at a time when a shortage of food would be evident to the birds. Since we have no information on the cone crops of 1935 in Utah, Arizona, and the Panamint Mountains of California, nor on the cone crop of 1955 in Utah, it is not possible to say whether the invasions recorded in those years resulted only from overcrowding, or whether food shortage was also a factor. The invasions in western California appear to correlate with food shortage and with the possibility of population build-up suggested by periods of high cone production prior to the cone shortage coincident with invasion.

ACKNOWLEDGMENTS

Frank A. Pitelka made the original suggestion that we gather information on the nutcracker invasion of 1955–56 on the Monterey Peninsula. We wish to thank the following persons for furnishing records of nutcrackers and other information: R. P. Parsons, L. R. Mewaldt, S. R. Turner, Ken Legg, Lila M. Lofberg, Beatrice Howitt, D. W.

McCullough, G. T. Hastings, and J. B. Dixon. G .H. Schubert was most helpful in supplying information on annual cone crops in the Sierra Nevada. We wish to thank especially Mrs. Fred E. Zimmerman, whose long series of records provided our major source of information on the behavior and length of stay of nutcrackers on the Monterey Peninsula in 1955–56. Specimens from the Stanford Natural History Museum and the Dickey Collection were forwarded through the courtesy of Drs. Margaret Storey and Thomas R. Howell, respectively.

SUMMARY

Irruptions of the Clark Nutcracker have occurred in California in 1898, 1919, 1935, 1950, and 1955.

The invasion of the Monterey Bay region in 1955 and the behavior of the invading birds are discussed.

Nutcrackers depend on pine cones for winter food. Californian irruptions appear to occur when an unusually large population of nutcrackers is faced with a low supply of food on the normal winter range. The irruptions correlate with severe and widespread failure of cone crops following two or more years of large crops, during which the nutcracker population in general, and the breeding population in particular, apparently increases significantly as a result of abundance of winter food.

Invasions in other parts of the southwestern United States in 1935 and 1955 seem to correlate with prior population build-up. Since cone-crop data are not available for these regions, the role of food supply in stimulating these invasions cannot be assessed.

LITERATURE CITED

Arnold, J. R.
 1937. Birds of the Coalinga area, Fresno County, California. Condor, 39:31–35.
Brattstrom, B. H., and Sams, J. R.
 1951. The Clark nutcracker in San Diego County, California. Condor, 53:204–205.
Childs, H. E., Jr., and Howard, W. E.
 1955. The vertebrate fauna of the San Joaquin Experimental Range. U. S. Dept. Agr., Forest Serv., Calif. Forest and Range Exp. Sta., Misc. Paper No. 19:1–20.
Clary, B., and Clary, M.
 1936. Clark nutcracker again visits Colorado Desert. Condor, 38:119.
Dawson, W. L.
 1923. The birds of California. Format de Luxe, Sunset Edition. Vol. 1 (South Molton Company, San Diego, etc.), xvii + 522 pp.
Dickey, D. R., and van Rossem, A. J.
 1923. Additional notes from the coastal islands of southern California. Condor, 25:126–129.
Dixon, J. B.
 1956. Clark nutcrackers preying on ground squirrels and chipmunks. Condor, 58:386.
Esterly, C. O.
 1920. Clark nutcracker on the Colorado Desert. Condor, 22:40.
Farner, D. S.
 1952. The birds of Crater Lake National Park (University of Kansas Press, Lawrence, Kansas), xi + 187 pp.
Ferris, G. F.
 1920. Clarke nutcracker at sea. Condor, 22:39.
Fisher, W. K.
 1920. The Clarke nutcracker at Point Pinos, Monterey County, California. Condor, 22:36.
Fortiner, J. C.
 1920. Clark nutcracker and white-winged dove in southern California. Condor, 22:190.

Fowells, H. A., and Schubert, G. H.
  1956. Seed crops of forest trees in the pine region of California. U. S. Dept. Agr., Tech. Bull.
    No. 1150:1–48.
French, N. R.
  1955. Foraging behavior and predation by Clark nutcracker. Condor, 57:61–62.
Gilman, M. F.
  1936. Additional bird records from Death Valley. Condor, 38:40–41.
Grinnell, J., Dixon, J., and Linsdale, J. M.
  1930. Vertebrate natural history of a section of northern California through the Lassen Peak
    region. Univ. Calif. Publ. Zool., 35:v + 594 pp.
Grinnell, J., and Linsdale, J. M.
  1936. Vertebrate animals of Point Lobos Reserve, 1934–35. Carnegie Inst. Wash. Publ. No.
    481:vi + 159 pp.
Grinnell, J., and Miller, A. H.
  1944. The distribution of the birds of California. Pacific Coast Avif. No. 27:1–608.
Grinnell, J., and Storer, T. I.
  1924. Animal life in the Yosemite (University of California Press, Berkeley), xviii + 752 pp.
Hoffmann, R.
  1920. Notes on some birds of Santa Cruz Island, California. Condor, 22:187–188.
Lack, D.
  1954. The natural regulation of animal numbers (Clarendon Press, Oxford), viii + 343 pp.
Mailliard, J.
  1920. Notes on nutcrackers in Monterey County, California. Condor, 22:160–161.
Mewaldt, L. R.
  1952. The incubation patch of the Clark nutcracker. Condor, 54:361.
Presnall, C. C.
  1936. Clark nutcrackers invade southwestern Utah. Condor, 38:36–37.
Rett, E. Z.
  1938. The Clark nutcracker at sea level. Condor, 40:125.
Schlesinger, J. L.
  1920. Clarke nutcracker at Carmel. Condor, 22:41.
Schubert, G. H.
  1955. California cone crop—1955. U. S. Dept. Agr., Forest Serv., Calif. Forest and Range Expt.
    Sta., Forest Res. Notes No. 97:1–3.
Taylor, W. P., and Vorhies, C. T.
  1936. The Clark nutcracker in extreme southwestern Arizona. Condor, 38:42.
Unglish, W. E.
  1937. A few unusual records from central California. Condor, 39:39–40.
Wetherill, M. A., and Phillips, A. R.
  1949. Bird records from the Navajo country. Condor, 51:100–102.
Willett, G.
  1912. Birds of the Pacific slope of southern California. Pacific Coast Avif. No. 7:1–122.
Woodbury, A. M., and Russell, H. N., Jr.
  1945. Birds of the Navajo country. Bull. Univ. Utah, 35 (14):1–160.

Hastings Reservation, University of California, Carmel Valley, California, and Carmel, California, June 9, 1957.

Peter Marler and Miwako Tamura

Department of Zoology
University of California, Berkeley

Culturally Transmitted Patterns of Vocal Behavior in Sparrows

Abstract. *Male white-crowned sparrows have song "dialects," acquired in about the first 100 days of life by learning from older males. In the laboratory an alien white-crowned sparrow dialect can be taught. Once the song is established further acoustical experience does not change the pattern. White-crowned sparrows do not copy recorded songs of other sparrow species presented under similar conditions.*

The white-crowned sparrow, *Zonotrichia leucophrys*, is a small song bird with an extensive breeding distribution in all but the southern and eastern parts of North America (*1*). Ornithologists have long remarked upon the geographical variability of its song. Physical analysis of field recordings of the several vocalizations of the Pacific Coast subspecies *Z. l. nuttalli* reveals that while most of the seven or so sounds which make up the adult repertoire vary little from one population to another, the song patterns of the male show striking variation (see *2*).

Each adult male has a single basic song pattern which, with minor variations of omission or repetition, is repeated throughout the season. Within a population small differences separate the songs of individual males but they all share certain salient characteristics of the song. In each discrete population there is one predominant pattern which differs in certain consistent respects from the patterns found in neighboring populations (Fig. 1). The term "dialect" seems appropriate for the properties of the song patterns that characterize each separate population of breeding birds. The detailed structure of syllables in the second part of the song is the most reliable indicator. Such dialects are known in other song birds (*3*).

The white-crowned sparrow is remarkable for the homogeneity of song patterns in one area. As a result the differences in song patterns between populations are ideal subjects for study of the developmental basis of behavior. If young male birds are taken from a given area, an accurate prediction can be made about several properties of the songs that would have developed if they had been left in their natural environment. Thus there is a firm frame of reference with which to compare vocal patterns developing under experimental conditions. Since 1959 we have raised some 88 white-crowned sparrows in various types of acoustical environments and observed the effects upon their vocal behavior. Here we report on the adult song patterns of 35 such experimental male birds. The several types of acoustical chamber in which they were raised will be described elsewhere.

In nature a young male white-crown hears abundant singing from its father and neighbors from 20 to about 100 days after fledging. Then the adults stop singing during the summer molt and during the fall. Singing is resumed again in late winter and early spring, when the young males of the previous year begin to participate. Young males captured between the ages of 30 and 100 days, and raised in pairs in divided acoustical chambers, developed song patterns in the following spring which matched the dialect of their home area closely. If males were taken as nestlings or fledglings when 3 to 14 days of age and kept as a group in a large soundproof room, the process of song development was very different. Figure 2 shows sound spectrograms of the songs of nine males taken from three different areas and raised as a group. The patterns lack the characteristics of the home dialect. Moreover, some birds from different areas have strikingly similar patterns (*A3*, *B2*, and *C4* in Fig. 2).

Males taken at the same age and individually isolated also developed songs which lacked the dialect characteristics (Fig. 3). Although the dia-

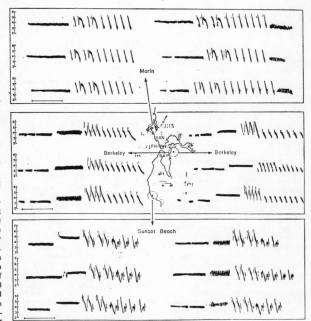

Fig. 1. Sound spectrograms of songs of 18 male white-crowned sparrows from three localities in the San Francisco Bay area. The detailed syllabic structure of the second part of the song varies little within an area but is consistently different between populations. The introductory or terminal whistles and vibrati show more individual variability. The time marker indicates 0.5 second and the vertical scale is marked in kilocycles per second.

lect properties are absent in such birds isolated in groups or individually, the songs do have some of the species-specific characterisitcs. The sustained tone in the introduction is generally, though not always, followed by a repetitive series of shorter sounds, with or without a sustained tone at the end. An ornithologist would identify such songs as utterances of a *Zonotrichia* species.

Males of different ages were exposed to recorded sounds played into the acoustical chambers through loudspeakers. One male given an alien dialect (8 minutes of singing per day) from the 3rd to 8th day after hatching, and individually isolated, showed no effects of the training. Thus the early experience as a nestling probably has little specific effect. One of the group-raised isolates was removed at about 1 year of age and given 10 weeks of daily training with an alien dialect in an open cage in the laboratory. His song pattern was unaffected. In general, acoustical experience seems to have no effect on the song pattern after males reach adulthood. Birds taken as fledglings aged from 30 to 100 days were given an alien dialect for a 3-week period, some at about 100 days of age, some at 200, and some at 300 days of age. Only the training at the age of 100 days had a slight effect upon the adult song. The other groups developed accurate versions of the home dialect. Attention is thus focused on the effects of training between the ages of about 10 and 100 days. Two males were placed in individual isolation at 5 and 10 days of age, respectively, and were exposed alternately to the songs of a normal white-crowned sparrow and a bird of a different species. One male was exposed at 6 to 28 days, the other at 35 to 56 days. Both developed fair copies of the training song which was the home dialect for one and an alien dialect for the other. Although the rendering of the training song is not perfect, it establishes that the dialect patterns of the male song develop through learning from older birds in the first month or two of life. Experiments are in progress to determine whether longer training periods are necessary for perfect copying of the training pattern.

The training song of the white-crowned sparrow was alternated in one case with the song of a song sparrow, *Melospiza melodia*, a common bird in the areas where the white-crowns were taken, and in the other case with a

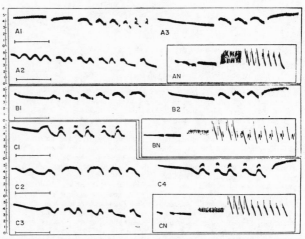

Fig. 2. Songs of nine males from three areas raised together in group isolation. *A1* to *A3*, Songs of individuals born at Inspiration Point, 3 km northeast of Berkeley. *B1* and *B2*, Songs of individuals born at Sunset Beach. *C1* to *C4*, Songs of individuals born in Berkeley. The inserts (*AN*, *BN*, and *CN*) show the home dialect of each group.

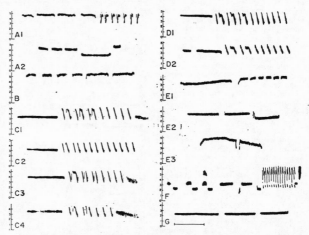

Fig. 3. Songs of 12 males raised under various experimental conditions. *A1* and *A2*, Birds raised in individual isolation. *B*, Male from Sunset Beach trained with Marin song (see Fig. 1) from the 3rd to the 8th day of age. *C1* to *C4*, Marin birds brought into the laboratory at the age of 30 to 100 days. *C1*, Untrained. *C2* to *C4*, Trained with Sunset Beach songs; *C2* at about 100 days of age, *C3* at 200 days, *C4* at 300 days. *D1*, Bird from Sunset Beach trained with Marin white-crowned sparrow song and a Harris's sparrow song (see *G*) from the age of 35 to 56 days. *D2*, Marin bird trained with Marin white-crowned sparrow song and a song-sparrow song (see *F*) from the age of 6 to 28 days. *E1* to *E3*, Two birds from Sunset Beach and one from Berkeley trained with song-sparrow song from the age of 7 to 28 days. *F*, A song-sparrow training song for *D2* and *E1* to *E3*. *G*, A Harris's sparrow training song for *D1*.

song of a Harris's sparrow, *Zonotrichia querula*. Neither song seemed to have any effect on the adult patterns of the experimental birds. To pursue this issue further, three males were individually isolated at 5 days of age and trained with song-sparrow song alone from about the 9th to 30th days. The adult songs of these birds bore no resemblance to the training patterns and resembled those of naive birds (Fig. 3). There is thus a predisposition to learn white-crowned sparrow songs in preference to those of other species.

The songs of white-crowned sparrows raised in isolation have some normal characteristics. Recent work by Konishi (4) has shown that a young male must be able to hear his own voice if these properties are to appear. Deafening in youth by removal of the cochlea causes development of quite different songs, with a variable broken pattern and a sibilant tone, lacking the pure whistles of the intact, isolated birds. Furthermore, there is a resemblance between the songs of male white-crowned sparrows deafened in youth and those of another species, *Junco oreganus*, subjected to similar treatment. The songs of intact juncos and white-crowns are quite different. Konishi also finds that males which have been exposed to the dialect of their birthplace during the sensitive period need to hear themselves before the memory trace can be translated into motor activity. Males deafened after exposure to their home dialects during the sensitive period, but before they start to sing themselves, develop songs like those of a deafened naive bird. However, once the adult pattern of singing has become established then deafening has little or no effect upon it. Konishi infers that in the course of crystallization of the motor pattern some control mechanism other than auditory feedback takes over and becomes adequate to maintain its organization. There are thus several pathways impinging upon the development of song patterns in the white-crowned sparrow, including acoustical influences from the external environment, acoustical feedback from the bird's own vocalizations, and perhaps nonauditory feedback as well.

Cultural transmission is known to play a role in the development of several types of animal behavior (5). However, most examples consist of the reorientation through experience of motor patterns, the basic organization of which remains little changed. In the development of vocal behavior in the white-crowned sparrow and certain other species of song birds, we find a rare case of drastic reorganization of whole patterns of motor activity through cultural influence (6). The process of acquisition in the white-crowned sparrow is interesting in that, unlike that of some birds (7), it requires no social bond between the young bird and the emitter of the copied sound, such as is postulated as a prerequisite for speech learning in human children (8). The reinforcement process underlying the acquisition of sound patterns transmitted through a loudspeaker is obscure.

References and Notes

1. R. C. Banks, *Univ. Calif. Berkeley Publ. Zool.* **70**, 1 (1964).
2. P. Marler and M. Tamura, *Condor* **64**, 368 (1962).
3. E. A. Armstrong, *A Study of Bird Song* (Oxford Univ. Press, London, 1963).
4. M. Konishi, in preparation.
5. W. Etkin, *Social Behavior and Organization Among Vertebrates* (Univ. of Chicago Press, Chicago, 1964).
6. W. Lanyon, in *Animal Sounds and Communication*, *AIBS Publ. No. 7*, W. Lanyon and W. Tavolga, Eds. (American Institute of Biological Sciences, Washington, D.C., 1960), p. 321; W. H. Thorpe, *Bird Song. The Biology of Vocal Communication and Expression in Birds* (Cambridge Univ. Press, London, 1961); G. Thielcke, *J. Ornithol.* **102**, 285 (1961); P. Marler, in *Acoustic Behaviour of Animals*, R. G. Busnel, Ed. (Elsevier, Amsterdam, 1964), p. 228.
7. J. Nicolai, *Z. Tierpsychol.* **100**, 93 (1959).
8. O. H. Mowrer, *J. Speech Hearing Disorders* **23**, 143 (1958).
9. M. Konishi, M. Kreith, and J. Mulligan cooperated generously in locating and raising the birds and conducting the experiments. W. Fish and J. Hartshorne gave invaluable aid in design and construction of soundproof boxes. We thank Dr. M. Konishi and Dr. Alden H. Miller for reading and criticizing this manuscript. The work was supported by a grant from the National Science Foundation.

14 September 1964

DISTANCE NAVIGATION IN THE ADELIE PENGUIN

J. T. EMLEN & R. L. PENNEY

Received on 26 November 1963

INTRODUCTION

The objective of this study was to obtain information on animal navigation in readily followed subjects in the absence of landmarks and under conditions which would permit contrast of potential navigational cues. The ice cap of Antarctica was selected as the area and the Adelie Penguin *Pygoscelis adeliae* as the subject.

Antarctica provides a wide choice of release sites, geographically separated but alike in the absence of landmark cues. The widely diverging lines of longitude in the polar region and the incorporation of the south magnetic pole within the area, permit clear contrast of several potentially usable navigation cues. Also, the continuous daylight and essentially horizontal azimuth course of the sun during the Antarctic summer present conditions favourable to studies of celestial orientation.

The Adelie Penguin, an abundant resident of coastal Antarctica, provides a subject with demonstrated navigational ability (Penney 1963, Sladen & Ostenso 1960). The bird is adapted to the cold climates characteristic of the ice cap and naturally resistant to prolonged fasting during the breeding season when navigation studies are best conducted. Important also, the restriction to terrestrial locomotion in penguins permits the following or tracking of experimental subjects and the accurate mapping of their routes over considerable distances.

All experiments described in this report were performed on birds taken from rookeries in the Ross Sea sector of Antarctica and released at inland sites from 340 to 1,500 km. away (see map).

The study was conducted under a grant from the National Science Foundation administered by the University of Wisconsin. We are much indebted to officers and personnel of the U.S. Antarctic Research Program (USARP), the Antarctic Support Activities of the U.S. Navy, and to many individuals whose help with technical and logistic problems made this project possible. Among these, special mention should be made of USARP representatives Phillip Smith and Robert Mason, surveyor Malchom Ford, pilots E. Hand, R. Herr, G. Maaske, S. Manning, B. Ogden, D. Roe and R. Spencer and field investigators John Cranfield, Brian Reid and Robert Wood.

METHODS AND PROCEDURES

Subjects. The birds selected for the experiments were males taken from their nest-sites at Cape Crozier and, in one series, Cape Hallett. Sex identifications was by direct observations of " ecstatic " display or copulatory position. Vigorous heavy birds were selected. Subjects for the November and December experiments (series I, II, III and IV) were individuals in the " pre-egg stage " of the nesting cycle. Those used in the January experiments (V and VI) were defending nest-sites during the chick stage of the breeding season, and were, in our best judgement, unsuccessful breeders or late arrivals (see Penney 1963).

IBIS, 1964, Vol. 106, pp. 417-431.

Transport. Experimental birds were captured with as little disturbance as possible either in a dip net or directly by hand. They were placed without delay in small individual compartments in well ventilated, double-carrying boxes. Transport, 20 birds at a time, was accomplished as quickly as possible in unheated planes. Whenever delays occurred (weather conditions or plane scheduling difficulties delayed operations for 10 days in one case) the birds were transferred from the boxes and temporarily housed in solid walled pens on the snow or in sub-surface snow pits. Fresh snow was provided for " drinking "; feeding was considered unnecessary. All birds were examined and individually marked for subsequent identification at the time of release.

Releases. On arrival at a release site the birds were transferred from the carrying boxes and placed in groups of four or five in snow pits measuring about 1 × 2 metres and 0·7 metres deep, covered with white muslin. They were taken singly from these pits as needed for release.

Each release constituted a separate experiment, and, with two planned exceptions (series IB), no birds were released until the previous bird had completely disappeared from view. This generally took from one half to one hour. In the first series of experiments all exposed equipment and camping gear were painted white for camouflage, and birds for release were placed in a white release box which, when tripped with a clock mechanism, opened out flat on the snow surface. Experience soon indicated that this elaborate procedure was unnecessary, and all subsequent releases were made directly from the hand between 30 and 100 metres from one of the observation transits. Most of the birds departed within a few minutes of release, a smaller number delayed departure for more than 15 minutes, and a few in each series remained for an hour or more, making it necessary to recapture them. With a single exception these recaptured birds departed without undue delay when used in a repeat experiment a day or two later.

Tracking. Departure routes were plotted by triangulating on the bird at five-minute intervals from two standard survey transits with 25 × telescopes mounted atop ten-foot-high tripods. The base line between the two transits was, with one exception, 200 metres long and established at right angles to the anticipated direction of departure. Azimuth angles to the nearest minute of arc were simultaneously recorded by the two observers on a signal from one of them. The distance to which birds could be followed with the telescopes varied from 1 to 4 km. depending on variations in the snow-ice surface (sastrugi), the wind (drift) and the type of locomotion used by the birds (upright walking or prostrate tobogganning). The positions of all points along a departure route were calculated using 5-place natural functions. These were then plotted at a scale of 1 cm. = 100 m., and the plots used for calculations of direction, straightness and speed.

Experiments. Six series of releases were planned with 20 birds in each. With the exception of Series II, the birds were divided about equally into two or three groups. One of these, a standard group, was handled as described above; the others differed from the standard birds with respect to (a) grouping at the time of release (Series I), (b) source of origin (Series IV), (c) previous homing experience (Series V), (d) stage of the breeding cycle (Series IV and V), (e) sun condition at time of release (Series III), and (f) exposure to artificial dark-light cycles before release (Series VI). Three widely spaced sites were selected for the releases in order to permit the drawing of sharp distinctions between true direction (based on the local meridian), grid direction (based on lines parallel to a selected primary meridian), magnetic compass direction and home direction. Pertinent details and results of these experiments are summarized in Table 1.

The first release site, used in Series I and II, was on the Ross Ice Shelf, a vast expanse of featureless compacted snow, at a point about 340 km. southeast of Cape Crozier and well beyond any possible view of the bordering mountains to the west or of " water sky ".

TABLE 1. *Circumstances of release and data performance of groups of Adelie Penguins transported for experimental release in inland Antarctica. Details are explained in the text.*

Expt. Series Number (No. of birds)	IA (10)	II (4)	IIIA (8)	IIIB (10)	IIIC (8)	IVA (10)	IVB (8)	V (17)	VIA (5)	VIB (6)	VIC (7)
A. RELEASE DATA											
1. Location of Source	C. Crozier Ross I. Sh.	C. Crozier Ross I. Sh.	C. Crozier Byrd Sta.	C. Crozier Byrd. Sta.	C. Crozier Byrd Sta.	C. Crozier Victorialand	C. Hallett Victorialand	C. Crozier Victorialand	C. Crozier Victorialand	C. Crozier Victorialand	C. Crozier Victorialand
2. Location of Release	80° S, 178° E.	80° S, 178° E.	80° S, 120° W.	80° S, 120° W.	80° S, 120° W.	75° S, 155° E.	75° S, 155° E.	75° S, 155° E.	75° S, 155° E.	75° S, 155° E.	75° S, 155° E.
3. Position											
4. Dates of Release	2-3 Nov.	3-6 Dec.	16-20 Nov.	16-20 Nov.	16-20 Nov.	6-9 Nov.	6-9 Nov.	1-5 Jan.	7-11 Jan.	7-11 Jan.	7-11 Jan.
5. Preparation of birds	—	—	—	—	—	—	—	—	—	Dark 15-21.00	Dark 9-15.00
B. CONDITIONS											
1. Sun cover	Clear	Clear-part	Clear	Partial	Complete cds.	Clear	Clear	Clear	Clear	Clear	Clear
2. Wind-Direction	Variable	W.-S.W.	W.S.W.-N.	S.S.W.-N.	S.S.W.-N.	S.W.	S.W.	W.-S.W.	W.-S.W.	W.-S.W.	W.-S.W.
3. Wind-Velocity	3-12 kn.	5-15 kn.	0-15 kn.	0-15 kn.	0-15 kn.	2-15 kn.	2-15 kn.	5-25 kn.	0-5 kn.	0-12 kn.	0-8 kn.
4. Temp. C°	-30° to -16°	0 to +12°	-10° to 0°	-8° to +5°	-10° to +10°			-24° to -5°	-24° to +3°	-24° to +3°	-24° to +3
5. Sastrugi	Vague (N.)	Vague (N.)	None	None	None	N.E. mod.	N.E. mod.	N.E. mod.	N.E. mod.	N.E. mod.	N.E. mod.
C. DIRECTION TAKEN											
1. ex. Merid. North	6·7° E.	27·5° E.	7·0° W.	25·3° W.	40·7° W.	54·1° E.	83·4° E.	59·7° E.	32·8° E.	35·2° E.	82·9° E.
2. ex. Grid. North	15·7° E.	36·5° E.	64·0° E.	45·3° E.	30·7° E.	40·1° E.	69·4° E.	45·7° E.	18·8° E.	21·2° E.	68·9° E.
3. ex. Magn. South	58·8° E.	80·0° E.	105·5° E.	88·3° E.	72·9° E.	75·5° E.	105·4° E.	80·7° E.	53·8° E.	56·2° E.	103·9 E.
4. Concentration (k)	8·82	2·88	6·80	2·59	0·65	75·00	3·28	8·00	6·66	3·25	0·75
5. Resultant (R)	9·49	3·74	7·47	8·26	2·65	9·94	6·67	16·00	4·70	5·23	2·94
6. R²/N	9·00**	3·60*	6·96**	6·81**	0·88 n.s.	9·89**	5·56**	15·56**	4·42*	4·56*	1·24 n.s.
D. STRAIGHTNESS											
1. Dist. Trav./str.	1·004 (10)	1·006 (4)	1·013 (8)	1·033 (10)	1·411 (8)	1·009 (10)	1·123 (8)	1·009 (17)	1·015 (5)	1·032 (6)	1·385 (7)
2. Deviation segments 20°	0/46	0/20	5/62	7/67	15/46	3/69	13/72	3/84	1/26	2/35	16/77
3. Change > 20° R.L.	0,0/6	0,0/2	0,0/8	1,3/9	1,3/6	1,1/10	4,0/8	0,1/12	0,1/4	0,1/4	1,1/7
E. SPEED (net)											
1. Km./hr	4·6	3·5	3·7	2·4	4·0	3·5	2·5	·3·9	2·9	2·6	2·2

Note. R²/N is the test of preferred direction where * indicates p < ·05 and > ·01 and ** indicates p < ·01; and n.s. indicates no practical direction (p > ·05).

to the north. (Low clouds over water receive less reflected light than similar clouds over a snow surface and are consequently darker; such an indication of water can sometimes be detected to distances of about 80 miles.) Twenty birds from Cape Crozier were used in Series I, 10 of them released individually and the other 10 in two groups of five as a test for the effect of social factors on departure performance. Series II was designed to test the effect of advancing season (one month after Series I). In this we were severely handicapped by accidents and delays beyond our control, and succeeded in releasing only four birds effectively.

The second site, used in Series III, was 1,500 km. east of Cape Crozier in Marie Byrd Land, near the New Byrd Station and at a point again selected for absence of topography. The 20 birds, all from Cape Crozier, were released under varying conditions of cloud cover.

The third release site, used in Series IV, V and VI, was on the Victoria Land Plateau, another flat and featureless expanse of snow, at a point about 460 km. northwest of Cape Crozier, and 550 km. southwest of Cape Hallett. Ten birds from Cape Crozier and eight from Cape Hallett were used in Series IV; the home direction for the Hallett birds was 85° to the left of that for the Crozier birds. Series V was designed to test the possible effect of advancing season (two months after Series IV), and the behaviour of birds with recorded performances at another release site (seven birds which had returned from Series I on the Ross Ice Shelf). The objective of Series VI was to test the effect of a 10-day exposure to artificial dark-light cycles prior to release.

Statistical Analysis. As an aid in the interpretation of our results several statistical procedures appropriate to directional data were kindly supplied to us by Dr. G. S. Watson (Watson & Williams 1956, Watson 1961, 1962).

For each of the experimental series a mean direction was determined by vector analysis of all the birds plotted mean routes. The concentration of directions within each series is given by the value $k = \frac{N-1}{2(N-R)}$ with N representing the number of birds in the series and R the length of the resultant vector. This measure may be thought of as $\frac{1}{\text{variance}}$. To test for a significant difference in concentration between two samples, the ratio k_1/k_2 is compared with $F_{(n_1-1)(n_2-1)}$; large values indicating a difference.

As a test for preferred direction, the value $\frac{R^2}{N}$ is compared with an exponential distribution, mean 1. Values exceeding 3·0 or 4·9 are significant at the ·05 and ·01 level respectively.

Comparison of mean directions between any two experimental series is done with a distribution-free test (Wheeler & Watson, in press). In this test the two samples are placed on a circle with successive observations spaced with an angle equal to $\frac{360°}{n_1+n_2}$ such that the resultant vector for both samples equals 0. A value, R_1^2, is computed by vector analysis for one of the series and compared with an expected value, $E(R_1^2) = \frac{n_1 n_2}{N-1}$ through the ratio $R_1^2/E(R_1^2)$, which is in turn compared with an exponential distribution as was done for the test of preferred direction.

OBSERVATIONS

BEHAVIOUR BEFORE AND DURING DEPARTURE

Upon release from the hands of the experimenter most birds backed off a few metres, squawked in protest, and then ran quickly towards the nearest conspicuous object, generally a tripod or the tent. If the release point was 30 metres or less from such an object, the bird characteristically covered from one half to most of that distance before pausing. From greater distances, the first pause generally came after 10 to 20 metres. A few birds left in the departure direction immediately and without pauses, apparently either not noticing or ignoring our poorly camouflaged gear.

During the ensuing 5–15 minutes most of the birds moved about erratically within a few hundred metres of the transits, pausing frequently for from a few seconds to several minutes. During these pauses they generally stood upright, turning the head from side

117

to side, stretching, shaking and occasionally preening. Some of the birds called and a few gave the "ecstatic" display, an inappropriate act which suggests a state of confusion. We attempted to remain immobile and inconspicuous, and the birds rarely appeared to be unduly disturbed by our presence. As they started to move off, however, many of the birds repeatedly paused to look back at us and our scant equipment on an otherwise featureless terrain. Calls from the stored birds in the subsurface pits constituted a rather serious source of distraction when they occurred. Fortunately they were infrequent and delayed departures only occasionally.

After the initial period of erratic activity, movements of from a few metres to 20 or 30 metres between pauses were generally in the departure direction and practically never widely diverging from it. This suggested that the route was often selected well before the bird was ready to leave the distractions of the release site.

The moment of final departure was usually fairly well defined and the duration of the pre-departure period determinable to within a minute or two. This varied from zero in three cases to several hours. Under clear skies most birds left within 15 minutes after release. Those which stayed longer often lay down and slept, and when this happened and the delay extended beyond an hour (19 instances), we usually chased, recaptured and returned the bird to a storage pit. Such birds, with a single exception, performed without an extended delay on second release, suggesting that the original delay was probably attributable to distractions or lack of motivation rather than inability to select a departure direction.

BEHAVIOUR ALONG THE ROUTE

The mode of locomotion of penguins in transit varied with the hardness and smoothness of the snow surface. When once under way nearly all birds moved swiftly and persistently, alternating tobogganning on the belly with running in an upright position. On smooth surfaces tobogganning predominated, on coarse surfaces and in the presence of transverse sastrugi (wind-formed snow ridges) as much as half and sometimes more of the route was covered running. Until well started the head of a tobogganning bird was raised and repeatedly turned 60° or more to right and left; but a bird under full speed held the head forward only occasionally turning it slightly. Brief stops to stand and look around were made at intervals of from a few minutes to 20 minutes or more; a few birds were never seen to pause until they had disappeared beyond the horizon.

Speeds of continuously moving birds over good surfaces varied from about 5 to 10 km. per hour, and over poor surfaces from 3 to 6. The fastest birds seemed almost frantic in their haste and raced along, without any rests, for the full 3 or 4 km. covered by the transit telescopes. Mean net speeds ranged from 2·2 to 4·6 km. per hour in the various Series (Table 1–E).

Distractions along the route of departing birds were minimized by the essentially featureless nature of the release sites. In Series V, however, a few snow blocks and pits constructed at a point about ½ km. away in an earlier experiment briefly diverted several passing birds which came within 100 metres of them. In Series III, a series of thin bamboo marker poles spaced 322 metres apart produced no detectable response, but may have diverted some of the birds slightly. As already noted social distractions in the form of calls from birds in the holding pits almost always delayed departures when calls occurred. The standard procedure of not releasing birds until the previous subject had departed beyond view prevented social distractions along the route. Two "accidents" in Series II and one planned series with group releases (IB), however, demonstrated that the presence of other birds does produce social responses and prolonged delays. In both these instances the birds eventually departed in the same general direction as the singly released birds of the series, and the return of six of the 10 grouped birds in Series IB compared with six of 10 in the control series indicates comparable navigational performance.

STRAIGHTNESS OF DEPARTURE ROUTE

With a few exceptions normal birds released under good sun held a relatively straight course as long as they could be followed (Fig. 1, IIIC). This conforms with the observations of Ostenso (Sladen & Ostenso 1960) on the tracks of two penguins encountered far inland on the Ellsworth Highland and the Filchner Ice Shelf.

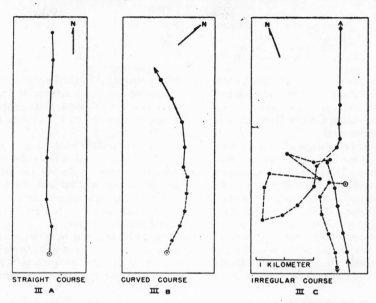

FIGURE 1. Sample departure routes of displaced Adelie Penguins showing straight, curved and irregular courses. The dots represent plotted positions determined by triangulation from the two observation transits at five minute intervals. The encircled dot indicates the starting position near the transits. Solid lines between dots indicate courses followed under a clear sun, dotted lines indicate courses followed under a cloud-covered sun. (For explanation of IIIC see Discussion.)

Measures of deviations from straightness were made on three scales or levels: (a) *a local scale*, for which plots of the snow tracks of departing birds were traced on a one metre scale for a sample of eight 50-metre segments of the route in Victorialand; (b) *an intermediate scale*, in which the units were successive 5-minute segments between observation points (averaging about 300 metres in length) along the departure route; and (c) *a long unit scale* in which the direction of the first two and last two segments on a route were compared (see Fig. 1).

On the local scale a straightness index based on actual route traversed divided by the straight line distance covered gave values of from 1·011 to 1·055 and an average of 1·026. In the total of 400 metres of track mapped, deviations from the mean direction ranged up to 40° for stretches of from 30 down to 2 metres (Table 2). Corrections back to the mean route direction were made within from one to six seconds according to the extent of the deviation (calculations on the basis of average speed).

On the intermediate scale, the straightness index (route traversed/straight distance) applied to individual birds gave values ranging from 1·000 (straight) to 33·470 (very crooked). Among 70 untreated Crozier birds released under good sun, 52 (74%) had indices less than 1·010, and only two (3%) had indices greater than 1·100. The mean for the eight Series ranged from 1·004 to 1·033 (Table 1–D1) and averaged 1·015.

119

Inferior performances were made by birds released without sun—1·411 (Series IIIC in Table 1), birds pre-treated with an artificial dark-light cycle—1·385 (Series VIC), and the birds from Cape Hallett—1·123 (Series IVB).

TABLE 2. *Analysis of irregularities in routes of departing Adelie Penguins on a local (one metre) scale.*

Deviations from mean direction	0–10°	11–20°	21–30°	31–40°
Percent of trail involved	50	30	15	5
Longest segment (metres)	30	12	4	2
Duration before correction (secs.)		6	2	1

In a separate measure of straightness of course, deviations of single 5-minute segments from the mean direction for each bird were measured and the incidence of segments deviating more than 20° tallied for each experiment series (Table 1–D2). Values for the series using Crozier birds under good sun ranged from 0% to 8%; values for the other series were 30%, 20% and 18% respectively.

Records of change of course over long distances were unfortunately, but inevitably, restricted to the first two to four kilometers by the limits of vision from the elevated telescopes. However, a comparison of the direction assumed during the first two observation intervals (10 minutes and generally about 600 metres) and the last two before disappearance provides a basis for comparison and correlation over the observable range (Table 1–D3). The angle subtended by these two lines reveals a good retention of straightness in most of the untreated Crozier birds under good sun and a poorer performance by the others. In some cases the change of course may have resulted simply from a delay in the selection of the departure direction; in others a continuing deflection is suggested. In no series was there a consistent swing to the left such as would be expected of birds orienting to the sun without corrections for apparent sun movement.

DIRECTION OF DEPARTURE ROUTE

With the exception of one rather abortive experiment with four birds (II), a definite preferred direction, significant at the ·01 level, was shown in all experimental series conducted with normal (not manipulated) subjects under partial or clear sun (Table1–C6).

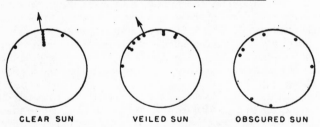

EFFECT OF SUN COVER ON ORIENTATION

CLEAR SUN   VEILED SUN   OBSCURED SUN

CAPE CROZIER BIRDS RELEASED IN MARIE BYRD LAND
NOVEMBER 16-20

FIGURE 2. Effect of sun cover on the departure directions taken by Adelie Penguins released on featureless ice plateaux in inland Antarctica. Each dot represents the direction taken by a single bird. The data are grouped in 10° segments about the circle. The arrow shows the mean direction for the group. The sun was considered to be veiled when thin clouds were drifting across its face, and occluded when the intervening clouds obscured the disc to the point where no shadows could be detected on the snow under an object moving six inches above the surface.

A positive correlation between the consistency of departure direction (sample concentration) and the visibility of the sun's position was demonstrated in Series III, where all records were grouped into three categories according to sun condition at the time of release and during departure. Under a veiled sun the consistency of direction selection deteriorated slightly (Table 1–C4 & C6), while under an occluded sun no preferred direction was detected (p < ·01) (Fig. 2). January releases in Victorialand showed

EFFECT OF SEASON ON ORIENTATION

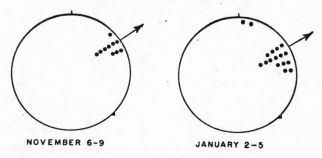

NOVEMBER 6-9   JANUARY 2-5

CAPE CROZIER BIRDS RELEASED UNDER GOOD SUN
IN VICTORIALAND

FIGURE 3. Effect of advancing season on departure directions of displaced Adelie Penguins. Symbols as in Fig. 2. The peripheral notch indicates the direction of " home ".

EFFECT OF LOCALITY OF SOURCE ON ORIENTATION

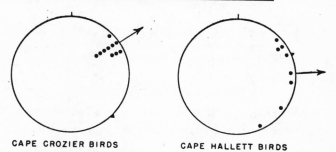

CAPE CROZIER BIRDS   CAPE HALLETT BIRDS

RELEASED IN VICTORIALAND UNDER GOOD SUN
NOVEMBER 6-9

FIGURE 4. Comparison of departure orientation of Adelie Penguins from two breeding localities. Symbols as in Fig. 2.

significantly greater variation (p < ·01) in selection of direction than those in November, but the two series did not differ significantly in their mean directions (Fig. 3). Birds from Cape Hallett were significantly more variable than those from Cape Crozier in Series IV, but again no difference in mean direction was found (Fig. 4). Subjects treated with artificial dark-light cycles in Series VI showed a significantly greater variation in departure direction than either controls (Fig. 5) or other normal releases in Victorialand. Those birds in which the dark period was imposed during the noon hours failed to show a preferred direction (p < ·01), while those with an evening dark period showed a preferred direction at only the ·05 level.

121

The mean departure directions selected by the birds at each of the three widely separated release sites appear roughly parallel and aligned with the N.E. compass direction at Cape Crozier, whence the birds came (see Map). These data suggest that the birds were orienting with respect to a rectangular grid pattern of directions (grid direction, insert A on Map) rather than to a radiating pattern of meridians emanating from the pole (compass direction, insert B on Map) (Table 1–C1 & C2, Fig. 6). Tests for comparison of mean departure directions at the three release sites using compass

EFFECT OF ARTIFICIAL LIGHT-DARK CYCLE ON ORIENTATION

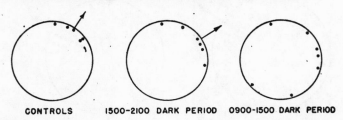

CONTROLS   1500-2100 DARK PERIOD   0900-1500 DARK PERIOD

CAPE CROZIER BIRDS RELEASED IN VICTORIALAND UNDER GOOD SUN
JANUARY 8–11

FIGURE 5.   Effect of 10-day exposures of Adelie Penguins to artificial light-dark cycles before release on departure direction.   Symbols as in Fig. 2.

EFFECT OF RELEASE LOCALITY ON ORIENTATION

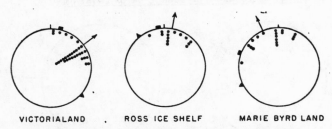

VICTORIALAND   .   ROSS ICE SHELF   MARIE BYRD LAND

CAPE CROZIER BIRDS RELEASED UNDER GOOD SUN

FIGURE 6.   Effect of locality of release on departure direction of displaced Adelie Penguins. Symbols as in Fig. 2.   The peripheral notch indicates the direction of home, and the block the direction of " grid north ".

direction show that of the three possible pairings, two, Ross Ice Shelf versus Victorialand and Marie Byrd Land versus Victorialand, are significantly different ($p < ·01$).   When the same tests are made using grid direction one pairing, Marie Byrd Land versus Victorialand, remains significantly different even though the two mean directions differ by only 8·5°.   The results of these tests should be interpreted with some caution since they may reflect, in part, differences in sample size and dispersion.   This seems particularly pertinent when comparing Marie Byrd Land with Victorialand, a pairing which also shows a significant difference ($p < ·01$) in sample concentration.

There was no direct or consistent correlation of mean departure direction with prevailing winds (Table 1–B2) or sastrugi (Table1–B5).   Analysis of departure directions with previous homing experience (seven subjects in Series V) revealed no correlations.

122

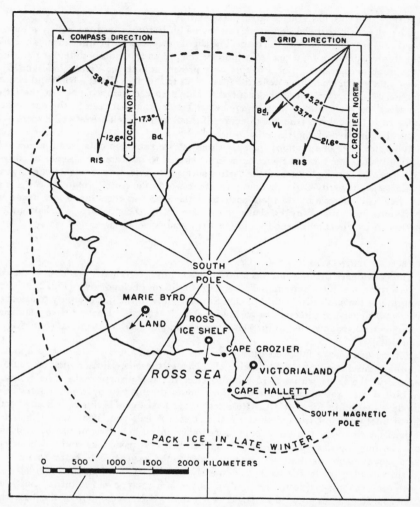

Map of Antarctica showing locations of the two sources of experimental birds and the three release sites. Mean departure direction of Cape Crozier birds released under good sun are indicated by an arrow at each release site. The three arrows in inset A show the mean departure direction for these sites brought together for direct comparison on a compass scale. Those in inset B make the same comparison on a grid scale based on the Cape Crozier meridian. The dashed line marking the outer limit of pack ice in September indicates in a general way the feeding range of the birds at that time.

DISCUSSION

The above observations indicate that Adelie Penguins transported in various directions and released on featureless ice plateaux in inland Antarctica will (*a*) display simple direction orientation rather than goal orientation, (*b*) use the sun azimuth position or an associated celestial cue as orientation reference, and (*c*) use an inherent timing sense or biological clock to hold a fixed orientation while using a "moving" orientation cue. The nature and basis of these conclusions are discussed below.

DIRECTION ORIENTATION VERSUS GOAL ORIENTATION

The essentially parallel departure courses of birds from the three widely separated release sites are clearly seen on the map. The slight deviations of the three mean directions from absolute parallelism, if real, may indicate the presence of subtly different conditions at the three release sites. Local factors were present at both the Victorialand and Byrd release sites which could have deflected these birds to the right (East)—wind and sastrugi direction at the former, several distant and widely spaced bamboo poles at the latter. The actual parallelism may thus be somewhat better than that seen in the data on the map. In so far as this is true, the direction of the Ross Ice Shelf arrow would seem to be the most indicative of the three.

While we have observations for only three release sites, the data would seem to be sufficiently consistent and the sites sufficiently spaced to indicate the absence of convergence towards any single goal on the earth's surface. Certainly there is no convergence or orientation towards Cape Crozier. In other words the birds provided no evidence that they had information on their position with respect to their home locality or any other point (no " map " in the sense of Kramer 1960); their departure behaviour was determined by direction orientation rather than goal orientation.

THE SUN AS ORIENTATION CUE

Direct evidence that the sun was used for orientation reference is best seen in the data on performance at Byrd Station under varying conditions of cloud cover (Fig. 2). Partial obscuring of the sun's disc with thin cloud interfered with the birds' ability to select the " correct " departure direction or to hold a straight course. Heavier cover, sufficient to eliminate all shadows, led to further deterioration and random dispersal (Series III in Table 1–C).

Several birds were followed during periods in which the sun alternately appeared and disappeared through slowly drifting clouds. In these cases disorientation could be detected in the birds within 5–10 minutes after the sun disappeared. The course of one bird which was followed for over four hours during two overcast and two clear periods is plotted in Fig. 1–IIIA. Released under heavy clouds this bird headed south (dotted line) until lost from view at 1,500 metres. A half hour later it was sighted on the horizon and near the point of disappearance in an area brightened by sunshine. Tobogganning northward (solid line) it approached and passed us under a clear sun. As the clouds again obscured the sun, our bird stopped less than 500 metres to our north and then headed off to the west. For nearly two hours it wandered irregularly and sometimes hesitatingly (dotted line); then as the sun re-appeared it turned north and without further pauses pursued a straight course to the N.N.W. (solid line), the " correct " direction, until it was lost from view on the horizon.

Definite loss of orientation seemed to occur in the birds when we ourselves could still readily locate the sun's position within a degree or two, with or without polaroid sun glasses. Records were kept on percent of sky cover as well as density of sun cover, and no effect of clouds was detected except as they partially or completely obscured the disc of the sun. Stars were never visible to us during the continuous daylight and are not regarded as potential cues during the summer months. The moon was generally visible when illuminated, but we found no evidence that it was used by the birds.

In sun-navigating animals the azimuth position of the sun rather than its altitude must inevitably supply the final reference for selecting an azimuth direction on the earth's surface. To use sun azimuth as reference for straight course or consistent course orientation, however, an animal must have additional " instructions " to tell it in which direction and how much its course should deviate from the azimuth position of the sun at any given moment. Such instructions can be obtained from information on the time of. day available through observations on the sun's altitude or reference to an intrinsic time sense or " biological clock ".

Information derived from sun altitude alone provides no basis for discriminating between morning and afternoon moments of equal sun altitude. No confusion in the performance of our penguins was noted that could be attributed to this situation. Time information from sun altitude, furthermore, relates to the local time at the locality of testing and, as applied to the selection of an azimuth departure direction, would therefore produce a response related to the local meridian of longitude. The essentially parallel departure routes displayed by our birds argues against the use of this time cue. Time information based on an internal clock would, by contrast, relate to local time at the home locality, and departure direction, so determined, would relate to the direction of the home meridian of longitude regardless of the locality of testing. Thus, a bird orienting towards the sun at Cape Crozier noon and suddenly transported 71° eastward from Cape Crozier to Byrd Station observes the sun at an azimuth position 71° west of the local noon sun position (Byrd Station meridian north) and orients accordingly. The course is parallel on a rectangular grid scale to that taken at Cape Crozier, but widely different from the north compass direction on the meridian scale.

On this basis the biological clock would seem to dominate the sun-altitude clock in determining the correct compensation for the observed sun azimuth position in our birds. This does not, however, exclude the possible use of sun altitude as a *Zeitgeber* cue for periodic setting of the biological clock. Other uses of sun altitude information in conjunction with a biological clock have been discussed by Braemer (1960) and Pennycuick (1960).

The direction of prevailing winds, and hence sastrugi if present, were roughly parallel at the three release sites and must therefore be examined as possible factors in determining departure directions. Wind direction and velocity varied during the releases, however, without conspicuously altering departure direction, and sastrugi were essentially absent or highly irregular at two of the three sites. A correlation of course direction with an angle roughly 80° (54°–105°) east of the local magnetic direction at each release site is thought to be fortuitous in the light of positive evidence on sun response and internal clock. A similar correlation with the direction of nearest open seas (300–700 km. away) is also thought to be fortuitous but remains an untested challenge.

THE BIOLOGICAL CLOCK AND DIRECTION MAINTENANCE

Evidence that the experimental birds in this study used a rather precise and persistent timing sense or biological clock in their orientation is provided by their ability to hold a straight course, their ability to select a common direction regardless of time of day, and the partial breakdown of orientation in birds exposed to 10 days of artificial dark-light cycles before release.

Evidence of ability to hold a straight course is unfortunately limited in our study to observation periods of less than an hour during which time the expected change of direction by a non-correcting sun-oriented bird would be only 15 degrees. The direction of change by such a bird would of course, invariably be to the left. As noted there was no prevalence of curving to the left in our records.

The grouping of departure directions around a mean throughout the day is convincing evidence of a functioning time sense. Constant direction regardless of hour would require not only a 15°-per-hour clockwise correction to observed sun position, but also a cycle of variation around this 15° mean to compensate for the cycles of variation in sun azimuth speed occasioned by the tilt of the earth's axis (Braemer 1960). A bird with a biological clock lacking such a compensating device would head east of the mean direction in the morning and west in the. afternoon. Examination of our data for deviation from mean departure directions by time of day at Cape Crozier reveals a 10°

shift to the east for 28 releases during the A.M. and a 12° shift to the west for 23 releases during the P.M. (Table 3). This difference is found to be significant at the ·01 level and suggests that the birds were operating with a uniform (non-compensating), 15°-per-hour clock. The observed deviations correspond roughly with those expected for the latitudes and seasons covered by the experiments.

TABLE 3. *Morning and afternoon deviations from mean departure directions of Adelie Penguins after release.*

Release time (nearest hour)	Releases	Mean deviation	Concentration (" k ")
06.00–11.00 a.m.	28	10·1° E.	9·37
13.00–18.00 p.m.	23	12·5° W.	4·26

Our attempts to demonstrate the biological clock experimentally was only partially successful. In theory, a bird in which the rhythm of activity and inactivity was reversed would select a departure direction directly opposite to that of an unmanipulated control bird. In the Antarctic environment, however, we were not altering a 24-hour dark-light cycle with our ten day conditioning programme, but introducing dark periods at 24-hour intervals into an otherwise continuous daylight regime. Under these circumstances one would scarcely expect the 24-hour activity rhythm to be reversed, and it is not surprising that the treated birds showed confusion rather than a systematic change of departure direction. Greatest confusion occurred in the group in which the dark period coincided with the noon portion of the day (Table 1, Series VIC).

It is of considerable interest that the birds in all our experiments showed good corrections for time of day despite the absence of a clear synchronizing cue or " time giver ". Light intensity and air temperatures did decline appreciably at Cape Crozier after about 11 p.m. as the sun dropped in altitude and disappeared behind the mountains of Ross Island. This conceivably served as the " time-giver " for a daily setting of the clocks of Cape Crozier birds. Quantitative records of several aspects of penguin behaviour indicated a slight reduction of activity during these periods of reduced light and increased cold; but no indicators of precise activity rhythms were detected. The slight deterioration in consistency of orientation in January as opposed to November releases in Victorialand (Fig. 3) may perhaps reflect a deterioration of synchrony in the absence of a precise environmental " clock-setter ". We have no explanation for the relatively poor performance of the Cape Hallett birds (Table 1, Series IVB).

THEORETICAL BIOLOGICAL VALUE OF A GRID-NORTHWARD ORIENTATION

Recent observations of what appears to be adherence to a fixed departure direction (" nonsense orientation ") in disregard of the home direction has been reported for terns by Griffin & Goldsmith (1955), for pigeons by Kramer (1959) and Schmidt-Koenig (1960) and for ducks by Bellrose (1958, 1962) and Matthews (1961, 1963, 1964). Several of these authors have shown that such behaviour, supplemented later by goal-directed orientation (using landmarks or coordinate navigation and based on experience), may be effective in steering a displaced bird to its home.

In our only penguin release series in which distance and available time were favourable for getting home before the end of the season, a majority (12 out of 20) of the birds got back despite a mean direction of departure about 40° from the home direction (Series I). Circumstantial evidence from the slow homing speed (three to four weeks for 340 airline kilometres) and the condition of the birds on arrival (clean and heavy) strongly suggests that the route taken included a visit to the feeding grounds a good many miles off shore and, if at a point designated by the departure direction (see map), a considerable distance east of Cape Crozier. Return from this " ice-edge refuge " would have required at least

126

a partial reversal of the direction assumed in departing from the release site, possibly aided by visual landmarks provided by the Ross Ice Shelf front and, as the subjects moved closer to home, by Mount Erebus and Mount Terror rising to 4,000 metres altitude behind Cape Crozier.

The term " nonsense orientation " for fixed direction departures was coined because of the lack of any immediate obvious biological value. Any consistent animal response, however, deserves consideration for its possible significance to the species. In the present case, the N.N.E. directional response of the Cape Crozier Adèlie Penguins in the approximate longitude of their rookery could be regarded as an escape orientation or an oriented escape possessing survival value in steering lost birds to the broad pack ice feeding grounds which lie off shore (see Map). Birds accidentally displaced to the east or west would, furthermore, be guided back into a common area as the broadly circular ice edge deflected their basically grid-north movements centripetally, to a regional " refuge " (feeding and resting ground) opposite the rookery.

This concept of a regional refuge has further logical appeal if birds from colonies at other points along the coastline of Antarctica have a similar escape orientation northward, i.e. outward from their coasts. We have no evidence that such orientation exists, and our efforts to obtain birds from rookeries across the continent were unsuccessful. The return from 3,800 km. of two and possibly three of five birds transported from Wilkes Station to McMurdo in 1960 (Penney 1963), however, could be explained by an escape orientation paralleling north along the meridian passing through Wilkes Station.

An obvious inadequacy of the northward escape theory is its inability to explain the movement of birds back to the coast at the onset of the breeding season. In the absence of any legitimate explanation we propose that the physiological changes of this period effect a reversal in the basic escape direction and cause an inshore migration which is guided by landmark orientation as the birds approach the coast. The problem is perhaps not dissimilar to that posed by the return of song-bird migrants to their breeding grounds, a problem which still defies satisfactory explanation.

SUMMARY

Male Adelie penguins *Pygoscelis adeliae* were transported from coastal rookeries in the Ross Sea area of Antarctica to three release points on featureless ice plateaux in the interior of the continent. Birds were released individually and their departure routes mapped for distances of 2–4 km., the position of the bird being determined by triangulation every five minutes. Precise data were thus obtained on the straightness of course and direction selected by each of 103 birds.

Birds released inland from a coastal rookery under favourable conditions consistently moved in straight courses N.N.E. toward the coast. Birds from the same rookery released at points to the east and west took courses essentially parallel to this departure direction, i.e., northwest and northeast respectively on a meridian scale rather than true north or in the homeward direction. These and other experiments under varying degrees of cloud cover and with birds prepared under artificial day-night light regimes indicate that the birds possessed a navigation mechanism which used the sun as the primary orientation cue plus a biological clock to compensate for changing sun azimuth positions. The mechanism effected a consistent escape direction for birds of a given population (source) regardless of the location of the release site.

The " grid N.N.E." orientation of these birds is compared with " nonsense orientation " as described for ducks and other birds. It is considered to have survival value in the present instance in steering lost penguins to the appropriate off-coast feeding areas and in segregating and concentrating the birds from the various circum-continental populations.

REFERENCES

BELLROSE, F. C. 1958. Celestial orientation in wild Mallards. Bird-Banding 29 : 75–90.
BELLROSE, F. C. 1958. The orientation of displaced waterfowl on migration. Wilson Bull. 70 : 20–40.
BELLROSE, F. C. 1962. Orientation behaviour of four species of waterfowl. Auk 80 : 257–289.
BRAEMER, W. 1960. A critical review of the sun-azimuth hypothesis. Cold Spr. Harbor Sympos. Quant. Biol. 25 : 413–427.
GRIFFIN, D. R. & GOLDSMITH, T. H. 1955. Initial flight direction of homing birds. Biol. Bull. 108 : 264–276.
KRAMER, G. 1959. Recent experiments on bird orientation. Ibis 101 : 399–416.

MATTHEWS, G. V. T. 1961. "Nonsense" orientation in Mallard *Anas platyrhynchos* and its relation to experiments on bird navigation. Ibis 103 : 211–220.
MATTHEWS, G. V. T. 1963. "Nonsense" orientation as a population variant. Ibis 105 : 185–197.
MATTHEWS, G. V. T. 1964. The astronomical bases of "nonsense" orientation. Proc. 13th Int. Orn. Congr. Vol. 1 : 415–429.
PENNEY, R. L. 1963. Territorial behavior and social interactions by the Adelie Penguin. Ph.D. dissertation, Univ. Wisconsin.
PENNYCUICK, C. J. 1960. The physical basis of astro-navigation in birds: theoretical considerations. J: Exp. Biol. 37 : 573–593.
SCHMIDT-KOENIG, K. 1960. Internal clocks and homing. Cold Spr. Harbor Sympos. Quant. Biol. 25 : 389–393.
SLADEN, W. & OSTENSO, N. A. 1960. Penguin tracks far inland in the Antarctic. Auk 77 : 466–469.
WATSON, G. S. 1961. Goodness-of-fit tests on a circle. Biometrika 48 : 109–114.
WATSON, G. S. 1962. Goodness-of-fit tests on a circle. II. Biometrika 49 : 555–561.
WATSON, G. S. & WHEELER, S. In press. A two sample distribution-free test on a circle.
WATSON, G. S. & WILLIAMS, E. J. 1956. On the construction of significance tests on the circle and sphere. Biometrika 43 : 344–352.

Professor John T. Emlen & Dr. Richard L. Penney, Dept. of Zoology, University of Wisconsin, Madison 6, U.S.A.

THE ADAPTIVE SIGNIFICANCE OF COLONIAL NESTING IN THE BREWER'S BLACKBIRD *(EUPHAGUS CYANOCEPHALUS)*

Early Summer 1968

Henry S. Horn

The structural simplicity of the study site allowed easy access to the nests and accurate measurement of their spatial distribution.

The effects of predation on breeding success were analyzed with respect to colony shape and the spatial distribution of the nests. On the study area the predation pattern favored more widely spaced nests in linear colonies, but more closely spaced nests in round colonies.

I examined the role of colonial nesting in aiding the exploitation of a spatially and temporally variable food supply by taking food samples from nestling birds, measuring patterns of food availability, and observing the foraging patterns of the adult birds. An idealized model relates the spatial distribution of nests to the efficiency of individual exploitation of different distributions of food. In addition to conforming to the conditions of the model, Brewer's blackbirds take advantage of each other's foraging success. In conclude that colonial nesting in the Brewer's blackbird is primarily adaptive to the variable nature of their food supply.

INTRODUCTION

Characteristic patterns of distribution of animals in space and time have aroused the interest of naturalists for a long time, but only recently have these patterns been studied from a functional as well as descriptive point of view. Such functional studies take advantage of the fact that when naturally occurring variations in distribution patterns can be correlated with differential reproductive success, the action of natural selection is directly demonstrated. Birds that nest colonially provide a natural model for the framing and testing of hypotheses involving natural selection, since they present a fixed and easily studied pattern of spatial distribution, and each pair of birds in the colony has a measurable reproductive output.

The functional analyses of colonial nesting to date have related its adaptive significance to two aspects of the breeding behavior of the birds: their behavioral interactions prior to mating and anti-predator behavior during the nesting period. A third aspect, the spatial distribution of the food exploited during nesting, has been discussed in theoretical reviews though relevant data are scarce in field studies of colonial nesting.

In some colonial sea birds, Darling (1938) observed a correlation between the number of birds in a colony and their average clutch size. Accordingly, he suggested that in the larger colonies a greater total amount of social behavior stimulated increased reproductive output. Attempts to confirm this hypothesis in the field have either been unsuccessful or subject to alternative interpretations (Coulson and White 1956, 1960, Orians 1961).

The mechanisms of a theory in which predation plays an important part have been reviewed by Kruuk (1964). A large body of data, consisting of comparisons of the nesting habits of different species (Cullen 1960), comparisons of colonies with outlying nests (Patterson 1965), and carefully controlled behavioral experiments and observations (Kruuk 1964), supports the idea that spacing of nests in colonies of gulls and terns is a result of a compromise between selection for

clumping to allow joint defense against predators and selection for dispersal of cryptic nests to avoid detection by predators.

In a review of avian spacing systems, Brown (1964) has suggested that where food is predictably and thinly spread over the environment, defending a territory with sufficient food to raise young is energetically feasible. Where food is highly clumped or unpredictable, however, it may not be possible to defend a territory large enough to assure an adequate food supply. In this latter case, some other system of spacing, such as colonial nesting, results.

The Brewer's blackbird *(Euphagus cyanocephalus)* in eastern Washington is particularly appropriate for examining the contributions of behavioral interactions, predation, and foraging to the adaptive value of colonial nesting, since the nests are abundant and accessible in a relatively simple environment. I report elsewhere (in prep.) the role of displays by individual birds in promoting aggregation and synchrony of nesting. In the present paper, I describe the general pattern of predation and analyze the effect of the spatial distribution of the nests on the likelihood of predation. The spatial and temporal variability of the food supply is then documented, and the efficiency of exploitation of different distributions of food is related to the spatial distribution of the nests by an idealized model. Finally, I assess the relative contributions of predation and foraging patterns to the adaptive value of colonial nesting.

The work reported here is part of a doctoral dissertation sponsored by Gordon H. Orians of the Department of Zoology, University of Washington. Constructive criticism of several manuscripts was given by Gordon Orians, Robert T. Paine, Donald S. Farner, and Elizabeth G. Horn. For permission to work on the Columbia National Wildlife Refuge, I am grateful to Phil Lehenbauer, Robert Nelson, and Jack Waddell. The study was supported by the National Science Foundation through a Predoctoral Fellowship to me and a grant to Gordon Orians for the study of vertebrate social systems.

ECOLOGY, 1968, Vol. 49, pp. 682-694.

The area of my study is about 30 km² of channeled scabland northwest of Othello, Grant and Adams Counties, Washington, known locally as the "Potholes." Parts of the main study site are on the Columbia National Wildlife Refuge. The topography consists of buttes and basins scoured in Columbia basalt by Pleistocene floods (Bretz 1959). The Columbia basin, in the "rain shadow" of the Cascade Mountains, receives about 20 cm of precipitation annually. Most of the standing water in the study area post-dates the advent of local irrigation at the turn of the century, and many of the ponds are presently growing because of seepage from more extensive irrigation which began in 1951. It is unlikely that Brewer's blackbirds bred on the study area prior to the formation of ponds and streams.

The dominant upland vegetation of the area is sagebrush (*Artemesia tridentata*), bluegrass (*Poa* sp.), and bunchgrass (*Agropyron spicatum*). Greasewood (*Sarcobatus vermiculatus*) and rabbitbush (*Chrysothamnus viscidiflorus*) dominate alkaline pans and sandy areas, respectively. Cheatgrass (*Bromus tectorum*) covers heavily grazed and well-watered areas. Sedges (*Carex* sp. and *Scirpus* sp.) grow near standing water and streams, and cattail (*Typha angustifolia*) occurs in patches. Willows (*Salix amygaloides*) are found along the older streams.

The Brewer's blackbird in the Potholes shows a combination of attributes especially appropriate to the study of colonial nesting. Colonies are large enough to form a level of organization higher than the aggregation of individual pairs, but small enough to allow analysis of the contribution of individuals to the properties of the colony. The young are altricial and are available for census and measurement since the nests are in sagebrush. The limited number of simple and discrete habitat types allows almost constant observation of the birds and permits a discrete classification of the areas where they forage.

Three characteristic features of the nesting colonies in the Potholes are: a foraging area, a nesting area, and a relatively high perch nearby. Most of the food brought to the young consists of emerging naiads and fresh tenerals of damsel-flies which the adults pick up while walking in the short grass along the edges of watercourses. The nests are built in the more densely foliated sagebrush. Nesting is usually confined to a portion of the potentially suitable sagebrush. Near each colony is a cliff or row of trees, providing perches at least 3–7 m higher than the ground where the nests are built. The males spend much of their time on these perches during the period when the females are laying eggs and incubating.

My study concentrated on 8 colonies of from 10 to 30 pairs of birds each. These colonies were named for nearby lakes whose locations are listed by Wolcott (1964). In 1964 and 1965 I camped continuously in the Potholes from mid-April to mid-June; in 1966, from late April through May. During this time I kept a daily or bi-daily log of the states of the nests.

Visits of the adult birds to the nest were monitored by an automatic camera, which exposed a single frame of 16 mm film when the bird cast its shadow on a photocell.

I took samples of the food brought to the nestlings by placing bands of pipe-cleaner around their necks (Orians 1966, after Klujiver 1933) and removing the food brought in during the next hour by the adults. A study of the distribution of insects in the Potholes allowed a determination of the foraging areas of the adult birds from analysis of these food samples. The emergence pattern of damsel-flies was monitored with traps.

The concealment of nests was measured by assuming that a terrestrial predator sees a nest as a dark object against a background of vegetation and sky; the more concealing vegetation around the nest, the less light penetrates through the vegetation. Concealment is then defined as the logarithm of the ratio of intensities of light above and about a foot below the nest. This measure correlates well with a subjective assessment of the concealment of the nest made before the light measurements.

After most of the young had fledged, I mapped the positions of the nests on extreme enlargements of aerial photographs taken in 1961 by the Agricultural Stabilization and Conservation Service. Scaling, distortion, and overall accuracy were checked by a few direct field measurements, which came within 5% of map measurements. On these maps, I measured parameters of the spatial distribution of the nests, such as the distance from each nest to its nearest neighbor and the distance of each nest from the center of the colony. The center of a colony is computed as the point that has as coordinates the mean coordinates of the nests considered; that is, the "centroid" of the nest locations.

Further details of the methods used in this study may be found in Horn (1966).

Most of the data were initially processed on an IBM 7094 computer. Where trends were found in the mean values, they were examined statistically. Results were judged statistically significant when the probability of observing a difference as large as that observed, when in fact there is no difference, is 0.05 or less. To minimize the effects of intercolonial differences in topography, predation, and foraging area, data were analyzed for each colony separately and the results were then pooled for statistical analysis. This procedure also minimizes the effect of the variability of the spatial distribution of nests from colony to colony. As a result of this procedure, however, the size of any sample that is homogeneous with respect to the hypothesis under test is limited by the number of nests in the individual colonies rather than by the total number of nests in all colonies. The small size of homogeneous samples is particularly restrictive when hypotheses involve statements about the relative amounts of variation within different samples.

RESULTS AND INTERPRETATIONS

Predation and Anti-predator Behavior

Predators of the Brewer's blackbird in the Potholes are listed in Appendix I.

During the period of egg-laying and incubation the male blackbirds spend much of their time on perches near the colony, from which they give alarm calls in response to predators in the distance and fly out to harry those that come too close to the colony. An incubating or brooding female shows two types of response to the male alarm call. She either crouches in the nest so that only her bill and tail protrude above the rim, or she drops from the nest and flies away close to the ground, reappearing on the cliff with the male.

When the young hatch, there are a number of changes in the anti-predator behavior of the adults. The males assist the females with care of the nestlings and spend little time on their perches near the colony. Harrying of potential predators is confined to a smaller area around the nest and is more intense, but flocking near potential predators often occurs at a greater distance from each pair's nest than during the periods of egg-laying and incubation. While the birds are in a state of alarm, they do not feed their young or approach the nest.

The pattern of nestling mortality due to predation is shown in Figure 1, where the logarithm of the number of young surviving to a given age is plotted against the age of the young. Since survivorship is expressed logarithmically, a constant slope of the survivorship curve indicates a constant likelihood of predation within a given period of time. A significant change in the likelihood of predation occurs at the time of hatching in both 1964 and 1965. This change is correlated with the change in anti-predator behavior of the adults,

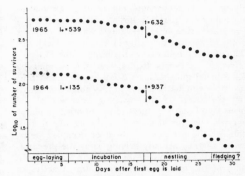

FIG. 1. Log (survivorship) curve of nestlings. The size of the initial cohort (l_o) is given for each curve. Also given is the t-statistic (Fisher 1958: 122) comparing the daily decrease in log (survivorship) before and after hatching. As both t's are greater than the critical value (t.05,23d.f. = 2.07), the difference in slope of the curves before and after hatching is significant.

increased activity around the nest, and the presence of nestlings rather than eggs in the nest.

There is direct evidence that the visual outline of the nest does not affect the likelihood of predation. The concealment measures and the heights of predated and nonpredated nests do not differ significantly (Horn 1966).

If predators locate a specific nest primarily by auditory or olfactory clues, a convex survivorship curve might be expected during the nestling period because an increasing rate of predation would be associated with the increase in noise and body mass of the nestlings. The form of the survivorship curve is linear, however, during the nestling period, suggesting that the increased activities of the adult birds are primarily responsible for the increased predation during this period. The activities of the adults around the nest increase with the hatching of the young, but the rate of feeding the young remains relatively constant through the nestling period (Horn 1966).

Thus, the pattern of mortality of the young is consistent with the hypothesis that the attention of predators is drawn to a nest by the normal activities of the adult birds. I doubt that these activities attract a predator's attention to a specific nest at a greater range than the distance from that nest to its nearest neighbor, because I found no tendency for predators to take nests at the edge of a colony before those in the center. Consequently, cessation of this activity in response to alarm calls should decrease the likelihood of predation.

In all the encounters with potential predators that I saw, the blackbirds were only able to deter

131

flying birds; they could not drive away snakes, mammals, or perched birds. LaRivers (1944) presented similar observations in an intensive study of nestling mortality in Brewer's blackbirds. The mobbing behavior of the birds in the Potholes effectively prevents flights over the colonies by Ring-billed gulls (*Larus delawarensis*), and thus probably eliminates losses to this abundant potential predator. If the mobbing behavior of the birds significantly reduces losses to other predator species, however, it must do so by making it difficult for the predator to discover occupied nests, rather than by actually driving away the predator. Both the distraction of the predator by the mobbing of the birds and the cessation of activities around the nest in response to alarm calls should enhance the crypticity of the nests.

After a given nest has been predated, the owners leave the colony and no longer participate in attacks on potential predators. This observation suggests that the mobbing behavior of the birds is not a defense of the colony as a whole, but of each nest by its owners. At outlying nests I was often attacked as a potential predator at a distance of more than 100 m from the nest, a distance at least 4 times as great as the mean distance between neighboring nests.

If the average radius of the area which each bird defends around its nest is greater than the average distance between nests, there is an advantage to close clustering of the nests. The closer together the nests are, the more defended areas overlap the position of a given nest, and the more birds are available to warn of predators or mob predators.

However, if the nests are close to a path that a predator routinely uses, rather than being spread over a wide, open area, a patterned search may not be necessary to locate them. In such a situation the mobbing behavior of the birds may even attract the predator to the area where the nests are most abundant.

To examine the effects of the spacing of the nests and the anti-predator behavior of the birds, colonies were first classified as linear or open on the basis of the number of parallel transects I had to run through the colony to locate all the nests. (See Fig. 2. The contrast shown in Fig. 2 between the two types of colony is typical; in no case was there any hesitation in assigning a given colony to one of the two categories.) The distribution of nests in the linear colonies was dictated by the distribution of suitable sagebrush along some topographic feature, a cliff or lakeshore, which was probably paralleled by the path of a terrestrial predator. The distance from each nest to its nearest neighbor was used as a measure of

TABLE 1. Effect of distribution of nests on predation

Nests predated during: Predated nests closer (C) together or farther (F) apart than median distance to nearest neighbor:	Egg-laying or incubation		Nestling period	
	C	F	C	F
12 Open colonies............	16*	35	21	20
8 Linear colonies...........	20*	9	10	16

Pairs of numbers marked by "*" are significantly different by a binomial test with $p=q=\frac{1}{2}$ (Siegel 1956: 36).

nest density since it gives a characteristic value for each nest. The active nests in a colony can then be divided into two density categories; half the nests are closer together than the median distance to nearest neighbor, and the other half are farther apart than the median distance to nearest neighbor. If predation has no relation to the density of the nests, a predator has an equal chance of taking a nest in either of the two density categories. Then the total number of nests taken that are closer together than the median should equal the number taken that are farther apart. However, if a large number of predations are totaled and the number of nests closer together than the median exceeds the number of nests farther apart than the median, this is evidence that the predators are more likely to take nests that are close together than those that are far apart. Stated in another way: this is evidence of selection for dispersal. The converse situation, an excess of predated nests farther apart than the median, is evidence of selection for clumping.

The distance to nearest neighbor of each predated nest was compared with the median distance to nearest neighbor of other nests in the colony that were active at the time of predation (Table 1). A significant tendency for differential predation is demonstrated during the period of egg-laying and incubation, when the male birds are on perches near the colony. In the open colonies nests farther apart than the median are taken by predators more often than those that are closer together. In the linear colonies, however, nests that are close together are taken more often. Under the observed pattern of predation, colonial nesting should be slightly favored in areas where there is a large expanse of sagebrush suitable for nesting. More distant spacing should be advantageous in linear colonies, where the area of suitable sagebrush is more restricted.

Foraging and the Distribution of the Food

The adults do most of their foraging in short vegetation at the edges of ponds and streams.

132

FIG. 2. Open and Linear Colonies.
Above: N. Teal Colony 1965, an open colony.
Below: E. Susan Pond Colony, a linear colony.
In each photograph the area that had to be carefully searched in order to locate all the nests is outlined.

Though the bulk of the foraging is in areas adjacent to the colony, foraging flights to a distance of a mile or more from the colony are occasionally observed. In colonies that are close to a number of foraging areas the birds are usually concentrated in one of these areas at a given time, presumably the area in which the food is most abundant at that time.

The contents of the food samples taken from the nestlings are analyzed by Orians and Horn (in prep.). The most important items in the diet of the nestlings are naiads and tenerals of damsel-

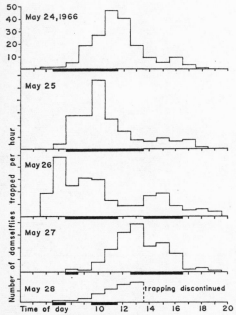

FIG. 3. Emergence of Damsel-flies on Pit-Teal Lake. Black bars show when blackbirds were foraging by the lake.

flies (Coenagrionidae). Orthopterans and cicadae provide a large amount of energy per item, but may be rarely encountered by the foraging adults. The small larvae and newly emergent adults of a white plume moth (Pterophoridae) and newly emerged dipterans (Chironomidae and Culicidae) are numerous in the samples but form only a small proportion of the caloric intake of the nestlings.

The most important food items, the damsel-flies, have a diurnal pattern of emergence, shown in Figure 3. Ten emergence traps, each with an opening 2 ft wide, were placed in fixed positions, spaced around Pit-Teal Lake. The traps were emptied hourly and the total number of damsel-flies plotted for 5 days. All 5 days were warm and sunny, but for a dust storm on the afternoon of the 26th. The bars below the histograms indicate hours during which a pair of Brewer's blackbirds foraged at the edge of the lake. This pair was the only pair with a nest near the lake at the time. The damsel-flies are available in high density only during a part of the day. The pattern of emergence on a given lake, particularly the timing of the peak emergence, varies from day to

day in a way that a single pair of birds does not appear to anticipate.

In addition to the temporal pattern there is a changing pattern of spatial clumping. Many tenerals on their maiden flights are caught by the wind and concentrated on the leeward shore of a lake. In a scabland area such as the Potholes, a small change in the direction of the prevailing winds may drastically alter the wind patterns on smaller lakes. Foraging Brewer's blackbirds appear to follow closely the resulting changes in local density of tenerals (see Fig. 4). The observations of Figure 4 are typical of a large number of observations recorded on field maps in 1965. Whenever a steady wind of more than 5 mph persisted, foraging Brewer's blackbirds were concentrated on the lee shores of the lakes. The ability of the Brewer's blackbird to capitalize on similar, ephemeral concentrations of food has been noted by Williams (1958) and by Howell and Bartholomew (1954).

The Brewer's blackbird characteristically exploits a food source that is very unevenly distributed in space and time. The nests of the birds are also spatially and temporally clumped. Since the spacing of the nests and the distribution of food can be expressed on the same scale, it is possible to examine the effect of colonial nesting on the exploitation of an unevenly distributed food source by means of an idealized model. Clumped and even nest distributions are superimposed on clumped and even distributions of food, and the average distance which the birds have to fly to gather sufficient food to the nest is calculated.

The following presentation of such a model is highly idealized for illustrative purposes. A more generalized presentation, with a derivation of the critical conditions favoring colonial nesting, is given in Appendix II.

The 4 situations to be examined are diagrammed in Figure 5. Exactly enough food to support 4 nests is distributed among 16 points 1 unit apart in a square that is 3 units on a side. Two patterns of food distribution are examined. The stable food distribution has the food evenly distributed among the 16 points at all times. For the moving food distribution, the food is assumed to be present at only 1 of the points at any particular time, but food is assumed to be present at different points at different times so that, in the long run, the same amount of food is provided at each point. Since the total amount of food has to be the same in both distributions, when food is present at a given point of the moving distribution it is 16 times more abundant than the food at any point of the stable distribution. Thus the 2 distributions

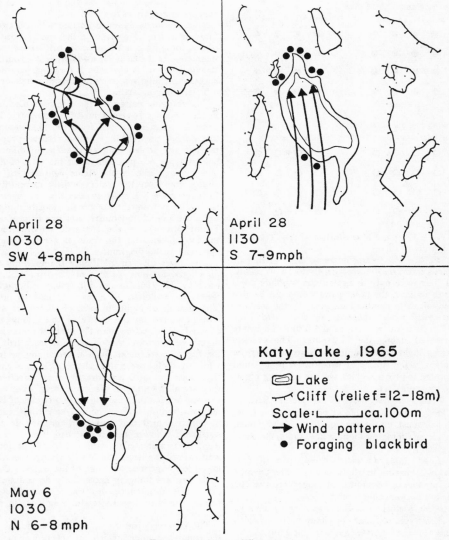

April 28
1030
SW 4-8mph

April 28
1130
S 7-9mph

May 6
1030
N 6-8mph

Katy Lake, 1965

⬭ Lake
⤙ Cliff (relief=12-18m)
Scale: ⌐_____⌐ ca.100m
➔ Wind pattern
● Foraging blackbird

FIG. 4. Foraging and Wind Direction.
The date, time, and direction of the prevailing winds are given for each observation.

of food can be characterized as: evenly distributed and stable, and highly clumped and transient. The patterns of distribution of the nests are: evenly spaced, 2 units apart, corresponding to "territoriality;" and all 4 nests in the center of the square, corresponding to "coloniality."

I assume that the nestlings must be fed con-stantly. The average distance that the adults fly on each foraging trip, from nest to food and back, is easily computed graphically.

(a) *Food stable; nests spaced.* Each pair of birds need only exploit the points immediately ad-jacent to its nest. The average foraging flight is 1.42 units.

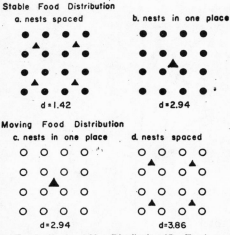

Stable Food Distribution

a. nests spaced   b. nests in one place

d = 1.42   d = 2.94

Moving Food Distribution

c. nests in one place   d. nests spaced

d = 2.94   d = 3.86

Fig. 5. Food and Nest Distribution (See Text).

(b) *Food stable; nests in one place.* Each pair of birds must, on the average, fly to all 16 points. If 1 pair were only to exploit the 4 points adjacent to its nest, the other pairs would not be able to exploit these points at all, since, by the assumptions of the model, there is only enough food for the 4 nests in the whole area and it must be evenly distributed among the 16 points. The average foraging flight is 2.94 units. (Note that there is no point in the square at which all 4 nests could be located to give a shorter average foraging flight. See Appendix II.)

(c) *Food clumped; nests in one place.* Because the food is only available at one point at a time, each pair must, on the average, fly to all 16 points. The average foraging flight is 2.94 units, the same value as in (b).

(d) *Food clumped; nests spaced.* As in (c), each pair must fly to all 16 points. The average foraging flight, 3.86 units, is longer because the nests are not centrally located.

The more efficient of the 2 spacing systems is, for each type of food distribution, that which results in the shorter average foraging flight. Thus, under selection for efficiency of food gathering, territorial spacing would be expected if the food source exploited is stable and evenly distributed. On the other hand, colonial aggregation would be favored for exploitation of a food source that is highly clumped in time and space. (The critical degrees of temporal and spatial clumping are derived in Appendix II.) Note that this model has been based on the average behavior of

individual pairs and not on the behavior of the colonial aggregate as a whole.

I have initially assumed no interaction between foraging pairs. However, if the spatial position of best foraging is not temporally predictable, such interaction is the basis for an additional advantage to aggregation. A bird who is foraging with little success can follow a more successful neighbor to a better foraging area.

The foraging pattern of the Brewer's blackbird in the Potholes is represented in Figure 6. The upper diagram is derived from the food samples taken from the nestlings. The relative proportions of the pooled samples taken from different habitat types are plotted against the time of day. The average size of the items delivered to the young from near the water (mostly damsel-flies, Coenagrionidae) is much greater than the average size of items from the sagebrush (mostly midges, Culicidae and Chironomidae, and tiny caterpillars, Pterophoridae); so the energetic importance of the food taken near the water is greater than is apparent in the diagram.

The lower diagram of Figure 6 represents the directional foraging pattern of 12 pairs of birds on May 20, 1965 in the Pit colony. Foraging flights were plotted on a map for half an hour. The number of flights to each of 16 sectors of a circle centered on the center of the colony was counted. The sectors with the greatest number of flights were darkly shaded until at least half of the flights were included; the remaining sectors with any flights were then shaded. It is obvious that when the birds are foraging most effectively they are all foraging in the same areas. Between the watches for the first and second circles of this diagram, within half an hour I saw three cases in which a bird that had been foraging in the sagebrush followed a bird that had just come in from the water's edge with a bill full of food, waited until the latter had fed its young, then followed to forage near the edge of the water. Thus birds that are foraging successfully do communicate, albeit "unintentionally," the location of better foraging to their less successful neighbors in the colony.

The observed pattern of foraging conforms to the conditions under which the theoretical model predicts that colonial nesting would be most efficient. I cannot examine the model critically, however, because I have not made comparable observations of the foraging pattern and food distribution of a non-colonial species.

The increased efficiency of foraging suggested by the observed communication of the location of best foraging can be examined. Birds nesting in the center of the colony should be able to take

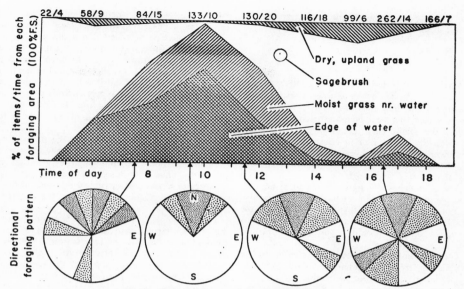

FIG. 6. Foraging Pattern of the Brewer's Blackbird.

In the upper diagram the percentage of food items obtained in each major. type of habitat is plotted against the time of day. Above each plotted point is the total number of items over the total number of samples that were taken at that time. The lower diagram is explained in the text. The amount of "spread" in the shaded areas is an indication of the degree of dispersal of the foraging birds at the times indicated by the arrows.

TABLE 2. Weight gain of young and nest location

Position in colony	Number of nests	Clutch size	Young hatched	Young 9 days old	Wt. gain/nest per day (grams)
Outer half	21	5.5	5.1	4.5	23.8
Inner half	20	5.7	5.4	4.6	27.5
t (testing difference above)			1.4		1.75
degrees of freedom			39		64
one-tailed t.05, —d.f.			1.7		1.67

advantage of the foraging success of a greater number of neighbors than birds nesting on the periphery of the colony. The pooled mean daily weight gain of nests in the inner and outer halves of several colonies is presented in Table 2. Each nest was classified as inner or outer by its relation to the median distance to the center of the colony of nests active at the time of the measurement of weight gain. Weight gain was measured during the period when the weight gained per nestling per day is roughly constant. The inner nests show a significantly greater weight gain than the outer nests.

It is possible that this weight difference is related not to coactive foraging, but to a tendency for the peripheral positions in the colony to be occupied by generally inferior individuals. However, the birds on the periphery are not inferior in clutch size or in proportion of eggs hatched; so it is unlikely that they are generally inferior.

The difference in weight gain per nest per day of inner and outer nests is 3.7 grams, which is of the same order of magnitude as the weight gained by a single nestling in a day (4.9 g, Horn 1966). However, the number of nestlings raised to an age of nine days shows no relation to the position of the nest in the colony. Therefore, the additional weight gain in the inner nests probably results in a higher weight of the young at fledging. If the weight at fledging is likely to affect the subsequent survival of the young, as Perrins (1963, 1965) has shown for the Great tit (*Parus major*), then

137

the foraging advantage of the inner nests would result in an increased reproductive potential.

DISCUSSION

Predation

Kruuk (1964) has observed that if predators are attacked by the owners of a nest over a greater distance from their nest than the average inter-nest distance, there will be more potential attackers within the colony than at the edge. If joint attacks on the predator or responses to alarm calls are effective in reducing predation, as Kruuk demonstrated for the Black-headed gull, close clustering of the nests is favored.

The advantages of aggregation and synchrony are countered by the greater likelihood of a predator's finding a colony than an individual nest (Cullen 1960), and, having found one nest, to capitalize on the proximity of others (Kruuk 1964).

These arguments have been supported in studies of gulls and terns by comparison of the incidence of predation in colonies with that in outlying groups of nests (Patterson 1965), contrast of the behavioral responses to predators and the nesting habits of different species (Cullen 1960), and experiments and observations on the behavior of predators and the anti-predator behavior of the birds (Kruuk 1964).

The arguments that I have advanced for the Brewer's blackbird are essentially identical to those reviewed by Kruuk. The only differences are related to the kinds of data sought to test the theory. I have attempted to test the theory by relating predation to variations of nest spacing within colonies, rather than between colonies. A contrast of linear and open colonies has shown that these are subject to different patterns of predation. This difference would have obscured the relations between nest spacing and predation, had I only made comparisons between colonies of different densities.

The predation pattern observed in the Potholes places a slight advantage on clumping in open colonies and dispersal in linear colonies. However, the anti-predator behavior of the blackbirds effectively prevents predation by the Ring-billed gull, which is but one of many potential predators.

Foraging

Brown (1964), interpreting the diversity of spacing systems in birds, has stressed the "economic defendability" of the food supply. Where food is evenly and thinly spread over the environment, assuring a food supply by defending a territory may well be worth the energy spent in territorial defense. On the other hand, if the food supply cannot be defended due to its motility or its transient nature, no territorial system is evolved to defend it. In this case, the area defended against conspecifics is usually restricted to the nest site. As examples of birds which depend on a motile or transient food supply, Brown cited colonial sea birds, nomadic and socially feeding passerines, and aerial feeders, all of which tend to be colonial nesters.

Brown's model concentrates on the differential defendability of different food distributions and does not consider the subsequent exploitation of the food. Thus while his model can interpret the presence or absence of territorial behavior, it does not present an adaptive significance for aggregation in space.

Fisher (1954) has suggested that colonial nesting may allow efficient exploitation of a food source that is "distributed in a scattered mosaic." When a bird finds a local concentration of food, his behavior may betray this fact to other members of the colony, who can then follow him to his source of food. Ward (1965) further suggested that this mechanism could only be expected to evolve where the local concentrations of food are larger than the individual finder can fully exploit.

The model that I have presented also suggests that colonial nesting is appropriate for exploitation of a food source that is spatially and temporally variable. The distribution of the food of the Brewer's blackbird and the foraging patterns of the bird conform to this model and to Fisher's suggesting that colonial nesting allows coactive foraging behavior, which increases the foraging efficiency of individuals.

The model makes no new predictions, but presents some advances over previous suggestions. First, it suggests a positive selective advantage to either territorial or colonial behavior for exploiting alternative food distributions, rather than suggesting that colonial nesting has evolved where territorial behavior is not advantageous. Second, the mechanism requires no initial interactions between pairs to derive the aggregation. Thus this model does not require as a precondition the aggregation that it is proposed to derive. Finally, the statement in quasi-mathematical terms specifies, in kind and degree, the clumping of the food source that is necessary for colonial behavior to be advantageous. Though the present study does not attempt to make precise predictions from the model and test them against data from the field, it takes a first step in this direction by making the interpretive arguments more precise.

CONCLUSION

This study has been concerned with the adaptive significance of 2 aspects of colonial nesting, antipredation and foraging behavior. Since I have not measured both on a common scale, I cannot assess their relative importance quantitatively. Therefore I rely on an interpretive evolutionary sequence to assess their relative generality. An evolutionary sequence can, of course, only be suggestive; it must not be viewed as a testable hypothesis.

The following evolutionary sequence would account for the presently observed colonial nesting of the Brewer's blackbird. Selection for efficiency of exploitation of a food supply that is variable in space and time led to an initial concentration of the nests, rather than to territoriality. This initial concentration of the nests allowed the birds to take advantage of each other's luck in foraging and brought about a high degree of overlap of the areas defended against predators by each pair. From this point differential reproduction would tend to fix the spatial patterns presently seen as a compromise depending jointly on predation patterns and foraging efficiency. The primacy of food exploitation in this sequence is favored for three reasons. No special social mechanisms need to be assumed initially. Many blackbirds that are territorial while breeding forage in flocks at other times of the year. Finally, the anti-predator behavior seen is not demonstrably effective.

Crook (1965) has concluded from an extensive survey of avian social systems that the social system is a joint adaptation to food distribution and the kind and degree of safety from predators afforded by available nest sites. The relation between nest spacing and predation has received extensive functional analysis with confirmation by comparative studies and by experiments. The present study suggests that the relation between nest spacing and food distribution deserves similar attention.

LITERATURE CITED

Bretz, J. H. 1959. Washington's channeled scabland. State of Washington Div. of Mines and Geology Bulletin 45: 1–57.

Brown, J. L. 1964. The evolution of diversity in avian territorial systems. Wilson Bulletin 76: 160–169.

Coulson, J. C., and E. White. 1956. A study of colonies of the kittiwake *Rissa tridactyla* (L.). Ibis 98: 63–79.

———. 1960. The effect of age and density of breeding birds on the timing of breeding of the kittiwake *Rissa tridactyla*. Ibis 102: 71–86.

Crook, J. H. 1965. The adaptive significance and avian social organizations. Symposia of the Zoological Society of London 14: 181–218.

Cullen, J. M. 1960. Some adaptations in the nesting behavior of terns. Proc. XII Intern. Ornithol. Congr.: 153–157.

Darling, F. F. 1938. Bird flocks and the breeding cycle a contribution to the study of avian sociality. Cambridge Univ. Press, Cambridge. 115 pp.

Fisher, J. 1954. Evolution and bird sociality. In Huxley et al. eds., Evolution as a process, Collier, New York. 1963: 87–102.

Fisher, R. A. 1958. Statistical methods for research workers, 13th edition. Oliver and Boyd, Edinburgh. 356 pp.

Freund, J. E. 1962. Mathematical statistics. Prentice-Hall, Englewood Cliffs, N.J. 390 pp.

Horn, H. S. 1966. Colonial nesting in the Brewer's blackbird (*Euphagus cyanocephalus*) and its adaptive significance. Ph.D. Thesis, University of Washington, Seattle. 85 pp.

Howell, T. R., and G. A. Bartholomew, Jr. 1954. Experiments on the social behavior in nonbreeding brewer blackbirds. Condor 56: 33–37.

Klujiver, H. N. 1933. Bijdrage tot de biologie en de ecologie van den spreeuw (*Sturnus vulgaris vulgaris* L.) gedurende zijn voortplantingstijd. Verl. Meded. Plantenziektenk. Wageningen 69: 1–145. (not consulted *fide* Lack, 1954, The natural regulation of animal numbers, Oxford.)

Kruuk, H. 1964. Predators and anti-predator behaviour of the black-headed gull (*Larus ridibundus*). Behaviour Suppl. 11: 1–129.

LaRivers, I. 1944. Observations on the nesting mortality of the brewer blackbird, *Euphagus cyanocephalus*. American Midland Naturalist 32: 417–437.

Orians, G. H. 1961. Social stimulation within blackbird colonies. Condor 63: 330–337.

———. 1966. Food of nestling yellow-headed blackbirds, Cariboo Parklands, British Columbia. Condor 68: 321–337.

Patterson, I. J. 1965. Timing and spacing of broods in the black-headed gull *Larus ridibundus*. Ibis 107: 433–459.

Perrins, C. M. 1963. Survival in the Great Tit, *Parus major*. Proc. XIII Intern. Ornithol. Congr.: 717–728.

———. 1965. Population fluctuations and clutch size in the great tit, *Parus major*. Journal of Animal Ecology 34: 601–647.

Siegel, S. 1956. Nonparametric statistics for the behavioral sciences. McGraw-Hill, New York. 312 pp.

Ward, P. 1965. Feeding ecology of the black-faced dioch *Quelea quelea* in Nigeria. Ibis 107: 173–214.

Williams, L. 1958. Brewer's blackbird, in Bent, A. C., Life histories of North American blackbirds, orioles, tanagers, and their allies. United States National Museum Bulletin 211: 302–334.

Wolcott, E. E. 1964. Lakes of Washington, volume II, Eastern Washington. State of Washington Div. of Water Resources, Water Supply Bull. 14: 1–650.

APPENDIX I.

The predators of the Brewer's Blackbird nests were as follows: Unidentified (probably mammal) 45, *Procyon lotor* 11, *Canis latrans* 3, *Lynx rufus* 2, *Mephitis mephitis* 2, *Taxidea taxus* 1, unidentified (probably snake) 28, *Pituophis catenifer* 3, *Crotalus viridis* 1, *Bubo virginianus* 3, *Larus delawarensis* 1, *Pica pica* 1, unclassified predator 14, cattle (rubbing on sagebrush) 4, human disturbance 3; wind (shaking contents from nest) 4.

APPENDIX II.

Nest Distribution and Foraging Efficiency

A model that minimizes the energy spent gathering food to the nest is presented below:

In the minimum area from which food can be gathered at a rate sufficient to raise a nestful of young, there is a single point to which this food can be gathered with a minimum amount of flying by the adult birds. Intuitively this point may be viewed as a "center of gravity" of the food distribution, but a more precise statement is necessary to prove that this point is indeed optimal.

The adults are assumed to make a constant number of foraging trips per unit time. Additional factors could be incorporated into the model to account for variability in the absolute net energy available at each point and its influence on the number of foraging trips per unit time, but the notation would become cumbersome and the conclusion would only be changed by the incorporation of further weighting distributions in the calculation of the optimal point for nest placement.

Points in the foraging area are assigned Cartesian coördinates (x_i, y_j). The nest site is at (x_o, y_o). The proportion of time during which foraging is better at (x_i, y_j) than at any other point in the area is $t(x_i, y_j)$. The number of foraging trips per unit time is a constant, k. The average distance flown gathering food to the nest in a large amount of time, T, is then:

$$2kT \sum_i \sum_j t(x_i, y_j) \sqrt{(x_i - x_o)^2 + (y_j - y_o)^2}$$

This distance can be minimized over the dimensions x and y separately by minimizing the second moments, weighted by $t(x_i, y_j)$, of x_i and y_j about x_o and y_o. It can be easily shown (See, e.g., Freund 1962) that these weighted second moments are minimized when:

$$x_o = \sum_j [x_i \sum_i t(x_i, y_j)]$$

and:

$$y_o = \sum_j [y_j \sum_i t(x_i, y_j)]$$

Thus in the minimum area from which food can be gathered at a rate sufficient to raise the young, the optimal location for a nest is the center of minimum second moment of the food distribution, weighted by the amount of time each point in the area is the point from which net energy can be exploited at the greatest rate.

If this minimum area has enough total food to support more than 1 nest, a single location would still be optimal for all the nests. Were there selection for efficiency of exploitation, an aggregation of nests near that location might be expected.

What are the conditions under which the minimum area that could support one nest, could also support more than one? The food must be highly clumped so that at certain, critical times foraging is best at only a single point. At that point during those times there must be more food than can be utilized by 2 foraging pairs. That these are necessary conditions is obvious from the results of their converse. Were the food not concentrated at 1 point during certain times (or at least restricted to a very small portion of the area), the area could be subdivided into smaller areas, each with enough food to raise a nestful of young. This would contradict the assumption that the initial area was the minimum necessary to raise a nestful of young. If this single point did not have enough food to support at least 2 foraging pairs, the whole area would be able to support only 1 nest during a critical period. This would contradict the assumption that the area could support more than 1 nestful of young.

Thus selection for efficiency of exploitation of a food supply that is very highly clumped in space and time, would favor aggregation of nests even in the absence of interactions between foraging individuals.

140

Underwater Vision of the Sea Otter

by
R. L. GENTRY
R. S. PETERSON
Division of Natural Sciences,
University of California,
Santa Cruz

A sea otter, *Enhydra lutris*, was trained to select the larger of two disks simultaneously presented under water, and its ability to discriminate between disks of nearly the same size was tested. The results provide an index of visual acuity, and suggest that *Enhydra* has slightly poorer underwater vision than *Zalophus* or *Phoca*.

As the ancestors of modern aquatic mammals moved from land to water, adaptation of sensory organs may have been critical. Variations in the underwater effectiveness of visual systems may therefore accurately suggest the degree of adaptedness of different species to the aquatic habitat.

Schusterman et al.[1] measured the ability of California sea lions (*Zalophus californianus*) to discriminate visually under water between disks of different sizes, and Feinstein and Rice[2] used the same technique to test harbour seals (*Phoca vitulina*). Both species could make very fine size discriminations under water, and their underwater visual acuity must be excellent. This finding is consistent with their high degree of aquatic adaptation.

In lacking pectoral limbs modified for swimming, and in lacking a streamlined body form, *Enhydra* seems less adapted to the open sea than do pinnipeds (for discussion compare ref. 3). Kenyon showed that sea otters are usually found in the littoral zone, although they make short trips on to land and to the open sea[4]. Otters and pinnipeds are morphologically and behaviourally dissimilar, so that sensory differences may be expected. We have tried to reveal existing differences in underwater visual discrimination between *Enhydra*, *Zalophus* and *Phoca*.

We tested the only sea otter known to us to be in captivity, a male at Point Defiance Aquarium, Tacoma, Washington. Captured in Alaska 14 months before testing, the animal was between 4 and 5 yr old and weighed 75 lb. Its daily food ration, 15 lb. of fish and squid, was maintained during testing, and was dispensed in three portions each day during the experimental procedures. Training and testing from March 13–26, 1967, were carried out in the $2 \times 4 \times 8$ ft. ($0.6 \times 1.8 \times 2.6$ m) wooden tank in which the animal had been held since capture.

We used a test apparatus (Fig. 1) similar to that used for testing the underwater vision of *Zalophus* and *Phoca*[1,2]. This device presented two targets 20 in. (50 cm) apart separated by an 18 in. (45 cm) divider. For test targets we used a size graded series of nine white painted metal disks of the following sizes: 67, 86, 96, 101, 108, 114, 122, 137 and 174 cm². After 4 h of training, the animal would dive, swim the length of the tank under water, and strike a training target (the 108 cm² or standard target of the series) to receive a reward of a 10 g piece of fish.

To determine whether the subject had a pre-existing preference when faced with two targets of different sizes, we simultaneously presented the largest and smallest targets in the series for thirty-five trials, rewarding responses to either target. The animal selected the larger target in twenty-one of the trials, suggesting a slight preference. In all subsequent experimentation we rewarded responses to the larger target only. To establish this response firmly, we then ran 360 additional presentations. At the end of these training trials, performance had reached virtually 100 per cent correct and testing was initiated.

The method of constant stimuli (ref. 5, page 118) was used in these tests. Each of the eight targets in the series was paired with the standard (108 cm²) target for ten trials in each test session. The position of the larger target was alternated randomly using a standard Gellerman series and the sequence of the target pairs was also randomized from one session to the next. The subject received usually three sessions of eighty trials each day during three days of testing.

We estimated the discrimination ability of the otter by the percentage of correct responses it made in ninety trials with each of eight pairs of targets (Fig. 2 and

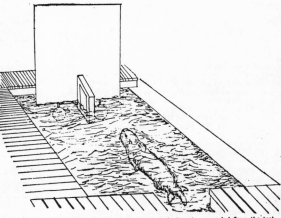

Fig. 1. Sea otter making an underwater approach to targets suspended from the test apparatus.

NATURE, 1967, Vol.216, No.5114, pp. 435-436.

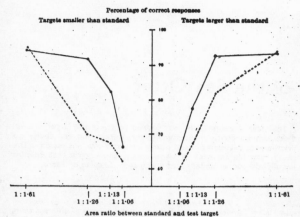

Percentage of correct responses

Targets smaller than standard   Targets larger than standard

Area ratio between standard and test target

Fig. 2. Comparative performance of *Zalophus* (——) and *Enhydra* (---) on a size discrimination task.

Table 1). When two very different targets were presented (area ratio of 1 : 1·61), the animal selected the larger target about 95 per cent of the time. When the two targets were nearly identical (area ratio of 1 : 1·06), the percentage of correct responses was approximately 60 per cent.

Table 1. SIZE DISCRIMINATION TESTS ON SEA OTTER

Ratios between areas of targets	No. of sessions of ten trials	Mean performance level	Standard deviation
(Targets smaller than standard)			
1 : 1·61	9	9·5	0·498
1 : 1·26	9	7·0	1·764
1 : 1·13	9	6·7	1·397
1 : 1·06	9	6·2	1·812
(Targets larger than standard)			
1 : 1·06	8	6·0	1·323
1 : 1·13	9	6·7	1·315
1 : 1·26	9	8·4	0·956
1 : 1·61	9	9·4	1·006

The table shows relative performance levels at different sessions.

Data given by Schusterman *et al.*[1] for two sea lions show mean levels of performance similar to those of the sea otter at very high and very low area ratios. The performance levels of the two species diverge at intermediate ratios, however. The amount of divergence can be measured by finding the 75 per cent performance level, a commonly used approximation of the threshold, at which discrimination ability becomes useful to an animal. At that level, *Zalophus* seemed able to make finer discriminations in area than *Enhydra*.

The data also suggest that the otter performed better when comparing targets with a large absolute size than when comparing those of smaller size, despite the fact that area ratios were exactly the same (see particularly the two points for area ratio 1 : 1·26, Fig. 2). It is possible that absolute size, as well as area ratio, may be involved in the otter's ability to make discriminations in the size range tested, although data on *Zalophus* and *Phoca* indicate no such dependence.

The optics of the eyes of amphibious mammals are poorly understood[7]. The morphology of the eye of *Zalophus* and *Phoca* is quite different from that of otters. The pinniped eye functions normally (is emmetropic) under water and possesses some special adaptations for aerial vision. The lens, adapted for use under water, is not used in air, but instead the iris is closed to a tiny aperture which serves as a "pin hole lens". Conversely, the eye of the otter (*Lutra*) is emmetropic in air and has some special adaptations for vision under water. While submerged, well developed ciliary and sphincter muscles in the otter's eye strongly distort the anterior part of the air-adapted lens, giving it a focal length similar to that of a spherical lens. It would not be surprising, then, to find that *Zalophus* and *Phoca* can see somewhat better under water than can *Enhydra*, as our data suggest, because the lens of the pinniped eye appears highly specialized to function under water, while that of the otter is amphibiously adapted.

It is possible that retention of sharp air vision has been ecologically more important to *Enhydra* than the evolution of adaptations for acute underwater vision. For example, terrestrial predators might have been more significant in the ecology of this littoral zone inhabitant than for a more pelagic species. Field studies have shown that *Zalophus* is slow to respond to threatening visual stimuli, such as an approaching man, in air[6]. R. J. Schusterman (personal communication), however, has recently tested the ability of this species to make size discriminations in air, and found it very similar to the underwater performance. We could not test aerial vision on the Tacoma sea otter, unfortunately; the animal did not respond when the targets were presented above the surface of the water.

If strong accommodation accounts for the otter's underwater visual abilities, we wondered whether a typical land mammal, such as man, could accommodate as well over short distances while submerged. We repeated the test procedures using two students as test subjects. When the pairs of disks of most nearly the same size (area ratio of 1 : 1·06) were presented, the humans achieved performance levels of approximately 80 per cent in forty trials at a distance of 3 ft. This was a decrease of 20 per cent from their performance in air. These results cannot be compared directly with results of tests on marine mammals because of testing differences, such as the longer response latency of humans. The trials show, however, that land mammals can probably accommodate as well at short underwater distances as sea otters can. The tests also show that comparison of disks for approximating visual acuity can reveal acuity differences of the magnitude of those experienced by a human entering water from air. This method is therefore useful for finding visual differences among some aquatic species. But when the differences in acuity become relatively small, as between *Zalophus*, *Phoca* and *Enhydra*, more sensitive measurements (such as Landolt's broken ring test) seem warranted.

We thank the US Fish and Wildlife Service and the Tacoma Zoological Society for permission to study their captive otter and for their assistance. We thank Cecil A. Brosseau, Dr M. L. Johnson, Karl W. Kenyon and Dr Victor B. Scheffer for their help. Ronald J. Schusterman lent the targets, and Victor Downing and Thomas Snyder were the human test subjects.

Received October 2, 1967.

[1] Schusterman, R. J., Kellogg, W. N., and Rice, C. E., *Science*, 147, 1594 (1965).
[2] Feinstein, S. H., and Rice, C. E., *Psychon. Sci.*, 4, 379 (1966).
[3] Mitchell, E., *J. Fish Res. Bd. Canad.*, 23, 1897 (1966).
[4] Kenyon, K. W., *The Sea Otter*, Smith. Inst. Wash. Rep., 1958, 399 (1959).
[5] Guilford, J. P., *Psychometric Methods*, 597 (McGraw–Hill, New York, 1954).
[6] Peterson, R. S., and Bartholomew, G. A., *Natural History and Behavior of the California Sea Lion*, 80 (Amer. Soc. Mammalogists, Spec. Publ. No. 1, 1967).
[7] Walls, G. L., *The Vertebrate Eye*, 785 (Hafner, New York, 1942).

142

GRAY WHALE CENSUSES BY AIRPLANE IN MEXICO[1]

CARL L. HUBBS and LAURA C. HUBBS
Scripps Institution of Oceanography
University of California, San Diego

Aerial censuses of the gray whale, *Eschrichtius gibbosus* (Erxleben), populations in the wintering waters in Mexico (from near San Diego to around Cabo San Lucas, with a few records from the shores of the Gulf of California), chiefly in and about the lagoons along the west coast of Baja California, from 1952 through 1964, yielded the following counts (counts plausibly explicable as too low in parentheses): 1952, *827*; 1953, *912* and *731*; 1954, *(276)* and *1,315*; 1955, *(584)*; 1956, *(960)*; 1957, *(631)*; 1959, *1,509*; 1960, *1,455*; 1961, *(959)*; 1962, *1,193*; 1964, *1,581*. When these explicably low counts are largely disregarded the following conclusions seem warranted: (1) higher counts after 1952 and 1953 suggest a growing population; (2) data for 1954–1964 suggest a leveling off of the population; (3) on assumption that about half the population was observed, the total population may be roughly estimated as about 3,000; (4) nearly identical low counts for 1952 and 1953 and high counts for 1959 and 1960 seem to refute the hypothesis that odd-year runs differ markedly from the even-year runs.

In the winter of 1946–47 we initiated an annual census of the eastern Pacific population of gray whales, *Eschrichtius gibbosus* (Erxleben), as they migrated past San Diego toward the lagoons of Baja California, Mexico, where all of the calves are born. Having continued this census for several years until others took over the project (Gilmore, 1960*a,b*; Rice, 1961), we began, in February 1952, an annual aerial census of this population. The census covered the coastline from San Diego southward to the Cape region of Baja California, at a time of year when almost the entire population winters there. From 1954 through 1957 the tally also included the small number of whales that winters along the eastern coast of Golfo de California (Gilmore and Ewing, 1954; Gilmore, 1958–1961; Gilmore and Mills, 1962; Gilmore et al., in press).

These aerial censuses were made with the aid and collaboration of Gifford C. Ewing, then on the staff of Scripps Institution of Oceanography. In addition to providing and piloting his plane, Dr. Ewing actively participated in the counts. His skill as a pilot, his intimate knowledge of the lagoon area, and his patience and dedication all contributed greatly to the thoroughness of the censuses (other aerial tallies are not comparable).

We accompanied Ewing on the February flights of 1952, 1954, 1959, 1960, 1961, 1962, and 1964. On the flights of 1959, 1960, 1962, and 1964 we were further assisted by several others (see footnotes to Table 1). Raymond M. Gilmore made the counts with Ewing in 1953 (closely following a trip made by Ewing and Andreas B. Rechnitzer), 1954, 1955, 1956, 1957. Thus, over the period 1952–1964 we have counts from 13 flights, including 2 each in 1953 and 1954 (but none in 1958 or 1963).

Some particulars regarding our trips of 1952 and 1954 and his trips

[1] Submitted for publication June 1966. This research was part of a program supported by grants from the National Science Foundation. Contribution from the Scripps Institution of Oceanography, University of California, San Diego.

CALIFORNIA FISH AND GAME, 1967, Vol.53, No.1, pp. 23-27.

TABLE 1

Counts of Gray Whales, from Airplane(s), from San Diego, California Southward

Details regarding flights of 1952 to 1957 were specified by Gilmore (1960a: 26–29). Later flights are discussed in text. The counts for 1954 to 1957 included a few whales on the east shore of Golfo de California.

Year of flight	Date of flight	Counter(s), with G. C. Ewing	No. of whales counted		
			Calves	Adults	Total
1952	II:16–20	C. L. and L. C. Hubbs	79	748	827[1]
1953	I:31–II:4	A. B. Rechnitzer	190	722	912[1]
1953	II:25–27	R. M. Gilmore	118	613	731[1]
1954	II:1–7	R. M. Gilmore	59	217	276[2]
1954	II:14–21	C. L. and L. C. Hubbs	227	1,088	1,315[3]
1955	II:26–III:3	R. M. Gilmore	148	436	584[4]
1956	II:14–17	R. M. Gilmore	138	822	960[5]
1957	II:27–III:3	R. M. Gilmore	98	533	631[6]
1959	II:20–26	C. L. and L. C. Hubbs[7]	286	1,223	1,509[8]
1960	II:18–21	C. L. and L. C. Hubbs[9]	244	1,211	1,455[10]
1961	II:25–27	C. L. and L. C. Hubbs	169	780	949[10]
1962	II:18–21	C. L. and L. C. Hubbs[11]	141[12]	1,052[12]	1,193
1964	II:20–24	C. L. and L. C. Hubbs[13]	209	1,372	1,581

[1] Total listed as 700 to 750 by Gilmore and Mills (1962: 27).
[2] Count not comparable with others, because incomplete (whole west coast north of Laguna San Ignacio was bypassed) and too early.
[3] Preliminary, approximate tally of 1,400 (200 calves and 1,200 adults) listed by Gilmore (1960a: 27) and by Gilmore and Mills (1962: 27).
[4] Very low count attributable to omission of Vizcaíno breeding area in main survey, only partly compensated for by inclusion here of early (February 4) aerial count of 69 calves and 121 adults by Gifford C. Ewing, Fred B Phleger, and Robert Langford; lateness of count also involved.
[5] Low count attributable in part to omission of several areas, as detailed by Gilmore (1960a: 28). Berdegué (1956: 105) who, along with D. Day, participated in the census, gave the count as 134 calves and 814 adults (total 948), and making estimates of numbers missed in areas not covered, arrived at a grand total of 1,008.
[6] "The flight was made in good weather and provided excellent coverage" (Gilmore, 1960a: 29); because of the late date many whales had probably returned north.
[7] George E. Lindsay participated in this flight and assisted in the count.
[8] This high count was not mentioned by Gilmore and Mills (1962: 27).
[9] On the 1960 flight we utilized a second, smaller plane provided and piloted by Lawrence C. Kuebler, and in the counting were further assisted by George E. Lindsay, Laurence M. Huey, and others.
[10] Gilmore and Mills (1962: 27) listed about 1,400 for each of the 1960 and 1961 flights. The 1961 count was abnormally low due to unavoidable haste, less than optimal weather, and omission of parts of the coast.
[11] On the 1962 flight we again utilized the plane provided and piloted by Mr. Kuebler and were assisted by George E. Lindsay, Earle Stanley Gardner, and Eva Ewing.
[12] Calves were not distinguished from adults in all areas.
[13] On the 1964 flight we were further assisted by Theodore J. Walker, Robert W. Elsner, and Jean Filloux.

of 1953 to 1957 were presented by Gilmore (1960a: 25–29). Berdegué (1956) gave an account of the 1956 flight. Our 1954 trip was in a Cessna 180 plane, which was excellent for observation. The 1959 and 1960 trips were in a Grumman Super Widgeon G44 amphibian, also very serviceable. Beginning in 1961 Ewing flew a larger plane, an Aero Commander 500 A, which served well for census taking.

Several circumstances may have favored higher counts as the aerial censuses continued. Beginning in 1959, additional personnel participated (except for the unsatisfactory count in 1961). On two of the last four flights a second and smaller plane, provided and piloted by Lawrence C. Kuebler, not only carried more observers but increased the width of the effective band of observation without requiring as much zig-zagging as on a single-plane operation. Greater skill in piloting and in observing tended to increase the counts. However, it is thought that there was only a moderate bias toward higher counts, particularly since Ewing very early in the series developed notable skill in zig-zagging his course along the coast to cover the band of migration (with occasional sorties beyond the limit of occurrence), and in circling over the lagoons just tightly enough to largely avoid either duplication or omission. Furthermore, the more complete and therefore more significant enumerations were made by the same personnel, and the two highest counts were made with a single plane.

Throughout our operations we stationed the prime observers in the pilot's and copilot's seats, so that both sides were scanned. Altitude was varied, so that a wide band was covered along the open coast and close-up observation was maintained in lagoons and other areas in which the whales congregated. Observations were usually recorded on tape, but a running tally was also maintained. Over the lagoons in which the whales abounded, adults were enumerated by hand tallies and the numbers of calves were jotted down by a third party as they were called out.

Sources of error in the aerial census as practiced do exist. In addition to factors favoring higher counts, visibility varied greatly with sea and wind state and with haze. To counteract these factors in and about Scammons Lagoon, where the greatest concentration of whales occurs, a count was usually made early in the day, when conditions for observation were best (once a count on a windy afternoon was followed early the next day by a much higher count, which was accepted). Counts made prior to mid-February or after February 27 are suspect, because the whale population seems to be at its height in the lagoons during the intervening period. In some years, few whales enter the lagoons before early February, and toward the end of the month the northward exodus seems to be underway. In fact, during the second half of February the last down-migrating stragglers meet the vanguard of the northward migrants along the open coast (both groups ordinarily proceeding without calves).

Despite these and other sources of error and variance, the summary data (Table 1 and Fig. 1) from the aerial censuses of the eastern Pacific gray whales appear to provide a significant basis for estimates of the population. When explicably low counts are disregarded, several conclusions regarding the population trend seem to be warranted.

(1) The initial low counts of 1952 and 1953, just before the high count of 1954, seem to confirm other indications that the population had not yet reached the level soon after attained. Early inexperience may explain in part, but we think in small part only, the lower counts on the first two censuses.

(2) The data for the 11-year period, 1954–1964, strongly suggest a leveling off (suggested by Hubbs, 1959) of the population increase.

(3) The nearly identical low counts for 1952 and 1953 and the similarity of the high counts for 1959 and 1960 seem to refute the hypothesis held by some observers (for example, Gilmore, 1958), that odd-year runs differ markedly in numbers from the even-year runs.

(4) On the assumptions that about half of the total population was observed in the area covered, and that almost all the individuals were concentrated in that area at the time of the counts, the entire population of gray whales in the eastern Pacific may be roughly estimated as about 3,000. Any major error in the admittedly rather intuitive estimate that about half of the population was observed on the flights should

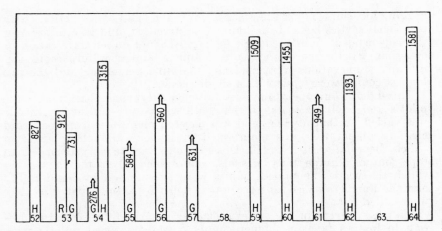

FIGURE 1—Aerial censuses of gray whales from 1952 through 1964, from San Diego southward.

The figure at the base of each column indicates the year, the figure at the top is the number of gray whales observed, and the letter represents the person who, with Gifford C. Ewing, made the counts (G = Raymond M. Gilmore, H = Carl L. and Laura C. Hubbs, R = Andreas B. Rechnitzer). An arrow surmounting a column indicates an obviously incomplete count.

not markedly vitiate conclusion (2), because the counting was closely comparable, except as noted, from year to year.

Estimates of a population as high as 5,000 to 9,000 (Gilmore, 1960a,b, 1961; Rice, 1961) seem unrealistic to us, and news dispatches from Mexico giving an estimate of 15,000 seem unbelievable.

Higher estimates by American cetologists have been based either on the assumption that only about one-fourth of the whales were counted on the aerial surveys in Baja California, or on counts from the shore station at the Cabrillo National Monument on Point Loma, San Diego, California. We are inclined to believe that aerial surveys are somewhat superior to the shore counts (begun in 1946–47), as well as being much more economical of time (5 days versus 2 months). The shore counts involve uncertainties chiefly due to: (1) frequent periods of fog, which may occlude the view for as long as several days; (2) inability to observe movements at night, and lack of information as to the nocturnal conditions under which migration is continued or interrupted (we have observed that migration continues under bright moonlight but is fully suspended during dark of the moon); (3) very real difficulty in deciding how many whales are in a migrating gam (some observers have tended to count spouts).

A source of error in censusing from shore, which may be time-dependent, is a change in migration route (tending more offshore), and in evasive behavior, which may well have resulted from the increase of small-boat traffic along the shore and especially from the increase in the number of commercial and private boats that chase the whales during their coastwise migration to obtain a closer view. Recent observations (Rice, 1965) indicate a southward movement near the Channel Islands of California in excess of any we had previously observed in that area. The tendency of gray and other whales to exhale under water when disturbed and to expose only their blowholes for inhalation

146

(Hubbs, 1965) renders them difficult to see and count. These factors seem to have been responsible for the surprisingly low numbers of whales observed passing San Diego during the southward migration of 1963–64. Wondering if there might have been a sudden depletion of the whales due to disease, or to exploitation in the Arctic or in the western Pacific, we resumed the aerial census in February 1964 (after the planned termination in 1962). To our gratifying surprise, the counts from the airplane were slightly the highest yet obtained.

In this paper, no attempt has been made to detail the counts for each lagoon and for each coastal sector, nor to include observations on migrational route, behavior, etc. Further analysis of the voluminous field notes will probably slightly modify the total counts. We also have many years of observations from shore, from vessels and small boats, and from other plane trips and from helicopters. To date our observations have barely been summarized in print (Hubbs, 1959).

LITERATURE CITED

Berdegué, Julio. 1956. Ultimo censo de la ballena gris, *Rhachianectes glaucus* (Cope), en aguas de Baja California. Ciencia (Méx.), 16(4–6) : 99–109, figs. 1–4.

Gilmore, Raymond M. 1958. The story of the gray whale. Privately published by author : 1–16, 10 figs.

————. 1960a. A census of the California gray whale, U.S. Fish and Wildl. Serv., Spec. Sci. Rept. : Fisheries, 342 : i–iv, 1–30, figs. 1–15.

————. 1960b. Census and migration of the California gray whale. Norsk Hvalfangst-Tidene, 49(9) : 409–431, figs. 1–7.

————. 1961. The story of the gray whale. Privately published by the author : 1–17, 10 figs.

Gilmore, Raymond M., Robert L. Brownell, Jr., James G. Mills, and Al Harrison. In Press. Gray whales near Yavaros, Southern Sonora, Golfo de California, Mexico. Trans. San Diego Soc. Nat. Hist.

Gilmore, Raymond M., and Gifford Ewing. 1954. Calving of the California grays. Pacific Discovery, 7(3) : 13–15, 30, 2 figs.

Gilmore, Raymond M., and James G. Mills. 1962. Counting gray whales in the Gulf of California. Pacific Discovery, 15(2) : 26–27, 3 figs.

Hubbs, Carl L. 1959. Natural history of the grey whale. XVth Intern. Congr. Zool., London, 16–23 July 1958, Proc. : 313–316.

————. 1965. Data on speed and underwater exhalation of a humpback whale following ship. Hvalrådets Skrifter, 48: 42–44, figs. 1–2.

Rice, Dale W. 1961. Census of the California gray whale, 1959/60. Norsk Hvalfangst-Tidene, 50(6) : 219–225, figs. 1–4.

————. 1965. Offshore southward migration of gray whales off southern California. Jour. Mamm., 46(3) : 504–505, fig. 1.

Diurnal Fluctuations in Censuses of
Migrating California Gray Whales

by
DONALD H. RAMSEY
Division of Natural Sciences
University of California
Santa Cruz, California
and
Marine Mammal Biological Laboratory
U.S. Fish and Wildlife Service
Seattle, Washington

Each autumn California gray whales, *Eschrichtius gibbosus*, leave their feeding grounds in the Bering and Chukchi Seas to migrate southward toward lagoons in Baja California where they calve and breed. Their migratory route south of Vancouver Island generally lies in shallow water within a few miles of the coast (Norris, 1967) and ovservers on shore can estimate the size of the population by counting passing animals:

While participating in a gray whale census during 1967--68 at Point Loma, San Diego County, California, I observed a diurnal fluctuation in the number of whales sighted: significantly fewer passed the counting station in the middle of the day than during the early morning or evening. Other investigators (Gilmore, 1960; Rice, 1961; Hubbs and Hubbs, 1967; Adams, 1968) have assumed that the whales migrate southward at a steady rate throughout the day. Population estimates have usually been based on extrapolations of the observed rate during periods of good visibility over those periods when the whales could not be seen. This paper analyzes hourly fluctuations in counts made during the 1954--55 (Gilmore, 1960) and 1967--68 censuses at Point Loma and compares them to the 1967--68 census at Yankee Point, Monterey County, California.

At the point Loma counting station observers maintained a daily watch from 0700--1700 hours, 27 December 1967 to 16 February 1968. This watch was divided into two five-hour shifts to facilitate observational accuracy. The number of whales in each pod were counted by carefully observing, with binoculars, the location and sequence of blows.

The numbers of whales counted during hourly periods throughout the 1967-68 census at Point Loma were added together (Fig.1, Table 1). A Chi-square goodness of fit test shows that these sums flutuate significantly

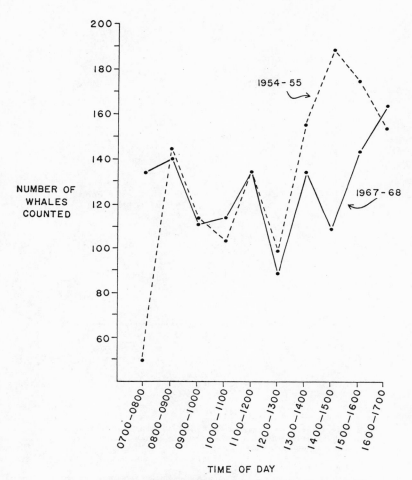

Fig. 1. Numbers of gray whales seen during hourly periods throughout the census period at Point Loma, California during censuses in 1954—55 (Gilmore, 1960) and 1967—68.

149

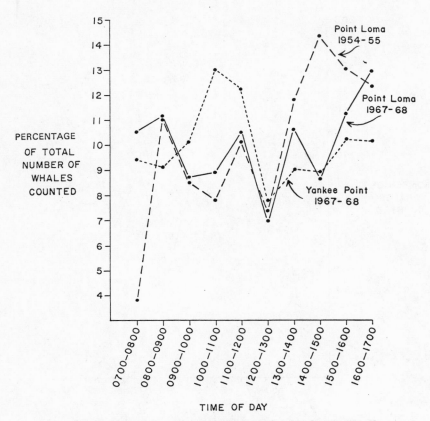

Fig. 2. Percentages of the total number of whales counted at Point Loma in 1954—55 (Gilmore, 1960) and 1967—68, and at Yankee Point in 1967—68 during hourly periods throughout the season.

(p. < .005). Confidence intervals for the four hours in the middle of the observation period, 1000—1300 hours, and the first and last two hours, 0700—0900 and 1500—1700 hours, show that there was a significant dip at midday (p. < .05). These tests and estimates suggest that there were significantly fewer whales seen in the middle of the day than in the morning and evening.

Gilmore (1960) also added together the number of whales seen during hourly periods in the 1954—55 gray whale census at Point Loma (Fig. 1, Table 1) to check for a diurnal fluctuation in the counts. A chi-square contingency test (to evaluate the hypothesis that two multinomials have the same mean) shows that with the exception of two very divergent periods, 0700—0800 and 1400 —1500, it is not possible to reject the hypothesis that

there is significant association between the 1954—55 and 1967—68 census data.

The results of the 1967—68 census at Yankee Point (Fig. 2, Table 1) also showed a significant diurnal fluctuation (p < .005) but do not show the same pattern as the two censuses at Point Loma. Confidence intervals for the Yankee Point data show that there were significantly more whales seen in the first four hours of the morning than in the last four hours of the afternoon (p < .05).

The fluctuations at Point Loma might have resulted from sampling errors, or could reflect a diurnal change in the behavior of the whales. Sampling error could result from changes in visibility due to fluctuating light conditions, fog or haze, or from changing conditions of the water's surface, any of which might interfere with accurate censusing. If real, the fluctuations may relate to a circadian

150

Table 1

Sums, chi-square goodness of fit values, and percentages of the total number of whales seen during hourly periods in the various censuses.

Place and Year		Hour										Total
		0700—0800	0800—0900	0900—1000	1000—1100	1100—1200	1200—1300	1300—1400	1400—1500	1500—1600	1600—1700	
Pt. Loma 1954—55	Sums	50	145	113	103	134	99	156	189	175	155	1319
	chi²	50.9	1.3	2.7	6.4	0	8.3	4.4	24.6	14.0	4.0	166.6
	%	3.8	11.0	8.5	7.8	10.1	7.4	11.8	14.3	13.0	12.3	
Pt. Loma 1967—68	Sums	133	142	112	114	136	93	136	111	146	169	1292
	chi²	0.1	1.3	2.2	1.7	0.4	10.0	0.4	2.5	2.2	12.4	32.2
	%	10.5	11.1	8.7	8.9	10.5	7.0	10.6	8.6	11.2	12.9	
Yankee Pt. 1967—68	Sums	283	273	304	391	366	234	271	268	308	304	3002
	chi²	1.0	2.4	0	27.6	14.5	14.5	2.8	3.4	0.2	0	66.4
	%	9.4	9.1	10.1	13.0	12.2	7.8	9.0	8.9	10.2	10.1	

behavioral rhythm, or changes in behavior due to disturbance by small boat traffic. Gilmore (1960) suggested that the fluctuations in the 1954—55 census were the result of sampling errors. He stated that the high figures for the afternoon were «probably the result of improved visibility — lifting of the haze. The low values at 7 a.m. and noon may (?) represent human errors of some kind.»

To test for a correlation between restrictions in visibility and fluctuations in the census, I added together the number of times during each hourly period in the 1967—68 census when visibility was less than two miles. For the ten periods from 0700—0800 to 1600—1700 these figures were: 14, 12, 10, 11, 11, 14, 14, 13, 14 and 11. A chi-square test indicates that there was no significant variation in the time of occurrence of the periods of restricted visibility and suggests that they were not responsible for the fluctuations.

It is more difficult to eliminate, with available information, the possibility that a diurnal change in the intensity and direction of sunlight is responsible for the fluctuations in the counts. To convincingly test this hypothesis it would be necessary to use other censusing techniques — observations from airplanes or ships — to determine the efficiency of shore observers under varying conditions of light.

In further criticism of Gilmore's (1960) hypothesis, it seems unlikely that the low figures at noon are the result of human error. At noon a fresh observer went on duty and would probably have missed fewer whales than an observer finishing a five-hour watch. It is possible that the low figures for the 1954—55 census from 0700—0800

could result from a lack of punctuality in beginning the count at 0700.

The observations at Point Loma, then, suggest that a diurnal cycle exists in the activity of the whales such as that reported for the Minke whale, *Balaenoptera acutorostrata* (Kimura and Nemoto, 1956) and for pinnipeds (Fiscus et al., 1965). But this hypothesis is difficult to defend in face of the Yankee Point data; one would expect a similar trend at both censusing areas. The effect of small boat traffic can not be evaluated because no record of it was made during the censuses, but there certainly are many fewer boats at Yankee Point than at Point Loma. Hubbs and Hubbs (1967) note that the increase in harassment from small boats in the Point Loma area might well cause gray whales to migrate further offshore. Thus, small boats might be responsible for a fluctuation there, but not at Yankee Point.

Although the causes of diurnal fluctuations are not yet known, the phenomenon must be carefully considered by cetologists estimating the number of gray whales. If the fluctuations result from a behavioral cycle, their effect upon population estimates will vary with the time of day when censuses are made. If the fluctuations are due to technical problems, such as changes in lighting, the effect will vary with the method of observation. The distortion will be greatest when estimates are based on very brief censuses, but the validity of any estimate which omits a correction for diurnal fluctuation may be seriously impaired.

I am grateful to Dr. R. S. Peterson for advice and assistance in the development of this manuscript, and to D. W. Rice who willingly gave access to the gray whale census data. Dr. M. Sylvan and A. M. Johnson gave valuable statistical advice and Dr. L. Adams read the manuscript critically. This research was supported in part by N.S.F. grant GY-2724.

References

Adams, L. 1968. Census of the gray whale, 1966—67. Norsk Hvalfangst-Tidende, 57 (2): 41—43.

Fiscus, C. H., G. A. Baines, and H. Kajimura. 1965. Pelagic fur seal investigations, Alaska, 1963. U.S. Fish and Wildl. Serv., Spec. Sci. Rept. — Fisheries, No. 489. 31 p.

Gilmore R. M. 1960. A census of the California gray whale. U.S. Fish and Wildl. Serv., Spec. Sci. Rept. — Fisheries, No. 342.

Hubbs, C. L. and L. C. Hubbs. 1967. Gray whale census by airplane in Mexico. Calif. Fish and Game, 53(1):23-27.

Kimura, S. and T. Nemoto. 1956. Note on a Minke whale kept alive in aquarium. Sci. Rept. Whales Res. Inst. (Tokyo), 11: 181—189.

Norris, K. S. 1967. Some observations on the migration and orientation of marine mammals. Pages 101—124 in R. M. Storm (Editor), Animal Orientation and Navigation. Corvallis: Oregon State Univ. Press, 134 p.

Rice D. W. 1961. Census of the California gray whale, 1959—60. Norsk Hvalfangst-Tidende, 50(6): 219—225.

Smith, M. S. R. 1965. Seasonal movements of the Weddell seal in McMurdo Sound, Antarctica. J. Wildl. Mgt. 29(3): 464—470. 30 p.

DDT RESIDUES IN THE EGGS OF THE OSPREY IN THE NORTH-EASTERN UNITED STATES AND THEIR RELATION TO NESTING SUCCESS

By PETER L. AMES

Museum of Vertebrate Zoology, University of California, Berkeley, U.S.A.

INTRODUCTION

The Osprey (*Pandion haliaëtus*) is a large fish-eating bird of prey found in nearly every continent in the world, always associated with large bodies of water. In many parts of the United States it may be seen in considerable numbers, nesting aggregations of several hundred pairs being spread over a few square miles. In common with nearly all other birds of prey, the Osprey has suffered a gradual decline since the early years of the twentieth century (Bent 1937). This decline, which cannot have averaged more than 2–3% per year during the first five decades of the century, has recently attained the rate of about 30% annually.

In 1957 I began an ecological study of a large breeding concentration of Ospreys near the mouth of the Connecticut River, where it empties into Long Island Sound. The colony extended over an area of about 10 square miles (25·9 km²) and numbered at least 100 pairs. About one-third of these were nesting on Great Island, a low salt marsh area of about 300 ac (120 ha), where many nests were on low structures and some on the ground. Almost from the start of the study it was evident that the production of young birds was extremely low. In 1960, the first season for which good data are available, the number of young Ospreys fledged was seven from seventy-one active nests, a rate of less than 0·1 young per nest. Nestling production in normal Osprey populations is 2·2–2·5 young per nest. The low production in 1960 was due in part to a high rate of egg predation, which was not repeated the following year, when thirty-one pairs produced twelve young (average: 0·4 young per nest). Even this rate is extremely low.

The five years from 1957 to 1961 were spent largely in gathering data on population trends and the factors affecting them. The situation was discussed by Ames & Mersereau (1964) and may be summarized as follows:

1. The number of nesting pairs of Ospreys in the Connecticut River colony has declined at an average rate of 31% annually since 1960. The maximum known population was 200 pairs in 1938 (J. Chadwick, personal communication) and this had dropped to twelve pairs by 1965.

2. The production of nestlings in the colony has been 0·1–0·4 fledglings per pair, as compared with 2·2–2·5 for healthy colonies in New York and Virginia.

3. Poor fledgling production, in this colony at least, is certainly due to poor hatching, for the observed fledging rates have been very close to hatching rates.

4. Courtship, nest-building, and other aspects of breeding behaviour appear normal. The usual clutch of three eggs is laid and incubation is continuous. There is no evidence of egg-eating nor other abnormal behaviour.

5. There is no correlation between the degree of isolation of the nest site and nesting success. In order to analyse the role of human interference, tidal flooding and egg predation, nesting platforms were provided for the marsh-nesting birds. By 1963 nearly half

JOURNAL OF APPLIED ECOLOGY, 1966, Vol.3, pp.87-97.

of the colony (then down to twenty-four pairs) nested on these elevated platforms. The rate of nesting success of the platform-nesting birds was about equal to that of those in trees.

6. By 1964 it was evident that nesting success is not randomly distributed, nor is it greater in one region or one nest site type. Certain pairs have produced young with nearly normal regularity; others have not produced within the 9 years of the study.

7. There do not appear to be any significant differences between successful and unsuccessful pairs in the number and species of fish eaten. Moreover, successful pairs under observation seem to have no difficulty in providing fish for three large young. The males at productive nests spend much time perched near their nests, suggesting that food pressures are not acute.

The situation found in Connecticut is mirrored in other parts of the Atlantic Coast, but the human variables are quite different. In eastern Maine Ospreys suffer very little harassment by man, but their population decline has paralleled that in Connecticut. In south-eastern Massachusetts the major drop apparently was between 1890 and 1930, and there are now only about thirty-five pairs in an area which once held about four times that number. 1965 production was about 0·15 young per nest (Memorandum, Massachusetts Audubon Society, 2 August 1965). Members of the Rhode Island Audubon Society have documented a similar situation in that state (Emerson & Davenport 1963) and have noted the low rate of fledgling production. Eight nests which produced only three young among them in Rhode Island in 1963 were located in a nearly impenetrable swamp, in which human interference seems unlikely. Elsewhere in Rhode Island the shooting of adults may have been a factor. A large Osprey colony on Gardiners Island, New York, directly across Long Island Sound from the Connecticut River colony, declined from about 300 pairs in 1900 to about twenty-one pairs in 1963. Wilcox, who has followed this colony closely for about 25 years, notes (personal communication) that the drop in the last 15 years has been about 50%. The fledging rate in 1963 was about 0·3 young per nest, the hatching rate about 0·4 eggs per nest.

In southern New Jersey the loss of nest trees through land development and other forms of human activity have greatly reduced the numbers of nesting Ospreys, a decline which continues. I know of no recently published reports on the population changes or rates of fledgling production. The present population appears to be about 5% that of 50 years ago.

A portion of the large Osprey population of Chesapeake Bay (Maryland and Delaware) is now being studied by Fred C. Schmidt of the United States Fish and Wildlife Service. The work is in too early a stage for a detailed evaluation of population trends, but the pesticide levels and rates of nestling production are discussed below.

From Virginia to Florida, Ospreys are found nesting in somewhat lower densities than in some of the northern states. The Florida birds do not appear to be in trouble (Alexander Sprunt, personal communication) but I know of no quantitative study of the species in any of the south-eastern states.

PESTICIDE STUDIES

In June 1962, six eggs were taken from Osprey nests on Great Island, Connecticut, when about 1 week past the expected hatching dates. All were in advanced state of decomposition. The eggs were analysed at the Connecticut Agricultural Experiment Station by paper chromatography and the well-known method of Schechter and Haller. As reported by Ames & Mersereau (1964), DDT residues (mostly DDE) averaged 555 μg per egg.

Three small samples of fish tissues, taken from Osprey nests, were also analysed and found to contain 0·7–1·8 ppm of DDT and 1·8–7·4 ppm of its metabolites.

In 1963 we felt that conclusive results might be gained by comparing the egg-pesticide levels and hatching data in the declining Connecticut Ospreys with the values obtained from the population in Chesapeake Bay, Maryland, where the species appeared to be maintaining its numbers. Other factors, such as human activity, nest site availability, and food fish species had not been analysed in the Maryland population, so Schmidt undertook to study various aspects of the nesting success, as well as to collect a series of eggs for analysis. Each of us, in his respective area, was to take for analysis one egg from each of a number of clutches. The remaining eggs in the nest (usually two) were to be checked for hatching and fledging rates. Because of the relative accessibility of Osprey nests in both colonies, there seemed little danger that our visits would prejudice the results of the remainder of the clutch. In June some overdue eggs were collected from the same nests as the early samples. In addition, a number of eggs were collected and analysed from Maine, Rhode Island and New Jersey, usually without complete nest histories.

During the first week of May 1963, thirty-eight eggs were taken from Osprey nests on the lower Potomac River, Maryland, at the western edge of the Chesapeake Bay area. Not all of the known nests in the area were sampled. Single eggs were taken from twenty-seven nests, two from one nest, and three (complete clutches) from three nests. The complete clutches were taken in order to determine the variability of pesticide distribution within a clutch. In the Connecticut colony fifteen eggs were taken in late April and early May, relatively earlier in the incubation period, as nesting is about 1 week later in Connecticut than in Maryland. As soon as possible after collecting, and in all cases within 24 h, each egg was weighed, its volume was measured by immersion in a graduated beaker (accurate to about ±3 ml), and it was opened to determine the developmental condition. All eggs (less shells) were stored in glass jars at about −18° C until analysed. They were analysed in the laboratory of the Patuxent Research Center of the Fish and Wildlife Service by thin layer (aluminum oxide) chromatography for the DDT group of chlorinated hydrocarbons only.

EGG FERTILITY AND NESTING SUCCESS

When examined fresh from the nests, most of the eggs were found to contain live, normal-looking, embryos. Of the fifteen Connecticut eggs taken early in the season, eleven had embryos (both alive and dead), and only one of the remaining four eggs had been incubated long enough for infertility to be positively established. Of the eleven fertile eggs, three contained decomposing embryos, indicating death prior to collecting. Even when an egg is found to be 'clear' (i.e. with no sign of development) after a week or more of incubation, one cannot be sure of its infertility; the embryo may have died at an extremely early age. The term 'infertile' is best applied to eggs which show no sign of development, not, as is often the case, to eggs which, for one reason or another, fail to hatch. In this sense, the fertility of the twelve Connecticut eggs which provide sure evidence was 92% and the minimum fertility of the fifteen eggs, assuming the three uncertain eggs to be infertile, was 73%.

Of the thirty-one Maryland eggs, twenty-nine were fertile, three with decomposing embryos. One of the remaining two eggs was crushed in handling, making accurate determination of fertility impossible. If present, the embryo must have been very small. The other egg appeared freshly laid. If these two are omitted as uncertain, fertility was

100%; if they are treated as infertile, fertility was 93%. Observed embryonic death in the Connecticut series was about twice as high as in the Maryland series, but the former were collected later in the incubation period than the latter, so the differences are probably not significant.

All four of the Maine eggs contained large, healthy-appearing, embryos. The Rhode Island and New Jersey eggs were collected when past due to hatch and their contents were too decomposed for fertility evaluation.

The 1963 breeding results of the Connecticut and Maryland Ospreys are summarized in Table 1. The upper half of the table shows the observed results in terms of hatching and fledging; the lower half gives an estimate of what the results would have been had not

Table 1. *Observed and theoretical nesting success in Connecticut and Maryland Ospreys, 1963*

| | Connecticut | | Maryland | |
	Total population	Sampled	Total population	Sampled
No. of nests	22	15	35	25
Total eggs (observed)	63	42	99	75
Eggs sampled	15	15	38	25
Eggs remaining after sampling	48	27	61	50
Observed hatch, eggs	9	4	27	27
Observed hatch (%)	18·8	14·8	44·3	54·0
Theoretical hatch, without sampling	12	6	41	41
Theoretical hatch, eggs per nest	0·54	0·41	1·25	1·60
Observed fledge, individuals	9	4	24	24
Percentage of eggs producing fledglings	18·8	14·8	39·3	36·0
Theoretical fledge, without sampling	12	6	39	36
Theoretical fledge, young per nest	0·54	0·41	1·1	1·4

about one-third of the eggs been taken for analysis. For each area data are given for the entire number of nests under observation and for that portion of the nests from which single eggs were taken. In Connecticut only single eggs were taken, so the table indicates all of the direct effects of sampling. In Maryland, however, the figure of thirty-five nests includes five in which no eggs remained after sampling (three clutches of three eggs each and two clutches of one egg) and one nest from which two out of three eggs were taken. A more meaningful evaluation of the possible effects of pesticides may be gained by considering only the twenty-five nests from which sample eggs were taken and in which some eggs were left for observation. It is interesting to note that none of the eight eggs in the four unsampled nests hatched. Three of these unsampled clutches were smaller than normal (one, two and two eggs), suggesting that predation may have taken place.

The estimates of the hatching and fledgling production which would have been observed in the absence of sampling were arrived at by applying to the total number of pre-sampling eggs the observed hatching and fledging rates of the eggs remaining after sampling. This method is probably more accurate in projecting hatching than fledging rates, for the survival of nestlings might be affected by lowering clutch-size.

It appears that the Maryland birds were about 2–2·5 times as successful as the Connecticut birds in hatching their eggs. The corrected hatch of about 0·40–0·54 eggs per nest in Connecticut was about equal to that observed in 1961 and 1962, when no sampling was performed during the incubation period. The hatchability of the Maryland eggs, 1·3–1·6 eggs per nest, appears to be lower than that observed in most vigorous Osprey populations, and one may well question whether the Maryland Ospreys are maintaining their numbers as well as is generally believed.

156

RESULTS OF CHEMICAL ANALYSES

The amounts of DDT residues found in Osprey eggs from the various regions sampled are shown in Table 2. To aid in comparisons with other Osprey populations and with other species, the values are given in average microgrammes (10^{-6} g) per egg and as average microgrammes per cubic centimetre of egg volume (including shell). The usual method of stating the amounts of pesticides in eggs, 'parts per million' (microgrammes per gramme), leads to erroneous conclusions when the various samples have undergone different amounts of drying, through decomposition or in the normal course of incubation. Stickel, Schmidt, Reichel & Ames (1965) discuss various methods of stating egg pesticide levels, using as examples early and late Osprey eggs from the Connecticut series. They

Table 2. *DDT and its metabolites in the eggs of Ospreys from the north-eastern United States*

Locality	Year	No. of eggs	Average volume (ml)	DDE µg	DDE µg/ml	DDD µg	DDD µg/ml	DDT µg	DDT µg/ml	Total residues µg	Total residues µg/ml	DDD (% of total)
Maine	1963	3	72	120	1·7	7	0·1	5	0·06	130	1·8	5
Rhode Island	1963	1	68	500	7·4	100	1·5	ND	ND	600	8·8	17
Connecticut	1962	6	68	450	6·7	100	1·5	Trace	Trace	550	8·1	22
Connecticut	1963	15	68	320	4·7	20	0·3	10	0·1	350	5·1	5
New Jersey	1963	2	Not measured	350	5·1	40	0·6	10	0·1	400	5·9	10
Maryland	1963	25	70	160	2·3	40	0·6	5	0·07	205	3·0	18

ND = None detected.

conclude that one of two methods should be employed. Either: (1) the fresh weight of the egg contents should be determined as a function of the entire egg volume and the pesticide amounts stated in parts per million (fresh weight), or (2) the amount of pesticide should be stated in microgrammes per millilitre of total egg volume. The latter of these methods is employed here because it allows ready comparison with the eggs of other raptors, and because the conversion factor from egg volume to weight of contents is not known for Ospreys.

The average microgramme amounts of residues listed in Table 2 are derived from single-egg estimates based on chromatograph spots. The values were stated by the chemist with an accuracy of ± 25–50%. The values are statistically valid when a good number of samples is analysed, as with the Connecticut and Maryland eggs. The values obtained from the Maine, Rhode Island and New Jersey eggs may be taken only as an indication of the widespread nature of the contamination. The amounts of all DDT residues in the individual eggs from Connecticut and Maryland are indicated in the histogram (Fig. 1), expressed in microgrammes per millilitre. The mean of the fifteen Connecticut eggs (5·1) is 1·6 times that of the twenty-five Maryland eggs on which the hatchability data are based (3·0), but both values are very small. It is interesting to note that DDD (=TDE) averages 18% of the total DDT residues in the Maryland eggs, but only 5% in the Connecticut eggs. This difference, which is also found in the fish samples, probably reflects the greater agricultural use of Rhothane (DDD) in Maryland. The amount of DDD in the Maryland eggs varies from 0 to 44% of the total residues; that in Connecticut eggs varies from 0 to 16%. What part of this DDD is produced by the metabolism of DDT cannot be determined on the basis of our present knowledge.

In 1964 we took several whole clutches of eggs from both Osprey colonies, in an attempt to learn whether there were differences which could be examined by artificial incubation.

157

The hatching success of both groups of eggs was so low that no comparisons could be made. Most of the clutches were taken early in the season and, as expected, most of the pairs laid replacement clutches. The hatching rate of the second clutches was about the same as the first clutches, 11%. We are still investigating methods of artificially incubating Osprey eggs and feel that this may prove a fruitful avenue of investigation.

RESULTS OF ANALYSIS OF OSPREY FOOD FISHES

In conjunction with the programme of egg analyses, fifteen samples of Osprey food fishes were collected from nests in Connecticut and thirteen from nests in Maryland. Most of the Connecticut samples were obtained at two nests with one and three young, respectively,

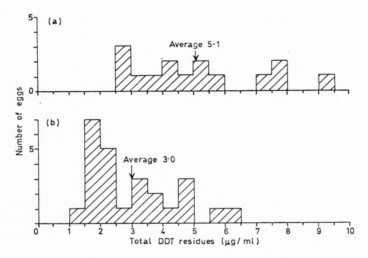

FIG. 1. Comparison of residue levels in eggs of Ospreys from (a) Connecticut, and (b) Maryland, in 1963.

and from which egg samples had been obtained. The Maryland samples were also obtained from nests with young. The results, shown in Table 3, must be evaluated with some caution, for several reasons.

1. Most of the samples were taken early in the season, when the young were small. For about 2 weeks after hatching the young and the adult female did not consume all of the fish supplied by the male, with the result that we were able to acquire uneaten parts of the prey, sometimes as much as 75 g, without interfering with nesting success. As the nestlings grew larger there was seldom any uneaten prey in the nests. Attempts to frighten the adult off the nest while she was feeding young resulted in her taking the fish with her. The single specimen of Shad from Connecticut was obtained on 25 August by frightening one of the grown young, who was feeding at the nest.

2. The samples represent the part of the fish normally eaten by the adult female and the young. The head of the fish, usually eaten by the male during the early part of the nesting season, was rarely included in the sample.

3. The basic validity of using late spring fish samples to evaluate early spring pesticide

158

intake might well be questioned, for the species of food fish utilized change with the shifts in abundance of one species or another. Early in the season Connecticut Ospreys were found to feed on Eels far more frequently than later in the season. Black-backed Flounder were eaten from March through June. For this reason the Eel sample known to be locally caught was purchased in a fish store. The rapid assimilation of pesticide by our experimental quail (see below) suggests that residues in Osprey eggs are the result of feeding during the few weeks or even days before the eggs are laid.

4. Smaller individuals and species are less represented in our fish samples than they are in the whole of the Ospreys' food, because they are more frequently eaten entirely.

5. The values obtained, although stated as 'ppm, wet weight', are often higher than would have resulted if the fish had been truly fresh, due to the unmeasured amount of drying before collecting. The Black-backed Flounders, Shad and Eel from Connecticut were nearly fresh when acquired, but the Windowpane Flounders, a species with a high surface-to-volume ratio, had lost perhaps half of their fluid weight when collected.

Table 3. *DDT residues in fish samples from Connecticut and Maryland*

Species	No. of individuals	Total wet weight (g)	DDE		DDD		DDT		Total residues		DDD (% of total)
			μg	ppm	μg	ppm	μg	ppm	μg	ppm	
CONNECTICUT											
Black-backed Flounder	6	376	160	0·4	30	0·1	300	0·8	490	1·3	6·1
Windowpane Flounder	2	70	50	0·7	10	0·1	140	2·0	200	2·9	5·0
Alewife	4	60	20	0·3	10	0·2	100	1·7	130	2·2	7·7
Shad	1	70	80	1·1	40	0·6	100	1·4	220	3·1	18·2
Cunner	1	19	Trace		Trace		60	3·1	60	3·1	5
Eel	1	40	80	2·0	40	1·0	100	2·5	220	5·5	18·2
MARYLAND											
Eel	4	572	60	0·1	110	0·2	60	0·1	230	0·3	48
Yellow Perch	3	256	20	0·1	10	0·04	30	0·1	60	0·2	17
White Perch	2	93	Trace		Trace		Trace		5	0·05	–
Striped Killifish	1	22	Trace		Trace		Trace		5	0·1	–
Menhaden	2	125	Trace		Trace		Trace		5	0·05	–
Toadfish	1	140	20	0·1	10	0·1	10	0·1	40	0·3	25

Scientific names of fish species: Black-backed Flounder, *Pseudopleuronectes americana*; Windowpane Flounder, *Lophosetta maculata*; Alewife, *Alosa pseudoharengus*; Shad, *A. sapidissimus*, Cunner, *Tautogolabrus adspersus*; Eel, *Anguilla rostrata*; Yellow Perch, *Perca flavescens*; White Perch, *Roccus americanus*; Striped Killifish, *Fundulus majalis*; Menhaden, *Brevoortia tyrannus*; Toadfish, *Opsanus tau*.

Despite the errors inherent in sampling, the values of DDT residues given in Table 3 probably show the relative residue intakes of the Ospreys of Connecticut and Maryland. The data are in the immediate range of residue found by Tompkins (1964) in fish from the upper waters of the Connecticut River (about 1·2 ppm in 1963; 3·5 ppm in 1964) and those reported by Ames & Mersereau (1964) for three samples of fish from Osprey nests (1·7, 3·9 and 7·4 ppm). Taken collectively, the data suggest that the amount of DDT and its metabolites in fish eaten by Connecticut Ospreys is 5–10 times higher than that in the food of Maryland Ospreys. Although these differences are easily sufficient to explain the differences in the residue content of the eggs from the two populations, neither group of fish samples contained residues sufficient to cause systemic poisoning in adults.

As indicated in Table 3, there are major differences between Connecticut and Maryland Ospreys in the fish species utilized for food, but the differences are not as profound as the table suggests. At a nest under observation in Connecticut at least one Yellow Perch was brought in by the male. Maryland Ospreys are sometimes seen carrying flatfishes.

159

Flounders, which make up about half of the observed prey of Connecticut Ospreys throughout the season, are certainly less often utilized by the Maryland birds. Extensive knowledge of the species and age classes of fish eaten by Ospreys would greatly facilitate determining the rate of pesticide intake. The current increase in the study of pesticides in fishes will certainly provide a better basis for evaluating intake levels in fish-eating birds.

DDT RESIDUES IN THE EGGS OF JAPANESE QUAIL

It is difficult to evaluate the effects of DDT residues in the eggs of Ospreys, mainly because of the paucity of data relating the residue levels to hatchability in any species under laboratory conditions. An attempt in this direction was made by Victor J. Hardaswick and myself in the winter of 1964–65 with the experiment described below. The analysis of eggs is not yet complete, but preliminary results are worth noting.

Japanese Quail (*Coturnix coturnix japonica*) were chosen because of their small size, high rate of egg production and polygamous breeding habits. Twenty cages of Quail were set up, in five racks of four cages each, with one male and three females in each cage. All were kept on a 16-h 'day', produced by fluorescent lights. Four racks were test groups; the fifth was controls. One group was dosed with technical Rhothane (DDD) at 10 ppm in the food, another at 50 ppm, a third group with *pp'*-DDE at 10 ppm, and a fourth with *pp'*-DDE at 50 ppm. The appropriate amount of pesticide was introduced dry into 10 kg of Purina Game Bird Layena, a commercial food prepared in 1 mm pellets. The entire 10 kg was slowly tumbled for 40 min in a cylindrical container on a skewed axis. The food was provided to the birds in gravity feed containers loaded from the top. Both food and water were continuously available.

Analysis of food samples has indicated that dry-mixing pesticide with pelletized food does not provide the anticipated dose rate. In our gravity feed containers, and probably also in the initial tumbling, the abrasion of food pellets results in food material being lost from the outsides of the pellets in the form of a coarse powder. This powder collects in the bottom of the feeding containers and is not consumed by the birds unless the feeders are allowed to become empty. Analysis of the powder from the bottom of a feeder of DDD at 10 ppm revealed a concentration of 27 ppm of DDD, while pellets from the surface of the feeder, where they were being consumed by the Quail, showed only 3 ppm. It is apparent that less pesticide than planned was entering the birds.

Eggs were collected from all cages at noon daily. Each egg was numbered and weighed shortly after collecting. For 2 consecutive days all of the eggs would be incubated, then for the following 2 days all would be saved for analysis, then 2 days' eggs would be incubated. The analyses were performed on the gas chromatograph at the Connecticut Agricultural Experiment Station by Mr Lloyd Keirstead. Incubation was performed in a 'Humidaire' forced-air incubator at 37·5° C and approximately 85% relative humidity. The eggs were automatically rotated 90 degrees around the short axis every 2 h. Hatches were scored daily by noting the empty shells, no attempt being made to separate the chicks or to study chick survival. Eggs which failed to hatch were removed when 2 days overdue and were examined for gross defects.

Dosing was not begun until fertile eggs had been obtained from all of the cages. During the acclimatization period several males were killed by females and there was some cannibalism among females, necessitating some substitutions in order to get workable cage groups. The shuffling of birds resulted in some loss of randomness, but definitely reduced the death rate during the experiment. The administration of pesticides was continued for

160

60 days, at the end of which time the birds were sacrificed and weighed. During the 60-day period 2881 eggs were laid by the entire flock, an average of about 580 eggs per test rack. About half of these, or about 290 eggs per rack, were incubated. The remainder were pooled by sample periods, providing about fifteen samples of sixteen to twenty-two eggs for each chemical at each dose. At the time of writing, four samples from each chemical/dose have been analysed, providing a basis for tentative conclusions regarding the deposition of DDE and DDD in eggs and their effects on hatchability.

1. During the test period deaths in the test groups were not significantly different from those in the control group: one or two birds per test rack. Only one male died, but data from his cage had to be discarded after his death, which was, fortunately, late in the experiment.

2. The weights of test birds remained as high as those of the controls, and all groups gained weight during the test period.

3. The amounts of DDE in the eggs of birds on the nominal 10 ppm rose from 0·27 μg/ml on the 4th day to 5·7 μg/ml on the 29th day, and 8·5 μg/ml on the 50th day. Apparrently the increase was considerably more rapid at the beginning of the period than at the end. At 50 ppm of DDE the amount in the eggs rose linearly from 7·7 μg/ml on the 5th day through 24·9 μg/ml on the 24th day, to 57·5 μg/ml on the 60th day, when the experiment ended.

4. The amounts of DDD were consistently much lower than those of DDE at the same dose and time. The nominal dose of 10 ppm produced 0·15 μg/ml in the eggs after 7 days, 0·40 μg/ml after 48 days, and 0·90 μg/ml after 64 days. DDD at 50 ppm produced a steady level of about 3·5 μg/ml in the eggs from the 6th to the 57th day.

5. At the egg pesticide levels attained in the 60-day period of the quail study there appears to have been no lowering of hatchability in any of the test groups. Other effects may turn up when the post-mortem examinations are evaluated. It is noteworthy that the hatching rates in all groups, including the controls, were less than 50%. Most of the losses occurred at a time close to hatching, when eggs would have benefited from higher humidity. We avoided the use of a separate, high-humidity hatching chamber because we did not wish to introduce an additional variable. It may prove difficult to separate eggs which may have died from the effects of the pesticides from those which died from desiccation at the critical point just before hatching. Further work is planned to elucidate this point.

6. There are a number of interacting factors in the cage behaviour of Japanese Quail which may influence or even counteract the effects of pesticides on fertility and hatchability. It is likely that some of the very attributes which make these quail (and many other galliform birds) good subjects for controlled studies also limit the applicability of the results. High egg production, large egg size, early maturation, polygamy and a good 'cage disposition' make the Japanese Quail appear an ideal experimental bird, but I urge other investigators to consider carefully all aspects of the behaviour and physiology of the species before using it for pesticide research.

ACKNOWLEDGMENTS

For the last 4 years I have been assisted in the Osprey study by Mr Gerald S. Mersereau, who has done much of the arduous field work. I am grateful to Dr and Mrs Roger T. Peterson, Mr William H. Stickel, Dr Lucille F. Stickel and Mr Frederick C. Schmidt for much material and intellectual aid. I am indebted to Mr Allen H. Morgan, Mr Robert C.

Woodruff, Mr LeRoy Wilcox and Mr Alexander Sprunt, IV, for information on the status of the Osprey on various parts of the Atlantic Coast.

I must express my appreciation to Mr Victor J. Hardaswick for permission to discuss the preliminary results of the quail study on which we worked jointly. The National Audubon Society deserves our gratitude for financial support of the study. DDT and DDD were generously provided by the manufacturers, the Geigy Chemical Corporation and the Rohm and Haas Company. For the analysis of quail eggs we are indebted to the Analytical Laboratory of the Connecticut Agricultural Experiment Station and, in particular, to Mr Lloyd G. Keirstead, who made a special effort to fit our samples into a pressing schedule. Mr Roland C. Clement deserves thanks for many helpful suggestions in planning the quail study.

SUMMARY

The Osprey (*Pandion haliaëtus*) population in coastal Connecticut has been declining for 9 years by 30% annually, due to embryonic death before hatching (0·40–0·54 eggs hatch per nest). Hatchability and egg pesticide values were compared with those of an apparently stable colony in Chesapeake Bay, Maryland (1·3–1·6 eggs hatch per nest). Osprey populations in Maine, Massachusetts, Rhode Island and New York are also declining.

DDT residues found were 350 μg per egg (5·1 μg/ml) in Connecticut, 205 μg per egg (3·0 μg/ml) in Maryland. Total DDT residues in fish from Connecticut nests were 5–10 times higher than in Maryland.

A laboratory study of Japanese Quail showed that 10 and 50 ppm DDE and DDT in the diet rapidly produced residues in the eggs. In the few analyses so far completed, 50 ppm DDE caused linear increase to 60 μg/ml after 60 days. 50 ppm DDD caused a stable level of 3·5 μg/ml in the eggs. These studies are continuing.

REFERENCES

Ames, P. L. & Mersereau, G. S. (1964). Some factors in the decline of the Osprey in Connecticut. *Auk*, 81, 173–85.

Bent, A. C. (1937). Life histories of North American birds of prey. Pt. 2. *Bull. U.S. natn. Mus.* 195, 352–79.

Emerson, D. & Davenport, M. G. (1963). Profile of the Osprey. *Naragansett Naturalist*, 6, 56–8.

Stickel, L. F., Schmidt, F. C., Reichel, W. L. & Ames, P. L. (1965). Ospreys in Connecticut and Maryland. I: Effects of pesticides on fish and wildlife. *Circ. Fish Wildl. Serv., Wash.* 226, 4–6.

Tompkins, W. A. (1964). *A pesticide study of the Westfield, Farmington and Connecticut watersheds.* Connecticut River Watershed Council, Greenfield, Mass.

THE ADAPTIVE SIGNIFICANCE OF SOME SIZE TRENDS IN ISLAND BIRDS

P. R. GRANT

Department of Zoology, University of British Columbia, Vancouver[1]

Accepted April 30, 1965

Species of animals living on islands may have morphological characteristics not possessed by their mainland counterparts, a fact which was recognized by Wallace (1881). He remarked that in the Celebes: "Nearly thirty species of butterflies, belonging to three different families, have a common modification in the shape of their wings by which they can be distinguished at a glance from their allies in any other island or country whatever, and all these are larger than the representative forms inhabiting most of the adjacent islands." Among birds there is an apparently undisputed tendency for island forms to have a plumage more drab than that of their most closely related mainland forms (Murphy and Chapin, 1929; Murphy, 1938; Amadon, 1953; Grant, 1965a). It has also been reported that island birds have long bills (Murphy, *loc. cit.*; Chapman, 1940; Amadon, *loc. cit.*) and long wings, the latter being interpreted as an indication of large body-size (Mayr and Vaurie, 1948; Amadon, *loc. cit.*). Yet these trends of large size in island birds are not universal, since there are reports of opposite trends (Hesse *et al.*, 1937; Bourne, 1955). For instance Bourne (*loc. cit.*) has pointed out that many of the birds of the Cape Verde islands have smaller dimensions than their mainland counterparts. He considered this to be a "character of sedentary species which is often particularly well shown by insular forms." Furthermore, even if a size trend among island birds can be demonstrated, its significance has yet to be explained satisfactorily. Attempts to interpret the greater bill-length and wing-length of island birds have been unable to

eliminate the effect of either of two potentially important factors—ecological and climatic characteristics of the environment.

To examine these trends and, should they be established, to explain their significance, a study has been made of the passerine birds of North America and México, and in particular those of the Tres Marías islands, Nayarit, México. These islands are especially suitable for study since their fauna is large, faunal affinities with the adjacent mainland are unequivocal, the species of interest exhibit little interisland variation and the habitat of two of the islands, María Magdalena and María Cleofas, has been scarcely disturbed (Zweifel, 1960) since both are without human inhabitants. The islands are situated at least 50 miles from the mainland between 21° and 22° N latitude. Their features are summarized by Grant (1965b).

The results of this study are presented as follows: The size trends, affecting the dimensions of exposed parts of island birds, are examined in a particular (Tres Marías) and a general situation. The relationship between the size of exposed parts and body-size is then considered. The environmental factors which influence the morphology of birds are investigated under two headings, climatic and ecological. The relative importance of these two environmental influences is assessed, both in the particular and the general situation, and a conclusion is reached concerning the adaptive significance of the morphological features of island birds.

LARGE WING AND BILL—INSULAR CHARACTERS?

On the Tres Marías islands 19 species of passerines are present in the summer months, most of which have been observed

---

[1] Present address: Zoology Department, McGill University, Montreal, Quebec, Canada.

TABLE 1. *Differences between the means of mainland and island samples of measurements of the Tres Marías passerine species, expressed as percentages of the mainland means.*

	Wing	Tail	Tarsus	Bill
*Platypsaris aglaiae	− 4.3	− 2.7	+0.8	− 5.5
Tyrannus melancholicus	− 1.1	− 2.6	− 3.2	− 0.2
Myiarchus tyrannulus	− 3.6	− 2.9	.− 3.2	− 3.8
Myiarchus tuberculifer	− 1.0	− 1.0	+0.3	− 1.9
*Myiopagis viridicata	− 1.7	− 1.0	+5.9	− 2.0
*Thryothorus felix	+4.4	+6.8	+1.7	+13.7
*Melanotis caerulescens	− 3.8	− 11.4	− 2.5	+15.1
*Turdus rufo-palliatus	+3.2	+3.2	+10.5	+14.5
*Myadestes obscurus	− 2.7	− 0.2	+11.7	− 3.8
*Vireo hypochryseus	+6.2	+8.5	+6.8	+3.4
Vireo flavoviridis	+2.9	+4.8	+6.0	+3.9
*Parula pitiayumi	+5.2	+14.8	+18.4	+1.0
*Granatellus venustus	+7.0	+9.7	+7.2	+2.3
*Icterus pustulatus	+8.7	+8.2	+6.0	+17.4
*Piranga bidentata	− 1.8	− 0.9	+6.4	+2.7
*Spinus psaltria	− 4.6	− 3.9	+1.7	− 10.1
*Richmondena cardinalis	+4.5	(− 4.9)	+11.8	+7.2

NB. A negative sign indicates that the mainland mean is the larger, and a positive sign that the island mean is larger. Male samples only used, usually comprising 15 specimens or more; the one figure in parentheses indicates that one of the two samples compared contains less than five individuals.
* Indicates an insular subspecies. *Camptostoma imberbe* and *Mimus polyglottos*, neither of them insular subspecies, have been omitted because their samples are small.

breeding (Grant and Cowan, 1964). Some are larger than their mainland counterparts in wing, tail, tarsus, and bill dimensions, others smaller or approximately of the same size (Table 1). For every dimension measured, the island birds are more frequently larger than their mainland relatives (Table 2). This is most noticeable for tarsus and bill measurements, but least for wings and tails. Thus, these results do not accord completely with the pattern of large wing and bill mentioned above.

To determine whether the predominance of forms with large bills and tarsi on islands is of local or widespread occurrence, use has been made of the large number of published measurements of North Ameri-

TABLE 2. *The number of differences between the measurements of mainland and island birds of the Tres Marías species.*

	Wing	Tail	Tarsus	Bill
Island specimens larger	7	6	10	5
No difference	6	6	5	9
Mainland specimens larger	4	5	2	3

NB. *Camptostoma imberbe* and *Mimus polyglottos* are not included (see footnote to Table 1). A difference is considered to exist when the ranges (two standard errors either side of the mean) of both male and female island measurements do not overlap those of the respective mainland measurements, and the samples of all four comprise at least five individuals. When only one sex is thus represented a difference is based upon this alone (*R. cardinalis*).

can and Mexican passerine birds (Ridgway, 1901–1907, and original descriptions of subspecies). This information has enabled 69 comparisons of taxonomically distinct mainland and island forms to be made (Grant, 1965b). Sample sizes are small and the mainland samples have not always been taken from the nearest area to the islands. However, there is no reason to suppose that a consistent bias in one direction is produced by these sampling errors. Therefore, if there are no differences of significance between the mainland and island samples, a comparison of means should yield the result that the island sample is larger in approximately half of the instances, and the mainland sample is larger in the other half. The results of these comparisons are summarized in Table 3, and show that for wing and tail measurements this expectation is met. In contrast, there is an apparent tendency for the bill and tarsus of island birds to be larger than those of mainland birds, and it is concluded that the trend among the Tres Marías birds is of widespread occurrence, at least in North America and México. The addition of the Tres Marías data to the contents of Table 2 does not alter this conclusion (Table 4), but brings tarsus and bill values closer to parity. Terrestrial non-passerines do not show the bill trend but do show the tarsus trend (Grant, 1965b).

164

	Wing	Tail	Tarsus	Bill
Island means larger	39	34	43	49
Means equal	0	2	2	1
Mainland means larger	30	33	15	16
x^2 test for 1:1 Ha[1]	0.59	0.01	4.50	8.25
Values of P	>0.1	>0.5	<0.05	<0.01

[1] Hypothesis states that the ratio of island means larger to mainland means larger is 1 : 1.

It should be noted that although the frequency of island birds with large tarsi and with large bills is approximately the same among the passerines, these two features are not always possessed by the same species (*e.g.*, *Melanotis caerulescens* and *Spinus psaltria*). Whereas there·are some birds which are different from the mainland forms to approximately the same degree (proportionate) in all measured dimensions (*e.g.*, *Myiarchus tyrannulus*), the majority is different to different degrees (disproportionate)'. For instance the island form of *Melanotis caerulescens* has a tail shorter than its mainland counterpart by approximately 11 per cent, yet its bill is longer by more than 15 per cent. Members of this latter group may be termed allomorphic (Huxley *et al.*, 1941). The distinction between them can only be made arbitrarily—if the differences between the mainland and island four sets of measurements of a species (Table 1) are themselves different by more than five per cent, the island bird may be considered an allomorph. The group comprises all the insular subspecies, with the exception of *Vireo hypochryseus*.

RELATIONSHIP OF EXPOSED PARTS TO BODY-SIZE

Presumably large tarsus and bill have evolved in one of two ways. Natural selection has acted either upon these parts directly or upon body-size which has produced allometric effects on the size of the parts. At the outset the latter explanation seems unlikely, because if an increase in body-size produces an increase in the size of external parts, all parts would probably be affected, whereas the data in Tables 3

and 4 show that tarsus and bill are more frequently larger on islands than are wing and tail.

It is generally agreed that body-size is best indicated by weight (Amadon, 1943) when the bird is not in a fat condition (Connell *et. al.*, 1960). Weights have been determined rarely in the past, and in the present study only small samples were obtained. Nevertheless they do indicate that the Tres Marías forms of at least nine species are less heavy than the mainland forms (Grant, 1965b). These include *Thryothorus felix*, *Vireo hypochryseus*, and *Icterus pustulatus*, whose island forms are larger in not one but all external parts (Table 1). Two species were of approximately the same weight in both regions and data were lacking for the rest. Thus there is no evidence among the Tres Marías passerines that large tarsus and bill are allometric consequences of large body-size. On the other hand the fact that many of the island forms are allomorphic supports the alternative view, that selection has acted upon each part individually.

Finally, it should be noted that a large tarsus (tarsometatarsus) is not necessarily accompanied by a large femur and tibiotarsus. For instance, island birds of *Icterus pustulatus* have a smaller weight but larger tarsus than mainland birds; between these extremes the femur and tibiotarsus of island birds are not significantly different from those of mainland birds (Grant, 1964).

IMPORTANCE OF CLIMATE

In the past, intraspecific variation in the size of continental birds has been inter-·

165

TABLE 4. *Comparison of mainland and island samples of North American and Mexican passerine-species, including those of the Tres Marías.*[1]

	Wing	Tail	Tarsus	Bill
Island means larger	47	41	56	59
Means equal	0	2	2	1
Mainland means larger	36	40	16	20
x^2 test for 1 : 1 Ha[2]	0.73	0.01	10.81	9.16
Values of P	>0.1	>0.5	<0.005	<0.005

[1] The endemic subspecies (see Table 1) and *Vireo flavoviridis*, which is as close to subspecific status (Grant, 1965b) as are several that are still recognized as subspecies (Ridgway, 1901–1907) and included in Table 3.
[2] See footnote to Table 3.

preted usually in the light of two principal ecogeographical rules, the Bergmann and Allen rules (Rensch, 1938; Snow, 1954a), yet rarely have these rules been applied to island situations. According to Rensch (*loc. cit.*), variation in the size of exposed parts of birds can be explained partly as an allometric consequence of body-size variation and partly as a result of selection for heat exchange. Under experimental conditions, mice (*Mus musculus*) do not achieve as large a body-size at high temperatures as they do at lower temperatures, but they do grow markedly longer tails at the high temperatures (Harrison *et al.*, 1964). Since many of the birds of the Tres Marías have a small body-size and yet a large tarsus and bill the question arises: "Are these insular characteristics of birds produced because the island environment is hotter than the mainland?" In other words, perhaps insular allomorphosis is the result of selection for heat exchange.

This encounters the difficulty discussed in the previous section namely that not all the exposed parts are large in island birds with the same frequency. Furthermore, in contrast to the richly vascularized skin over parts of the wing musculature (Eliassen, 1963) and basal members of the hind limb, the cornified surface of tarsus and bill is probably of little value in heat exchange. Finally, the heat exchange interpretation receives no support from the climatic conditions of Tres Marías islands and the adjacent mainland. As Huxley (1942) has pointed out, in semitropical regions, where winter minimum temperatures are not extreme, selection should act most strongly in the summer months, when temperatures are at their highest; and under these conditions birds should show adaptations to the dissipation of heat. However, there is little difference in summer maximum temperatures between the Tres Marías islands and Puerto Vallarta and Mazatlán on the mainland (Fig. 1). Heat exchange is also influenced by humidity. No data are available for this factor but, being dryer than the mainland, the islands may also be less humid. If this is true, heat dissipation is probably less difficult on the islands. But, despite the smaller need of large surfaces for heat dissipation, island birds have longer tarsi and bills.

For these reasons, it is concluded that the size of these structures cannot be explained as adaptations to climatic conditions.

IMPORTANCE OF ECOLOGICAL CONDITIONS

A difference in size between the bills and tarsi of mainland and island birds may reflect a different usage of those structures in the two environments. Thus, the large size of bill and tarsus in island birds may be a product of natural selection, which has acted upon these structures individually and resulted in a better adaptation to biotic and topographical features of the environment. The significance of differences in size of the structures needs to be appraised before the differences themselves can be related to ecological conditions.

TABLE 5. *Comparison of differences in bill-length, between mainland and island birds, with differences in their diet.*

Species	Bill differences[1]	Differences in diet[2]			
		Gizzard		Observations	
		N[3]	% difference	N	% difference
T. melancholicus	proportionate	84	8.5		
M. tyrannulus	proportionate	34	6.5		
M. tuberculifer	proportionate	24	3.0	88	17.0
V. hypochryseus	proportionate	52	8.0	173	6.0
V. flavoviridis	proportionate	60	2.5		
P. aglaiae	disproportionate	49	33.5		
M. viridicata	disproportionate	45	19.0		
M. caerulescens	disproportionate	24	36.0	105	96.0
I. pustulatus	disproportionate	112	18.0	453	45.7[4]
P. bidentata	disproportionate	35	46.0		
S. psaltria	disproportionate	37	18.5		

[1] Proportionate or disproportionate in relation to differences of other dimensions (see Table 1 and text).
[2] Percentage difference in frequency of animal or vegetable material. On the mainland, specimens were collected for gizzard analysis from several localities, 1961–1963; observations were made only at Tepic, March–August, 1962–1963.
[3] N gives complete mainland and island sample size.
[4] Average of four differences (21.0–87.0 per cent) in separate months.

Bill.—Variations in the shape and size of the bill can be correlated frequently with the nature of the food taken (Hinde, 1959; Bowman, 1961). An analysis of the gizzard contents of Tres Marías and mainland birds shows that bill differences are paralleled by dietary differences. Birds with proportionately similar bills in the two regions have diets differing by no more than 8.5 per cent, while those with disproportionately large or small bills on the islands have a diet different from that of their mainland relatives by more than twice that amount (Table 5). Observations support this conclusion. However, no further correlations with bill-size are possible, since some of the Tres Marías birds with large bills feed on a predominantly animal diet, others on a predominantly vegetable diet. Food particles were usually to comminuted to be measured. In this study also, no support was found for the theory of Voous (1957) that island birds (*Mimus polyglottos* on the Caribbean islands in particular) have longer bills because they feed on a greater variety of types of food.

Baldwin (1953), found that although three Drepaniids on Hawaii took the same size-range of insects, there was a correlation between the length of bill of each species and the mean size of prey. According to the work of Kear (1962), birds with large bills have an advantage over

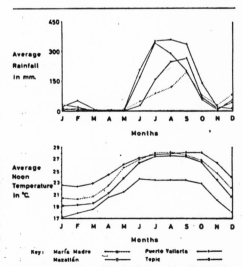

FIG. 1. Annual distribution of rainfall and temperature at four stations in western México. Data from Contreras (1942).

TABLE 6. *The use of perches in feeding, by two species on the Tres Marias islands and adjacent mainland.*

| Species | Locality | N[1] | Percentage use of perches | |
			Thin[2]	Thick[3]
Vireo hypochryseus	Tres Marías	44	77	23
	Tepic	129	89	11
Icterus pustulatus	Tres Marías	189	53	47
	Tepic	264	91	9
	Sauta	83	87	13
	Puerto Vallarta	83	94	6

[1] Sample size.
[2] Perches less than 1 cm. in diameter of cross section: *e.g.*, leaves, flowers, twigs.
[3] Perches more than 1 cm. in diameter of cross section: *e.g.*, branches, trunks, and including ground.

those with short bills, at least among finches (subfamily *Fringillidae*), in that their efficiency is greater in dealing with large food and a wide range of food-particle sizes. From these findings, it has been suggested that the long bill of many island birds is an adaptation permitting the exploitation of a large range of food-sizes (Watson, 1962; Grant, 1964), since there is no reason to suppose that the size of the food available to island birds is, on the average, larger than that available to mainland birds. The size of the bill is probably related to the upper half of a size-range of food rather than to the mean or the size-range *per se*, because the performance of birds with bills of different size is almost the same at the lower levels of the range but different in the upper half (Kear, *loc. cit.*). Thus it is the upper half of this greater range of food-size to which the bills of island birds are adapted.

Tarsus.—Variations in the length of tarsus in birds have received less attention. The leg serves the function of support and locomotion. Palmgren (1932) showed that in birds which feed in a hanging position from slender perches not only is the leg musculature different from those which feed in a more upright position, but the tarsus is a shorter member of the limb. Members of the families *Picidae* and *Certhiidae*, whose locomotion on tree trunks is performed in an essentially hanging posture, are also characterized by short tarsi. On the other hand it is known from

several studies that cursorial animals tend to have longer limbs than arboreal ones (*e.g.*, Dilger, 1956). A long tarsus is presumably advantageous in bipedal locomotion (Davis, 1957). The length of tarsus is thus probably correlated with the nature of the perch and the way in which it is used. Birds which feed and move on slender, not rigid, perches are likely to have a shorter tarsus than those which make a greater use of firm perches, in an upright posture.

Accordingly, on islands many species of birds might be expected to use firm perches to a greater extent than on the mainland. On the Tres Marías islands *Icterus pustulatus* (allomorphic) meets this expectation ($x^2 = 71.27$, $P < 0.001$) while *Vireo hypochryseus* (isomorphic) does not ($x^2 = 2.70$, $P > 0.1$). On the mainland both species feed predominantly on the periphery of tree and shrub canopies, from twigs, leaves, etc., but on the islands *I. pustulatus* feeds to a greater extent on branches and trunks of trees (Table 6). This evidence is meager but does support the contention that a different morphology is related to a different behavior. The contention is further supported by correlations of relative tarsus length with foraging behavior among other mainland birds (Grant, 1965c).

It is possible that feeding on the ground partly accounts for a greater use of firm perches on the islands. Such was not the case with either of the two species studied in detail.

168

Influence of Habitat

If the characteristic morphology of island birds corresponds with a characteristic behavior, such behavior may be determined by a habitat which is different from the mainland habitat. For instance *Turdus merula* and *T. ericetorum* nest on the ground of the almost treeless Orkney islands, a habit rarely observed elsewhere in the British Isles, where the two species occur in woodland (Lack, 1942); and differences in habitat occupancy between mainland and island birds have been reported frequently (*e.g.*, Hatt *et al.*, 1948; Lack and Southern, 1949; Svärdson, 1949; Miller, 1951; Amadon, 1953; Bourne, 1955; Voous, 1957; Keast, 1961; Rand and Rabor, 1960).

Even if the habitats on the mainland and islands are the same, they may be occupied differently by each species, which may thus influence their behavior. Lack and Southern (*loc. cit.*) have noted that *Parus coeruleus*, which occupies only broad-leaved woodlands on the continent of (North) Africa and Europe, feed in all types of woodland on the island of Tenerife, including pine forest.

Both possibilities are contradicted by the evidence from the Tres Marías islands. Here the vegetation is almost entirely Tropical Deciduous Forest, the same as that occurring at medium elevations on the mainland; and at least 15 of the 19 species occupy it in both regions. It is possible that fine structural features of the habitats present only on the islands influence the behavior of island birds (Grant, 1964). However, it does not seem likely that these structural features will occur on all islands and affect the behavior of the birds in the same way. The widespread and characteristic morphology of island birds cannot be explained solely in terms of habitat influences.

Numbers of Species

The behavior of one animal species is influenced by the presence or absence of others. Lack and Southern (1949) have

TABLE 7. *The number of species on the Tres Marías islands and adjacent mainland, recorded in the months May–August and considered to be summer-resident in the census area.*

		Tres Marías islands[1]	Mainland[2]
Area of:	10 acres	23	25
Area of:	20 acres	30 (+2)	29 (+5)
Area of:	40 acres	?	33 (+6)
Area of	90,000 acres	34	>39

[1] Areas of 10 and 20 acres censused on María Magdalena.

[2] Areas of 10, 20, and 40 acres censused at Tepic, Nayarit.

Numbers in parentheses refer to Falconiforms seen flying over the census areas; they are included in the totals in the last row.

correlated the habitat-extension (see above) displayed by some species of birds on Tenerife with the absence of closely related species. Similarly, it is known that two closely related species are often most similar, ecologically and morphologically, when in allopatry, and most dissimilar when in sympatry (Brown and Wilson, 1956).

It is a characteristic of islands that a smaller number of species are present than in an equivalent area of mainland (Hatt *et al.*, 1948; Preston, 1962). The Tres Marías islands (area approximately 90,000 acres) contain a smaller number of bird species than 40 acres of mainland censused near Tepic, in Nayarit (Table 7). Probably this difference would have been much greater if 90,000 acres of mainland had been censused. It is also probable that a larger number of congeneric pairs of species would have been recorded in a mainland area of that size (Grant, 1965b); in contrast to the two pairs on the Tres Marías (*Myiarchus* and *Vireo* spp.). Certainly the occurrence of congeneric species together on an island is a rarity (Mayr, 1931; Rand and Rabor, 1960). Congeneric pairs of species are often similar in ecology too. Thus, if on islands there are fewer species which are ecologically similar, and the amount of environmental resources is assumed to be approximately the same in the two regions, island birds have more resources available

TABLE 8. *Comparison of the number of individuals recorded on repeated surveys of ten-acre census areas at Tepic and Maria Magdalena.*

	Maria Magdalena	Tepic	Per cent difference[1]
Average number recorded on one survey	137*	103	32.7
Estimated maximum number of territories	148	126	17.5
Number of territories, exclusive of single-occurrence records	128**	93	34.7
Number of territories, exclusive of two-occurrence records	110**	80	34.1

NB. The census method of Enemar (1959) was used with modifications, with six surveys of each area in May (Tepic) and June (María Magdalena), 1963.

[1] The amount by which the M. Magdalena values exceed those for Tepic, expressed as a percentage of the latter.

* t test: difference significant at 0.05 level.

** x^2 test: difference significant at 0.01 level.

to exploit than mainland birds. It may be suggested that the morphological and behavioral characteristics of island birds are related to this greater exploitation (niche-extension), viz: a larger bill is an adaptation to a larger range of food sizes (see Kear, 1962), and a larger tarsus is an adaptation to a greater variety of perch dimensions.

Numbers of Individuals

Island faunas are often characterized by high densities (Lack and Southern, 1949; Crowell, 1962). At such densities some members of a population acquire different feeding grounds (Tompa, 1964) or nest-sites (Lack, 1942; Svärdson, 1949). Although only short-term effects, like these, have been demonstrated, it is possible that permanent changes in behavior arise in this way, facilitated on islands by the absence of closely related species.

Census results show that the density of birds on María Magdalena may be as much as 35 per cent greater than on the mainland (Table 8); but this difference is the result of the most common two species on the island, *Parula pitiayumi* and *Vireo flavoviridis*, being exceedingly common, a situation similar to that on Bermuda (Crowell, *loc. cit.*). Of the seven species recorded in both mainland and island censuses only two, *Vireo hypochryseus* and *Piranga bidentata*, were more frequent in the latter (Table 9). It is possible that when the species first colonized the island they

existed at a high density, their behavior and morphology underwent modification and later the level of density fell. But on present evidence, there is no satisfactory correspondence between high density and allomorphosis, and changes in form must be considered to have evolved in the absence of exceptional conditions of density.

EXCEPTIONS TO THE TREND OF LARGE BILL AND TARSUS ON ISLANDS

It is pointed out above that Hesse *et al.* (1937) and Bourne (1955) have reported instances of birds with smaller dimensions on islands. In the absence of the relevant information it is impossible to offer a single explanation for these instances. Added to the ecological factors and the consequential effects of body-size differences, climatic factors (Allen's rule) may be important. All these factors may interact to produce birds with small bills and tarsi on islands. For example, the ecological interpretation given to the large bill of *Parus coeruleus* on Tenerife, by Lack and Southern (*loc. cit.*), was contested by Snow (1954a), who pointed out that a cline of increasing size with decreasing latitude would account for it. However, this does not explain the characteristic shape of the bill of the Tenerife birds, and it would seem that a complementary action of climatic and ecological factors has been involved in the selection of this bill (see also Snow, 1954b).

The two species which, on the Tres

170

Marías islands, show the greatest reduction in exposed parts (*P. aglaiae* and *S. psaltria*), are allomorphic, their tarsi, for instance, being approximately the same size in the two regions. The smallness of their bills may be a consequence of their bodies being smaller, or it may be attributable to an ecological factor, such as the presence of an ecologically similar species. The latter seems plausible in view of the well-known tendency for two closely related species (systematically and, presumably, ecologically) to be markedly different in size of bill when in sympatry (Chapin, 1949; Vaurie, 1951; Amadon *loc. cit.*; Brown and Wilson, 1956; Selander and Giller, 1963).

Several of the Tres Marías birds are neither greatly larger or smaller than their mainland relatives, but are isomorphic with them, which indicates that selection has not favored a change of form. This may be because ecologically similar species hinder a change of niche, and it is perhaps significant that four of the isomorphic group are related systematically (the two *Myiarchus* and the two *Vireo* species), and perhaps ecologically too. Alternatively, or additionally, there may not have been sufficient isolation, in time or space, for selection to be effective. Three of the isomorphic group are partial or complete migrants (*T. melancholicus*, *M. tyrannulus*, and *V. flavoviridis*); it is possible that a few mainland individuals accompany the migrants on their return to the islands, and disrupt the effects of selection (see Mayr, 1963).

DISCUSSION

The absence on islands of species with similar ecological requirements has permitted some of those present to extend their activities and occupy at least part of the vacant niches, sometimes in new habitats.

Concomitant with this extension, these birds have undergone morphological change. Adaptation to the ecological conditions has resulted in a larger tarsus and bill. Not all birds have adapted in this way, or to the same degree, because other factors, including ambient temperature and changes in

TABLE 9. *Comparison of the maximum number of territories occupied by species occurring in both mainland and island ten-acre census areas.*

Species	Maria Magdalena	Tepic
Myiarchus tuberculifer	3	7
Myiopagis viridicata	1	6
Thryothorus felix	7	8
Melanotis caerulescens	3	9
Vireo hypochryseus	6	5
Piranga bidentata	6	2
Spinus psaltria	2	2–5*

NB. The census data are summarized in Table 8.
* Number in doubt.

body-size, have influenced the size of tarsus and bill.

There is considerable evidence that the specifically insular, ecological characteristics of birds are prevalent among island forms of other animals (*e.g.*, Hatt *et al.*, 1948; Wilson, 1961). From this it might be supposed that the feeding and locomotor apparatus of non-avian animals will have undergone adaptive modification. Foster (1963), in comparing the Queen Charlotte Island and mainland populations of Marten (*Martes americana*) in British Columbia, found a dietary difference, which he was able to relate to the "heavier dentition and associated areas in the skull" of the island form. But such examples have been reported rarely, which suggests that a trend, paralleling that in birds, does not exist (see Postscript). On the other hand there are numerous reports of "gigantism" and "dwarfism" on islands, applying to gastropod molluscs (Bole *et al.*, 1961), reptiles (Kramer and Mertens, 1938; Schuster, 1950), and mammals (Krumbiegel, 1943) particularly. Since the tendencies toward size-change are in opposite directions it is difficult to arrive at a clear idea of a general trend from these reports, if one exists at all. A trend can only be established from a large number of examples. Foster (1964), using the published measurements of a large number of mammal species, established that a trend toward large body-size exists among insular rodents, and an opposite trend exists among larger mammals. Of 68 species in the

171

former group, 60 insular forms were found to be larger than their mainland counterparts. The environmental factors believed to affect body-size have been discussed by Rensch (1960) and are considerably more numerous than those which affect exposed parts, such as appendages. Hence body-size differences are the more difficult to interpret.

Nevertheless there is evidence that those same ecological conditions which have permitted the evolution of bill and tarsus characteristics of birds on islands, have also permitted the evolution of large rodents on islands. Chapman (1940) and Watson (1962) have drawn attention to the fact that large bills are characteristic of birds living on both mountaintops and islands, two environments which are ecologically similar. It is of interest therefore, that large body-size is characteristic of five species of rodents living on mountains and islands in Europe (Zimmermann, 1950). The relict hypothesis, proposed by Barrett-Hamilton and Hinton (1914) and Zimmermann (*loc. cit.*) to explain this feature, has been contested recently by Mayr (1952), Steven (1953), and Cook (1961), who consider the large size to be an adaptation to the prevailing conditions. In temperate regions, large body-size is of metabolic advantage to warm-blooded animals (Rensch, *loc. cit.*); but since there are few ecologically similar species on islands and mountains, it may also facilitate a greater exploitation of environmental resources.

Whereas large size may be a disadvantage on the mainland in the face of heavy predator pressure (Falconer, 1953), it is not so on islands because this pressure is presumably less (Foster, 1964). If it is indeed true that the adaptations of a species are influenced by the presence or absence of others to this extent, it may help to explain why, in the course of evolution, there has been a tendency for individual species of mammals to become larger (Cope, 1896), which has parallels in several other groups of animals (Huxley and Haldane, 1929; Newell, 1949).

SUMMARY

1. In North America and México there is a strong tendency for island birds to have a longer tarsus and bill than their mainland counterparts; but there is no such tendency for them to have a longer wing and tail.

2. Although climate and body-size are known to influence the size of tarsus and bill the larger dimensions on islands are considered to be adaptations primarily to ecological conditions. The bill is longer because it deals with a greater range of food-sizes, and the tarsus is longer because a greater variety of perches is used.

3. The differences in usage have arisen as a result of the absence, on the islands, of species with similar ecological requirements; which has permitted some of those present to extend their activities and occupy at least part of the vacant niches, sometimes in new habitats.

4. It is suggested that the same ecological conditions and responses have influenced the evolution of large body-size of island rodents in particular, and of mainland animals of several phyla in general.

ACKNOWLEDGMENTS

The study of the Tres Marías birds was undertaken with the cooperation of the Dirección General de Caza, Departamento de Prevención Social, México D.F., and B. Villa R. and A. R. Phillips of the Universidad Nacional Autónoma de México. It was financed by the National Research Council of Canada during 1961–1963, and partly by H. R. MacMillan during 1961–1962; additionally, a Frank M. Chapman Award from the American Museum of Natural History met the expenses of working at that institution.

I am grateful to D. Amadon, H. G. Deignan, J. W. Hardy, T. R. Howell, P. S. Humphrey, J. D. MacDonald, A. H. Miller, R. T. Orr, A. R. Phillips, and K. E. Stager for providing specimens of birds on loan. To G. G. E. Scudder, D. Amadon, and I. McT. Cowan I am grateful for much helpful criticism, and to my wife for assistance in many ways.

172

POSTSCRIPT

Recent publications indicate that island mammals may possess unusual skull and dental features more frequently than is generally supposed. The Newfoundland beaver (*Castor canadensis*) has a zygoma quite different in shape from that of its mainland relative, and also feeds on a partly different diet in a partly different habitat (Cameron, 1958). More striking is the pattern of variation shown by some rodents. On some of the Scottish islands either *Clethrionomys glareolus* occurs alone, *Microtus agrestis* occurs alone, or both occur together. Where *Clethrionomys glareolus* occurs alone it shows a high incidence of elaboration of the posterior loop of the third upper molar, and only a low incidence of this feature in most mainland regions and on islands which also support *Microtus agrestis* (Corbett, 1963, 1964). It is not known whether *Microtus agrestis* displays a similar feature when alone on an island. But it is to be expected because a closely related North American species, *Microtus pennsylvanicus*, does show a similar feature on Newfoundland, an environment notable for the absence of *Clethrionomys gapperi* (Cameron, 1958). In this case it is the posterior loop of the first upper molar which is elaborate. Although detailed information on the diet of these forms is lacking, it is noteworthy that in those island situations in which the unusual dental feature occurs the animals occupy unusual habitats, habitats which are more typical of the species, either *Microtus* or *Clethrionomys*, which is absent. It is probable therefore that the dental peculiarities are correlated with an unusual diet. It is perhaps also significant that the posterior parts of the upper molars in *Microtus pennsylvanicus* are phenotypically the most variable parts of structures which appear to have undergone rapid evolution (Guthrie, 1965). Therefore adaptation to a new habitat (and diet?) on islands has been achieved by selection acting upon a phenotypically variable character. The bill length of birds, which has also undergone change, is similarly variable.

LITERATURE CITED

AMADON, D. 1943. Bird weights as an aid in taxonomy. Wilson Bull., **55**: 164–177.

——. 1953. Avian systematics and evolution in the Gulf of Guinea. Bull. Amer. Mus. Nat. Hist., **100**: 397–431.

BALDWIN, P. H. 1953. Annual cycle, environment and evolution in the Hawaiian honeycreepers. Univ. California Publ. Zool., **52**: 285–398.

BARRETT-HAMILTON, G. E. H., AND M. A. C. HINTON. 1910–1921. A history of British mammals. Gurney and Jackson, London, vol. 2, 748 pp.

BOLE, J., S. BRELIH, AND M. ZEI. 1961. Les Pulmonés et les Lézards insulaires et le problème de leur speciation dans l'archipel de Rovinj (Rovigno). *In* Le peuplement des Iles Mediterranéenes et le problème de l'insularité: Colloques internationaux du Centre National de le Recherche Scientifique. Editions du Centre National de la Recherch Scientifique, Paris.

BOURNE, W. R. P. 1955. The birds of the Cape Verde Islands. Ibis, **97**: 508–556.

BOWMAN, R. I. 1961. Morphological differentiation and adaptation in the Galápagos finches. Univ. California Publ. Zool., **58**: 1–302.

BROWN, W. L., JR., AND E. O. WILSON. 1956. Character displacement. Syst. Zool., **5**: 49–64.

CAMERON, A. W. 1958. Mammals of the islands in the Gulf of St. Lawrence. Bull. Nat. Mus. Canada, **154**: 1–165.

CHAPIN, J. 1949. Relationship and voice in the genus *Calamocichla*. Ornithologie als biologische Wissenschaft (Heidelberg), pp. 7–16.

CHAPMAN, F. M. 1940. The post-glacial history of *Zonotrichia capensis*. Bull. Amer. Mus. Nat. Hist., **77**: 381–438.

CONNELL, C. P., E. P. ODUM, AND H. KALE. 1960. Fat-free weights of birds. Auk, **77**: 1–9.

CONTRERAS A., A. 1942. Mapa de las provincias climatológicas de la República Mexicana. Sec. Agric. Fomento, Inst. Geográfico, México, 54 pp.

COOK, L. M. 1961. The edge effect in population genetics. Amer. Nat., **95**: 295–307.

COPE, E. D. 1896. Primary factors of organic evolution. Chicago.

CORBETT, G. B. 1963. An isolated population of the bank vole *Clethrionomys glareolus* with aberrant dental pattern. Proc. Zool. Soc. London, **140**: 316–319.

——. 1964. Regional variation in the bank-vole *Clethrionomys glareolus* in the British Isles. Proc. Zool. Soc. London, **143**: 191–219.

CROWELL, K. L. 1962. Reduced interspecific competition among the birds of Bermuda. Ecology, **43**: 75–88.

DAVIS, J. 1957. Comparative foraging behaviour of spotted and brown towhees. Auk, **74**: 129–166.

173

DILGER, W. C. 1956. Adaptive modifications and ecological isolating mechanisms in the thrush genera *Catharus* and *Hylocichla*. Wilson Bull., **68**: 171–199.

ELIASSEN, E. 1963. Preliminary results from new methods of investigating the physiology of birds during flight. Ibis, **105**: 234–237.

ENEMAR, A. 1959. On the determination of the size and composition of a passerine bird population during the breeding season. Vår Fagelvärld, Suppl. **2**: 1–114.

FALCONER, D. S. 1953. Selection for large and small size in mice. J. Genet., **51**: 470–501.

FOSTER, J. B. 1963. The evolution of the native land mammals of the Queen Charlotte Islands and the problem of insularity. Ph.D. thesis, Univ. British Columbia, Vancouver.

——. 1964. Evolution of mammals on islands. Nature, **202**: 234–235.

GRANT, P. R. 1964. The significance of some insular characteristics in birds. Ph.D. thesis, Univ. British Columbia, Vancouver.

——. 1965a. Plumage and the evolution of birds on islands. Syst. Zool., **14**: 47–52.

——. 1965b. A systematic study of the terrestrial birds of the Tres Marías Islands, México. Postilla, Yale Peabody Mus. Nat. Hist., **90**, in press.

——. 1965c. Further information on the relative length of tarsus in birds. Postilla, Yale Peabody Mus. Nat. Hist., **93**, in press.

GRANT, P. R., AND I. McT. COWAN. 1964. A review of the avifauna of the Tres Marías Islands, Nayarit, México. Condor, **66**: 221–228.

GUTHRIE, R. D. 1965. Variability in characters undergoing rapid evolution, an analysis of *Microtus* molars. Evolution, **19**: 214–233.

HARRISON, G. A., R. W. HIORNS, AND J. S. WEINER. 1964. The growth of mice in a fluctuating temperature environment. Proc. Roy. Soc. B, **160**: 137–148.

HATT, R. T., J. VAN TYNE, L. C. STUART, C. H. POPE, AND A. B. GROBMAN. 1948. Island life: a study of the land vertebrates of the islands of eastern Lake Michigan. Cranbrook Inst. Sci., **27**: 1–179.

HESSE, R., W. C. ALLEE, AND K. P. SCHMIDT. 1937. Ecological animal geography. Wiley, New York.

HINDE, R. A. 1959. Behaviour and speciation in birds and lower vertebrates. Biol. Reviews, **34**: 85–120.

HUXLEY, J. S. 1942. Evolution: the modern synthesis. George Allen and Unwin Ltd., London.

HUXLEY, J. S., AND J. B. S. HALDANE. 1929. Animal biology. Clarendon Press, Oxford.

HUXLEY, J. S., J. NEEDHAM, AND I. M. LERNER. 1941. Terminology of relative growth rates. Nature, **148**: 225.

KEAR, J. 1962. Food selection in finches, with special reference to interspecific differences. Proc. Zool. Soc. London, **138**: 163–204.

KEAST, A. 1961. Bird speciation on the Australian continent. Bull. Mus. Comp. Zool., **123**: 307–495.

KRAMER, G., AND R. MERTENS. 1938. Rassenbildung bei westistrianischen Inseleidechsen in Abhangegheit von Isolierungsalter und Arealgrosse. Arch. Naturg., **7**: 189–234.

KRUMBIEGEL, I. 1943. Zur kenntnis der säugetierfauna von Fernando Po. Arch. Naturg., n.s., **11**: 305–349.

LACK, D. 1942. The birds of the Orkney Islands. Ibis, ser. 14, **6**: 461–484.

LACK, D., AND H. N. SOUTHERN. 1949. Birds on Tenerife. Ibis, **91**: 607–626.

MAYR, E. 1931. Birds collected during the Whitney South Sea Expedition XVI. Amer. Mus. Novit., **502**: 1–21.

——. 1952. Notes on evolutionary literature. Evolution, **6**: 138–144.

——. 1963. Animal species and evolution. Belknap Press, Cambridge, Massachusetts.

MAYR, E., AND C. VAURIE. 1948. Evolution in the Dicruridae (birds). Evolution, **2**: 238–265.

MILLER, A. H. 1951. A comparison of the avifaunas of Santa Cruz and Santa Rosa islands, California. Condor, **53**: 117–123.

MURPHY, R. C. 1938. The need of insular exploration as illustrated by birds. Science, **88**: 533–539.

MURPHY, R. C., AND J. CHAPIN. 1929. A collection of birds from the Azores. Amer. Mus. Novit., **384**: 1–23.

NEWELL, N. D. 1949. Phyletic size increase, an important trend, illustrated by fossil vertebrates. Evolution, **3**: 103–124.

PALMGREN, P. 1932. Zur Biologie von *Regulus r. regulus* (L.) und *Parus atricapillus borealis* Selys. Acta Zool. Fennica, **14**: 1–113.

PRESTON, F. W. 1962. The canonical distribution of commonness and rarity, I and II. Ecology, **43**: 185–215 and 410–432.

RAND, A. L., AND D. S. RABOR. 1960. Birds of the Philippine Islands: Siquijor, Mount Malindang, Bohol and Samar. Fieldiana: Zool., **35**: 223–441.

RENSCH, B. 1938. Bestehen die Regeln klimatischer Parallelität beider Merkmalsausprägung von homöothermen Tieren zu Recht? Arch. Naturg. (N.F.), **7**: 364–389.

——. 1960. Evolution above the species level. London.

RIDGWAY, R. 1901–1907. Birds of North and Middle America. Bull. U. S. Nat. Mus., **50**, parts I–IV.

SCHUSTER, O. 1950. Die klimaparallele Ausbildung der Körperproportionen bei Poikilothermen. Abh. Senckenb. Naturf. Ges., **482**: 1–89.

174

SELANDER, R. K., AND D. R. GILLER. 1963. Species limits in the woodpecker genus *Centurus* (Aves). Bull. Amer. Mus. Nat. Hist., **124**: 217–273.

SNOW, D. W. 1954a. Trends in geographical variation in Palaearctic members of the genus *Parus*. Evolution, **8**: 19–28.

——. 1954b. The habitats of Eurasian tits (*Parus* spp.). Ibis, **96**: 565–585.

STEVEN, D. M. 1953. Recent evolution in the genus *Clethrionomys*. Symp. Soc. Exp. Biol., **7**: 310–319.

SVÄRDSON, G. 1949. Competition and habitat selection in birds. Oikos, **1**: 156–174.

TOMPA, F. S. 1964. Limitation of numbers in a population of song sparrows (*Melospiza melodia*) on Mandarte Island, B.C., Canada. Acta Zool. Fennica, **109**: 4–73.

VAURIE, C. 1951. Adaptive differences between two sympatric species of Nuthatches (*Sitta*). Proc. 10th Internat. Ornith. Congr., pp. 163–166.

VOOUS, K. H. 1957. Studies on the Fauna of Curaçao and other Caribbean islands (P. W. Hummelink, ed.) VII. The birds of Aruba, Curaçao and Bonaire.

WALLACE, A. R. 1881. Island life. Macmillan, London.

WATSON, G. E. 1962. Three sibling species of *Alectoris* partridge. Ibis, **104**: 353–367.

WILSON, E. O. 1961. The nature of the taxon cycle in the Melanesian ant fauna. Amer. Nat., **95**: 169–193.

ZIMMERMANN, K. 1950. Die Randformen der Mitteleuropaischen Wühlmäuse. *In* A. Jordans and F. Peus (eds.), Syllegomena Biologica Festschrift Kleinschmidt, Leipzig, pp. 454–471.

ZWEIFEL, R. G. 1960. Results of the Puritan-American Museum of Natural History expedition to western Mexico. 9. Herpetology of the Tres Marías Islands. Bull. Amer. Mus. Nat. Hist., **119**: 81–128.

Coordinated singing by black-crested titmice

ROBERT E. LEMON

Department of Zoology, McGill University, Montreal, Quebec

Received April 10, 1968

Tape recordings made in Texas reveal that neighboring black-crested titmice, *Parus atricristatus*, share a repertoire of several song types. When singing together, neighbors frequently sing the same song type, and, similarly, individuals often replied with the pattern played to them from a tape recorder. Thus the manner of singing of this species is similar to that of some other tits and certain richmondenine finches which often match patterns when singing.

Canadian Journal of Zoology, 46, 1163 (1968)

Introduction

Vocal communication in birds frequently involves the synchronization of patterned sounds by two or more individuals (Armstrong 1947, 1963). Frequently the most precise synchronizations are those between mated pairs, such as in African shrikes, Laniarius (Grimes 1964; Thorpe and North 1965; Thorpe 1967), the orange-chinned parakeet, *Brotogeris jugularis* (Power 1966), North American quail (Odontophorinae) (Stokes and Williams 1968), and a variety of tropical species (Skutch 1940; Diamond and Terborgh 1968). In these groups the birds usually sing antiphonally with a reply by one given precisely after another initiates.

A different manner of coordination occurs in the territorial singing of some richmondenine finches, the cardinal, *Richmondena cardinalis*, (Lemon, in press) and the pyrrhuloxia, *Pyrrhuloxia sinuata*, (Lemon and Herzog, in press), in which the males and the females in the same neighborhood have common dialects of several distinctive patterns and frequently use the same patterns when singing together. A similar phenomenon is shown by the great tit, *Parus major* (Gompertz 1961) and other members of the Paridae, such as the plain titmouse, *Parus inornatus* (K. Dixon, personal communication).

During a recent visit to Texas, the author noted that black-crested titmice, *Parus atricristatus*, which held neighboring territories and presumably were males, often countersang with song patterns which were the same. Since documentation of such vocal interactions is still scarce, this paper presents the evidence of the phenomenon and compares some of the variables of song of this species with those of others showing the same behavior.

Methods

The birds were studied at the Welder Wildlife Refuge near Sinton, Texas, in May 1967. Recordings were made with either of two Uher 4000 tape recorders. The recordings of higher quality (Fig. 1) were made at a speed of 7 1/2 in. per sec with the microphone mounted at the focal point of a 30-in. parabolic reflector; recordings during playback to bird 4 (Fig. 2) were made at 1 7/8 in. per sec without the aid of a reflector. Playback was done at a rate of 13 songs per minute by means of short loops of tape on a Uher recorder connected to a Fanon-Masco 12-watt amplifier and an Atlas HU-12N horn. Playback of a single song type was used to stimulate birds 1, 2 and 3 into singing. Analysis of recordings was by a Kay Electric Sonagraph, model 6061a.

Observations

The Song Patterns

Recordings were obtained from three neighboring birds, presumably males, holding territories in the vicinity of the Welder Refuge headquarters. Two kinds of vocalization were noted, songs and calls. The songs were loud pure whistles (Figs. 1.1 to 1.11), whereas the sounds considered as calls were quieter and frequently showed complex harmonics resulting in wheezy or nonwhistled sounds. Some calls not recorded also included whistles of high frequency as well as buzzy parts. The call shown in Fig. 1.12 was frequently interjected between series of songs.

Eleven distinctive song patterns were recorded from the three birds, of which eight were common to at least two (Fig. 1). Since the bird stimulated longest by playback (bird 1) showed the most patterns (nine), it is probable that the others possessed more patterns which were not recorded.

A striking feature of the songs is the remarkable simplicity of most of the component sounds or syllables, especially syllables 2 to 5 (Fig. 1). Syllables 2 and 3 were so similar that the prime distinction between them appeared to be the interval of silence between successive syllables: for syllable 2 this was approximately 0.13 sec and for syllable 3 it was 0.05 to 0.07 sec. The two syllables also differed in their frequency ranges, approximately 2.3 to 2.6 kHz for syllable 2, and 1.9 to 2.5 kHz for syllable 3. Syllables 10 and 11 of bird 2 were quite similar to syllable 6 of the other two and may represent individual variations. Syllables 7, 8, and 9 were notable for their rapid and frequent changes in direction of slurring. The most complex syllable, number 1, consisted of two distinct whistles of higher and lower frequencies, separated by a consonant-like sound of broad frequency range.

By comparison the great tit in England has fewer patterns per bird, normally 5 to a maximum of 7, according to Gompertz (1961), but the syllables generally consist of at least two or more parts; however, each song still consists of repetitions of a single type of syllable. Cardinals at the Welder Refuge usually have about 10 songs per bird and pyrrhuloxias about 14 songs (Lemon and Herzog, in press). Generally, the cardinals' songs consist of two distinct types of syllables whereas the pyrrhuloxias more frequently use a single syllable, as do the titmice.

The songs were given in a series or bouts of repetitions, the durations of which were measured from the time of the first utterance of a particular pattern to the first of the next pattern used. The 11 recorded bouts of bird 1 had a mean duration of 11.9 min, ranging from 3 to 38 min, which is roughly comparable to those from cardinals in the same area, although both are longer than those frequently sung by pyrrhuloxias. The bouts of song were frequently interrupted by calling, as noted above, but these interruptions were ignored in the definition of the bouts just given.

The rate of singing of bird 4 (described below) reached a maximum of 15 to 17 songs per minute, roughly twice the maximum recorded for cardinals and pyrrhuloxias in the same area.

The Matching of Song Patterns

During natural singing and during the recording of songs from birds 1, 2, and 3, the birds were heard to match patterns between themselves or with recorded songs from the speaker. Since some of the patterns were similar to the human ear, and since the matching might occur by chance, a series of five patterns was played to bird 4, an individual not previously exposed to playback, in the expectancy that he would match most of the patterns played to him. With reference to Fig. 1, the series of patterns played was as follows, with the duration of bouts in minutes shown in parentheses: 3 (5), 9 (7), 8 (1/4), 4 (6 1/2), 8 (5 1/2), 2 (5).

Bird 4 matched the first two and the last two presentations; in the middle two presentations the bird did not sing, although it gave calls in the second of these. The brief duration of the third presentation, caused by mechanical difficulties with the tape recorder, probably was too short to permit a proper response. The proofs that the patterns of the bird matched those from the tape recorder are shown in Fig. 2 where the recorded sounds are shown first, followed by the response of the titmouse. The two series of sounds were readily distinguished on the recording for the songs from the speaker were given at a more regular rate and higher volume than those from the titmouse.

The time from the onset of the tape recording to the correct reply by the titmouse varied, approximately 1/2 minute with the first recording to 2 1/2 minutes to the last recorded song during which the bird continued to sing the previous pattern. The timing of the individual songs of bird 4 with those of the speaker were usually unsynchronized, for although sometimes he sang during the intervals of silence between the songs of the tape recorder, frequently his songs overlapped in time with those of the recorder.

An interesting sidelight of the playback was the continued singing of a mockingbird, *Mimus polyglottos*, throughout most of the period. At times this bird matched patterns played from the speaker as Fig. 2E shows. The mockingbird did not match the patterns for very long, however, but instead continued its normal output from a very large repertoire.

Discussion

Vocal coordination ranges from the precisely synchronized singing of mated birds to the more leisurely interactions of counter singing by territorial males. The evidence to date suggests that the most precise synchronizations occur more often among tropical birds, perhaps because the birds there remain paired and with territorial interests for longer periods than do birds in the temperate zones where most are migratory. In spite of this contention, Diamond and Terborgh (1968) estimate that only 3% of the birds of New Guinea exhibit such coordination, or "dual singing", as they call it. In general, however, this estimate may be rather low, especially if one broadens the definitions and recognizes the great range of such interactions.

The precise coordinations by male and female are usually interpreted as a means of keeping the pair in contact, thereby maintaining the pair bond, especially where visual contact may be difficult (Skutch 1940; Thorpe and North 1965). That contact is important has been shown by Thorpe (1967), who cites an example of a bou-bou shrike, which, in the presence of its mate, was never heard to utter the full duet of the pair, but when the mate died the bird sang the complete duet. Also, Stokes and Williams (1968) have shown that antiphonal calling in North American quail is readily induced in captives by separating members of a pair. Vocal contact in quail may also have a sexual connotation as well for the same authors have observed unmated males calling antiphonally with females separated from their mates, the unmated males in this context using sexual calls rather than the more

usual contact calls. In contrast, antiphonal calling in mated pairs of the orange-chinned parakeet seems unrelated to contact for it occurs when the two are close together and are performing aggressive displays toward other parakeets (Power 1966).

Whether coordinated singing occurs in mated pairs of black-crested titmice I do not know, but if females do sing, as do female great tits, it is probable that some coordination occurs. Certainly in cardinals, the females frequently match the patterns sung by their mates (Lemon, in press), thereby enhancing the advertisement of the male. At times matching has been noted while the female sat on the nest and replied to the male, suggesting that matching functions as a means of contact.

In spite of the actual or possible coordination of singing by mates, the emphasis of song in tits and cardinals is territorial advertisement by the males. No doubt song serves to attract unmated females to potential mates, especially early in the season, but primarily it seems to be related to the territorial stability. At least in the cardinal (Lemon 1965), the plain titmouse (Dixon 1956), and the great tit (Kluyver 1951), individuals have longer tenures of territory both during the breeding season and from one season to another than do migratory birds living in the same area, and, as a result, the configurations of the territories are remarkably constant from year to year. It appears then that song is employed throughout the breeding season in stabilizing the territorial behavior of the males, for the matching of patterns may be especially effective in monitoring the positions of neighbors. Also, there is some evidence from cardinals that the amount of matching may vary with the circumstances (Lemon, in press): high scores of matching were obtained experimentally in circumstances where higher intensities of interaction might be expected.

It should be mentioned that other birds broadly satisfy the ecological conditions just mentioned, and yet the organization of song may be very different. For example, the Carolina chickadee, *Parus carolinensis*, a close relative of the black-crested titmouse, is a permanent resident with a similar life history (Dixon 1963), yet it has few song patterns per bird, possibly as many as four, and does not match often when using its repertoire (Ward 1966).

A major similarity of the coordinated singing of tits and cardinals is the leisurely way in which it is accomplished, lacking the remarkable temporal precision frequently shown in song duets of mated birds cited above. Precision by a pair may be accomplished readily if the patterns of the two birds are different, as in the orange-chinned parakeet and especially if the patterns are unique to the pair itself, as in the bou-bou shrikes. On the other hand when communications are between several birds, as in the black-crested titmouse and cardinals, it is obviously more efficient to have several patterns common to all.

It is as yet difficult to appreciate the importance of all the variables of song, although some may be considered. For example, what is the importance of the number of song patterns; why do cardinals use more complex patterns than do titmice? The number of patterns reflects the amount of uncertainty that a sequence of songs may exhibit, and hence should relate to the degree of coordination obtainable by the singers. One might argue that under circumstances of higher density there should be a need for more song types, but evidence from cardinals in Texas and Ontario showed no more patterns in the former place than in the latter, even though the concentrations of cardinals in Texas were frequently greater (Lemon and Herzog, in press). The question of complexity of the patterns of sound must relate to the need for specific identification and the importance of redundancies. In cardinals the redundancies include complex syllables and combinations in the songs of two or more different kinds of syllables; in black-crested titmice where the syllables are much simpler in structure, the song patterns are sung at a higher rate.

Since the emphasis in some birds is on the local use of common song patterns, there arises the question of the importance of conformity of song for social and reproductive success. Or, does the possession of one or several song patterns which differ from the local norm interfere with normal social interactions? The question is essentially one of perception. There is evidence that in man perception of speech patterns is determined by a comparison of the auditory stimulus and the vocal motor patterns (Lane 1965); in other words we can perceive those speech sounds which we have learned to reproduce. Relating this idea to birds, it may be suggested that they can perceive as their specific patterns only those sounds which they have developed in their own vocabularies. There is evidence that such is the case in some birds. Species which exhibit local dialects usually do so as the result of learning, as in the chaffinch, *Fringilla coelebs* (Thorpe 1958) and the cardinal (Lemon and Scott 1966; Dittus and Lemon, unpublished), and in the two species cited there appears to be a connection between the patterns learned and those which elicit response: wild cardinals respond more to recorded songs of their own dialects than to those of other dialects (Lemon 1967), and the songs of chaffinches are reinforcing to chaffinches which have been previously exposed to such song, but not to chaffinches reared in acoustic isolation (Stevenson 1967; from Thorpe 1967).

Yet there seems no reason why birds should not learn to associate certain sounds with certain individuals, even though they may be unable to reproduce the sounds these individuals sing. It should be pointed out that in chaffinches and cardinals the ability to learn new patterns terminates during the first months of the bird's life, say up to 8 to 11 months. If the perception of individual traits does occur without the ability to reproduce them, then perception would appear to be independent of the motor centers for song production.

Also, the problem of perception of sound in birds must not be generalized from studies of those with dialects, for frequently some species show so much individual variation of sounds that there is little in common between different birds. In such cases it appears that specific recognition is achieved through syntax, as Brémond (1967, 1968) has indicated occurs in the European robin,

PLATE I

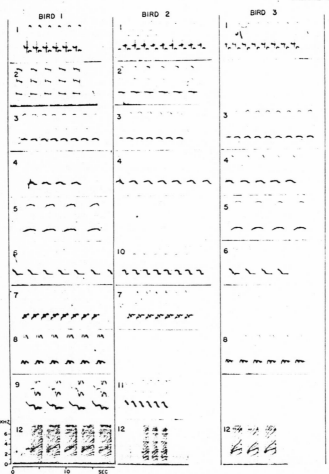

FIG. 1. Sonagrams of song patterns by three neighboring male black-crested titmice, Welder Wildlife Foundation, Sinton, Texas. Similar patterns are so numbered. Note that most patterns are common to at least two birds.

PLATE II

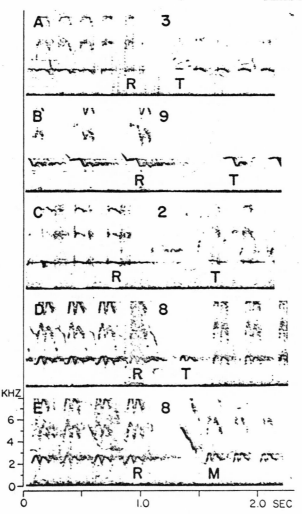

FIG. 2. The replies of titmouse 4 (A to D) and by a mockingbird (E) to recordings of titmouse songs, illustrating the matching of the recorded pattern by the bird. The numbers refer to the song patterns as in Fig. 1; *R* represents the last syllable of the utterance of recorded song and *T* or *M* represents the first syllable of the reply by the bird.

181

Erithacus rubecula, and the wren, *Troglodytes troglodytes.*

Acknowledgments

The author expresses his gratitude to the directors of the Welder Wildlife Foundation, Sinton, Texas, who acted as hosts in the spring of 1967 when this study was conducted. Dr. D. B. McMillan and Mr. Andrew Herzog assisted in the recording of data and the latter also in its analysis. Dr. Wallace Lambert has kindly discussed the problems of bird song. The National Research Council of Canada supported the work financially.

ARMSTRONG, E. A. 1947. Bird display and behaviour. Lindsay Drummond, London.
——— 1963. A study of bird song. Oxford Univ. Press, London.
BRÉMOND, JEAN-CLAUDE. 1967. Reconnaissance de schémas réactogènes liés à l'information contenue dans le chant territorial du rouge-gorge (*Erithacus rubecula*). Proc. XIV Internat. Ornithol. Congr. pp. 217–229.
——— 1968. Valeur spécifique de la syntaxe dans le signal de défense territoriale du troglodyte (*Troglodytes troglodytes*). Behaviour, 30: 66–75.
DIAMOND, J. M. and TERBORGH, J. W. 1968. Dual singing by New Guinea birds. Auk, 85: 62–82.
DIXON, K. L. 1956. Territoriality and survival of the plain titmouse. Condor, 58: 169–182.
——— 1963. Some aspects of social organization in the Carolina chickadee. Proc. XIII Internat. Ornithol. Congr. pp. 240–258.
GOMPERTZ, T. 1961. The vocabulary of the great tit. Brit. Birds, 54: 369–394, 409–422.

GRIMES, L. 1964. Antiphonal singing in *Laniarius barbarus barbarus* and the auditory reaction time. Ibis, 107: 101–104.
KLUYVER, H. N. 1951. The population ecology of the great tit, *Parus m. major* L. Ardea, 39: 1–135.
LANE, HARLAN. 1965. The motor theory of speech perception: a critical review. Psychol. Rev. 72: 275–309.
LEMON, R. E. 1965. The song repertoires of cardinals (*Richmondena cardinalis*) at London, Ontario. Can. J. Zool. 43: 559–569.
——— 1967. The response of cardinals to songs of different dialects. Animal Behav. 15: 538–545.
——— 1968. The relation between the organization and function of song in cardinals. Behaviour, in press.
LEMON, R. E. and HERZOG, A. 1968. The vocal behavior of cardinals and pyrrhuloxias in Texas. Condor, in press.
LEMON, R. E. and SCOTT, D. M. 1966. On the development of song in young cardinals. Can. J. Zool. 44: 191–197.
POWER, D. M. 1966. Antiphonal dueting and evidence for auditory reaction time in the Orange-chinned Parakeet. Auk, 83: 314–319.
SKUTCH, A. F. 1940. Social and sleeping habits of Central American Wrens. Auk, 62: 489–517.
STEVENSON, JOAN G. 1967. Reinforcing effects of chaffinch song. Animal Behav. 15: 427–432.
STOKES, A. W. and WILLIAMS, H. W. 1968. Antiphonal calling in quail. Auk, 85: 83–89.
THORPE, W. H. 1958. The learning of song patterns in birds, with special reference to the song of the Chaffinch. Ibis, 100: 535–570.
——— 1967. Vocal imitation and antiphonal song and its implications. Proc. XIV Internat. Ornithol. Congr. 245–263.
THORPE, W. H. and NORTH, M. E. W. 1965. Origin and significance of the power of vocal imitation: with special reference to the antiphonal singing of birds. Nature, 208: 219–222.
WARD, R. 1966. Regional variation in the song of the Carolina chickadee. Living Bird, 5: 127–150.

INTRASPECIFIC COMBAT AND THE EVOLUTION OF THE CAPRINI

WILLIAM M. SCHAFFER[1]

Department of Biology, Princeton University

Received April 30, 1968

Among the animals belonging to the mammalian tribe Caprini (sheep and goats), intraspecific conflict between males often takes the form of violent head-to-head butting. This paper correlates differences in fighting behavior among the various genera with the relative development of the neck muscles in each. Fighting style and horn shape are analyzed with reference to the production of torques about the occiput which, if unopposed, would cause violent and injurious rotation of the head. Areas of muscle insertion on the skull were used as the major indicators of muscle size, but dissections were also performed. Further studies of both musculature and behavior are desirable to clarify details which remain obscure.

The tribe Caprini is composed of five genera: *Hemitragus*, tahr; *Capra*, goats, ibexes; *Ammotragus*, Barbary "sheep"; *Pseudois*, blue "sheep"; and *Ovis*, true sheep—mouflons, argalis, and bighorn. All of these animals possess large, massive horns which are used to deal and receive blows of considerable force. In contrast, their ancestors are believed to have resembled the living Rupicaprini (Pilgrim, 1939; 1947), light-limbed creatures with small horns, quite aptly referred to as "goat-antelope (McCann, 1956)." Rupicaprini are not adapted to withstand, nor do they engage in, the furious head-on collisions of male caprines. Instead, horn-locking and head-to-head pushing occur, along with some body-butting (Couturier, 1938; Geist, 1964; 1966*b*). Such behavior is considered to be ancestral to the patterns observed in the Caprini (Geist, 1966*b*). Evolution in the latter group has thus involved alteration of both behavior and morphology, and

---

[1] NSF Pre-doctoral Fellow in Biology.

it is to the details of that evolution that we now turn.

MATERIALS AND METHODS

Sixty skulls were examined and measurements made with a calipers and tape. Specimens were obtained from the American Museum of Natural History, the Yale Peabody Museum, and the Museum of Comparative Zoology (Harvard). Areas of insertion were determined by dividing the surfaces into plane figures amenable to mensuration. In addition, the neck muscles of a domestic sheep (*Ovis aries*, Dorset stock) and a domestic goat (*Capra hircus hircus*) were dissected out and weighed. Both animals were young, uncastrated males whose upper third molars had nearly completed eruption. The specimens were perfused with formalin shortly after death and then preserved in a mixture of ethanol and water. Muscles and skulls were weighed on a postal balance, skull weights determined without the mandibles, but with the horn sheaths. Relative magnitudes of impact force (F_i) were estimated for each genus as indicated in the section on behavior. Relative values of dorso-ventral torques (torques promoting upward rotation of the skull in the sagittal plane) were calculated by multiplying the estimated force of impact times the appropriate lever arm (x). Measurement of the lever arms is discussed in the section on torques.

FIGHTING BEHAVIOR AND FORCE OF IMPACT

The force of impact has not been successfully measured in any caprine, hence the necessity of using estimates of *relative* force. In three genera—*Capra*, *Ammotragus*, and *Ovis*—sufficient behavioral data

TABLE 1. *Estimation of relative forces of impact from mass of the combatants and estimated closing velocity. See equation 2.*

Species	Mass (m) (kg)	Closing velocity (v) (m/sec)	mv (m kg/sec)	Relative force (F_i)
Capra hircus aegagrus	80	9.1	728	0.16
C. ibex sibirica	100	13.4	1340	0.29
Ammotragus lervia	85	22.1	1879	0.40
Ovis musimon .	70	18.0	1260	0.27
O. canadensis canadensis	115	26.9	3094	0.66
O. ammon darvini and *O. a. poli*	175	26.9	4708	1.00

are available to make such estimates. The most primitive fighting style occurs in *Capra*. Typically, both combatants stand on their hind legs, take two or three steps forward, and then with necks down-arched, bring the horns together with a resounding crash. Often, only the subdominant challenger attacks bipedally (Reed, pers. comm.), while the dominant male simply braces himself and extends the horns in front of and above the vulnerable face and eyes. Walthers (1961 and pers. comm.) stresses that the opponents are not oriented frontally (confirmed by Scott, 1960); rather, they are side by side and butt with a sideways thrust of the head. On impact, the horns are crossed. This type of behavior has been observed in *Capra ibex causica* (Schaffer and Reed, in prep.; Walthers, 1961 and pers. comm.); in *C. ibex ibex* (Couturier, 1962); in *C. ibex sibirica* (Grzimek, 1966); in *C. falconeri* (Walthers, 1961); and in *C. hircus hircus* (Collias, 1956; Haefez and Scott, 1962; Scott, 1960),

and is presumed to occur throughout the genus.

In marked contrast to the pattern of agonistic behavior observed in *Capra* is that characteristic of *Ovis* and *Ammotragus*. These animals, in the words of Geist (1966b) are "true rammers." Both contestants back off a good distance (up to 30 ft in *Ovis canadensis*—Welles and Welles, 1961), charge, and collide at full tilt. The closing velocity is greatest in the large sheep (*Ovis canadensis* and *O. ammon*), and these animals complete the charge on their hind legs (Mills, 1937; Murie, 1944; Walthers, 1961; Welles and Welles, 1961; Walker et al., 1964; Geist, 1966a; 1966b). In the smaller sheep (*Ovis aries*, Scott, 1960; pers. obs.; and *O. musimon*, Geist, 1966b) and in *Ammotragus* (Katz, 1949; Haas, 1959) the combatants remain on all fours and close at a slower rate. Impact in all these forms is directed frontally, the animals' heads being in line with their bodies. In *Ovis*, contact is nearly always

TABLE 2. *Estimation of relative dorso-ventral torques from average lengths of the lever arm x and F_i. See Fig. 1.*

Species	Lever arm (x) 90° (cm)	Lever arm (x) 135° (cm)	$\bar{x}$ (cm)	F_i	$F_i\bar{x}$ (cm)	Relative torque (T_i)
C. h. aegagrus	19.0	16.9	18.0	0.16	2.88	0.52
C. i. sibirica	16.8	20.6	18.7	0.29	5.42	1.00
A. lervia	8.8	8.0	8.4	0.40	3.36	0.63
O. musimon	2.0	2.0	2.0	0.27	0.54	0.10
O. c. canadensis	3.5	3.8	3.7	0.66	2.44	0.45
O. a. darvini and *O. a. poli*	3.1	4.2	3.7	1.00	3.70	0.68

horn-to-horn, whereas in *Ammotragus* interdigitation occurs frequently (Haas, 1959). Barbary sheep also indulge in other seemingly more primitive forms of combat. These include head-to-head pushing, horn-hooking, and wrestling with the neck and horns. Such behavior does not appear to be an important part of the repertoire of true sheep.

Concerning the remaining genera, little is known. Lydekker (1898) states that male *Pseudois* charge each other bipedally, but does not elaborate. This sounds reminiscent of the behavior of the larger sheep, and the exceptionally sturdy construction of the skull in this genus (Schaffer and Reed, in prep.) lends credence to the supposition that the closing velocities are comparable. No information is available concerning the behavior of *Hemitragus*.

From the above descriptions it is possible to estimate relative values of impact force. If the deceleration that occurs during impact is linear,

$$F_i = \frac{m \Delta v}{\Delta t}, \qquad (1)$$

where m is the mass of one of the animals, Δv the change in velocity during impact (equals the closing velocity, since the final velocity is 0), and Δt the time interval during which deceleration occurs. Assuming Δt to be constant for each genus,[2]

$$F_i = k m v, \qquad (2)$$

where k is a constant of proportionality, and v the closing velocity. Estimated closing velocities, masses, and estimated, relative values of impact force are presented in Table 1. Masses were taken from the literature (Anthony, 1928; Ward, 1935; Welles and Welles, 1961; Couturier, 1962; Walker et al., 1964) and must be considered rough estimates (I have used data for mature males, as these are the type of skulls studied). Closing velocities vary

[2] Preliminary attempts to measure the force of impact in *Ovis aries*, though unsuccessful, indicate the time during which deceleration occurs to be of the order of 3.3 msec.

TABLE 3. *Relative magnitudes of the three torques produced by impact and predictions concerning the relative development of the neck muscles.*

Species	Torque/mass[1]			Predicted size of muscles/mass	
	T_s	T_l	T_r	Lateral	Ventral
C. h. aegagrus	+	+	−	+	+
C. i. sibirica	+	+	−	+	+
A. lervia	−	−	+	+	−
O. musimon	−	−	−	−	−
O. c. canadensis	−	−	−	−	−
O. a. darvini and O. a. poli	−	−	−	−	−

[1] "+" indicates that the ratio of torque or muscle size to body mass will be "large"; "−" indicates that it will be "small."

with the size of the animals and also with the nature of the combat. The behavioral differences cited above suggest that the charges of sheep result in closing velocities considerably faster than those resulting from the lunges of goats. For a practical estimation, I have assumed that the closing velocity is twice as great in sheep as in goats of the same weight. Welles and Welles (1961) have observed male bighorn butt and estimate the closing velocity to be between 50 and 70 miles per hour. From high-speed motion pictures, I have estimated the closing velocity of domestic rams (horned Dorsets) to be about 40 miles per hour. One expects a similar figure for *Ovis musimon*. Since *Ammotragus* is slightly larger, but fights in the same manner, its closing velocity has been estimated to be 50 mph.

POINT OF IMPACT AND THE GENERATION OF TORQUES

Photographic evidence (Haas, 1959; Welles and Welles, 1961; Geist, 1966a; 1966b; Grzimek, 1966; and pers. obs.) and observations of damage to the horn sheaths indicate that male caprines hold the head at an angle that ranges from 90° (perpendicular to the ground) to about 135° (tucked under the neck) when butting. The manner in which the head is oriented will determine the point of impact for a

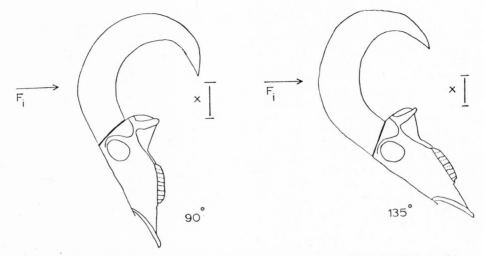

FIG. 1. Determination of the lever arm x for dorso-ventral torques. Caprini hold the head in a position that varies from 90° (left) to 135° (right). In each case the lever arm was measured as illustrated. In computing dorso-ventral torques (T_s), the average of the two values of x was used.

given horn, but the shape of the horn will also be important. Thus, impact occurs closer to the horn base in *Ovis* than in *Capra* because sheep's horns are more tightly coiled than those of goats. The angle at which the horns emerge from the skull also plays a part. The location of the impact site determines the length of the lever arm (x) through which the impact force acts to produce rotation of the skull about the occiput. Note that

$$T = F_i x, \qquad (3)$$

where T is the torque causing rotation. There are three torques that can act on the skull during impact. The first is what I should like to call a "dorso-ventral torque acting in the sagittal plane," because it rotates the skull upward in the sagittal plane. It will be signified by T_s. Values of T_s are presented in Table 2. Figures 1 and 2 illustrate how varying the orientation of the skull and the shape of the horns affects the length of the lever arm. Lever arms were measured for each species studied (Fig. 2; Table 2) for two different orientations of the skull (90° and 135°), and the average

values used for computing relative estimated torques. Note that the habit of rearing up on the hind legs and then lunging downwards in *Capra* will probably cause the actual values of x to be larger than those measured. This is because the direction of the impact force vector will be directed upward from the position shown in Figures 1 and 2. The difference, however, should not be great due to the curved shape of the horns.[3]

The second torque which can act on the skull I should like to term a "lateral torque," since it promotes left–right rotation in the transverse plane. The lack of detailed photographs prevents measurement of the appropriate lever arm, but it can be stated that T_l will be much greater in *Capra* than in *Ammotragus* or *Ovis* because only *Capra* butts with a sideways thrust of the head. A third rotary torque, T_r, shall be called "rotational." It pro-

[3] Changes in orientation of the head and the direction of F_i do not greatly affect the value of the lever arm x since the horn is curved about a point not too far distant from the center of rotation (the occipital condyles).

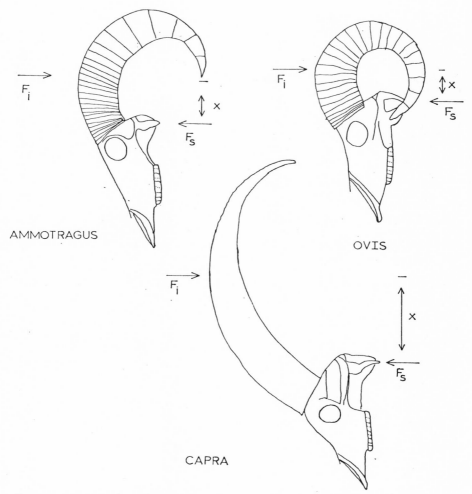

AMMOTRAGUS

OVIS

CAPRA

FIG. 2. Variation of the length of the lever arm x in the three genera discussed. The order is *Capra* > *Ammotragus* > *Ovis*.

duces rotation of the head about the axis of the cervical spine as it joins the skull. Neck wrestling of the sort observed in *Ammotragus* would be presumed to produce large values of T_r. Table 3 summarizes the probable distribution of occurrence of these torques throughout the Caprini. Note that these refer only to the results of normal combat. Bighorn sheep can, for example, misjudge their approaches and impact with

only one horn (Welles and Welles, 1961). The result is the production of large lateral torques which can, and presumably do, cause violent wrenching of the neck and severe injury. Indeed, most authors report the occurrence of one or more injuries, particularly when their observations coincide with the height of the rut. However, injury is the exception, not the rule, and natural selection has operated to prevent

187

TABLE 4. *Areas of muscle insertion in various Caprini. Compare with Table 3.*

Species	N	T.L.A.[1] (cm²)	T.L.A.[2] Mass (cm²/kg)	B.O.A.[3] (cm²)	B.O.A.[4] Mass (cm²/kg)
C. h. aegagrus	3	7.7	0.10	12.6	0.16
C. i. sibirica	9	13.8	0.14	18.7	0.19
A. lervia	7	11.1	0.13	12.3	0.14
O. musimon	4	4.2	0.06	7.0	0.10
O. c. canadensis	6	6.7	0.06	13.0	0.11
O. a. darvini and O. a. poli	11	16.0	0.09	17.2	0.10

[1] Total lateral area of insertion = mastoid process + paramastoid process + temporal crest.
[2] t-test between *Capra* +*Ammotragus* and *Ovis* yields $0.98 < P(t) < 0.99$.
[3] Basioccipital area.
[4] t-test between *Capra* and *Ovis* yields $0.98 < P(t) < 0.99$.

the seemingly violent form of agonistic behavior preferred by this group from seriously damaging the participants (Geist, 1966b; Hutchinson, 1963).

NECK MUSCLES AND THE PREVENTION OF RAPID ROTATION OF THE HEAD

The medical profession has long recognized that rapid rotation of the head can cause severe, and often fatal, damage to the brain independent of fracture to the skull and direct bruising of the cortex (Holbourne, 1945). The brains of Caprini would, like our own, be damaged by the repeated rotations of the skull that would result from butting if the torques discussed above were unopposed. Obviously, the torques are opposed, and we now turn to the evidence that this is accomplished by contraction of the neck muscles inserting on the skull.

If the neck muscles efficiently oppose these torques, one expects the size and strength of the muscles to vary from genus to genus in a manner proportionate to the magnitude of the torques produced by im-

pact in each. Accordingly, those muscles capable of opposing T_s should be larger, relative to body size, in *Capra* than in the other genera, as should those muscles countering T_l. On the other hand, those muscles that would counter T_r should be relatively larger in *Ammotragus*. However, the muscles that would work in opposition to T_l would also oppose T_r. Hence there are only two classes to deal with. The first I shall call "ventral muscles." These insert on the basioccipital bone and oppose T_s. The second I shall call "lateral muscles." These insert on the mastoid process, the paramastoid process, and on the ridge of bone directly above the mastoid process which may be called the temporal crest. Acting singly, the lateral muscles are capable of opposing T_l and T_r. Acting in pairs, they will oppose T_s. In accordance with the preceding analysis of torque production, one would expect the ventral muscles to be relatively larger in *Capra*, and the lateral muscles in *Capra* and *Ammotragus*. These considerations are presented in Table 3.

TABLE 5. *Areas of insertion and muscle mass in a domestic goat (*C. h. hircus*) and a domestic ram (*O. aries*). Compare with Tables 3 and 4.*

Species	Weight skull (kg)	T.L.A. (cm²)	Wt. lateral muscles (g)	B.O.A. (cm²)	Wt. ventral muscles (g)
Capra hircus hircus	1.0	6.5	410	8.5	36
Ovis aries	1.1	3.9	92	6.6	19

Among closely related species, the force exerted by homologous muscles can be taken as being roughly proportional to their areas of insertion. The mass of the muscles will also provide an indication, but it is recognized that force is strictly proportional to cross sectional area. Skulls and preserved specimens, not freshly killed material, were available for this study, and so areas of insertion and muscle mass were the two indices used. Table 4 presents areas of insertion for six species. The areas are compared with body mass, and the results are in good agreement with the predictions summarized in Table 3 (see also Figure 3). The sole exception is the basioccipital area of *Ammotragus* which appears to be larger than it ought. Instead of falling with the sheep, it falls between *Ovis* and *Capra*. This deviation from the theory may be the result of inaccurate estimation of body mass or F_i, or it may be due to the fact that the lever arms are actually longer than measured. This could result from the tilting of the heads that Haas (1959) has reported to occur during most of the more violent encounters. It is instructive to compare the observed areas of insertion with the estimated forces of impact (Fig. 4). The amount of scatter is large, the correlation coefficient being 0.40 for Basioccipital area vs. F_i, and 0.52 for Total lateral area vs. F_i. The areas of insertion do, however, correlate with the estimated torques. Only values of T_s could be estimated due to the lack of lever arms for T_l and T_r. The correlation between Basioccipital area and T_s, however, was high, r being equal to 0.94 (Fig. 5). Analysis by F test indicates this correlation to be significantly different from the others at the 0.05 level.

Table 5 presents the summed weights of ventral and lateral muscles in a domestic sheep and a domestic goat. Again the agreement with the predicted results is striking, the muscles being significantly larger in the goat. It is interesting to note that not only the muscles inserting on the skull, but also those having post-cranial insertions, were larger, indicating that torques

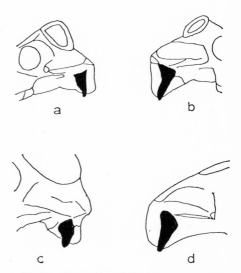

FIG. 3. Comparison of the lateral areas of insertion (shaded) in four species of Caprini. (a) *Ovis musimon*; (b) *Capra hircus aegagrus*; (c) *Ovis canadensis canadensis*; (d) *Capra ibex sibirica*. The areas are larger in the two species of *Capra*. Skulls a and b are about the same size as are c and d.

are probably generated not only about the occiput, but about a series of points extending the entire length of the cervical spine. Such a situation is to be expected since the model in this paper is obviously a simplification of reality.

DISCUSSION

This analysis is preliminary in nature and could stand considerable refinement. Nonetheless, it is sufficient to call attention to the link between anatomy and behavior and to suggest that each is adaptive within the context of the other. Geist (1966*b*) has summarized a good deal of the thinking with regard to the evolution of horns. However, insufficient attention has been devoted to the proposition that anatomy and behavior must have evolved together, and that different behavioral patterns, in order to be adaptive, must be joined with different morphologies. It is not now known why the ancestral caprine

189

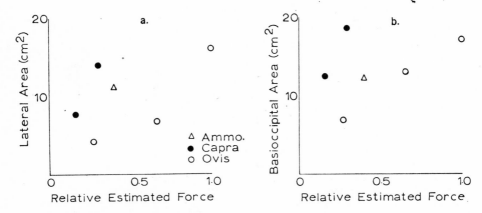

FIG. 4. Comparison of areas of insertion with force of impact (relative and estimated). (a) Lateral area vs. F_i, $r = 0.519$; (b) Basioccipital area vs. F_i, $r = 0.400$. Compare with Fig. 5.

diverged behaviorally and morphologically into the five existing genera. Although one can describe a progression of increasing impact force from *Capra* to the larger sheep, it is not sufficient to state simply that the one is more primitive, the other more advanced. Indeed, in their own way, goats are as divergent from the ancestral condition as sheep are in theirs. The fact that horns are used as display organs (Geist, 1966a; 1966b) should not be ignored. However, it is doubtful that the diversity in horn shape observed in the Caprini is explicable solely on the basis of display. In this paper, I have dealt primarily with the relation between the relative development of the neck musculature and the physical stresses resulting from agonistic behavior. The shape of the horns might similarly be analyzed as might the morphology of the skull. Indeed, there are morphological adaptations common to the entire group which are no doubt linked with the form of intraspecific combat the males have adopted (Reed and Schaffer, 1966; Schaffer and Reed, in prep.). It may well be that mammals do not need to evolve horns in order to bang their heads together in a violent way (Geist, 1966a; 1966b). However, once the decision (phylogenetically speaking) was made to have

horns, these structures had to become adapted to the physical use to which they were put, in this case butting. That this is true seems incontrovertible.

SUMMARY

The agonistic behavior of various sheep and goats (tribe Caprini) was discussed and the resulting physical stresses analyzed. It was proposed that butting would cause violent and injurious rotation of the head if the torques produced by impact were unopposed. It was further suggested that these torques are indeed opposed by contraction of the neck muscles. Since the magnitude of the torques varies from genus to genus, the theory was tested by measuring the relative development of the neck muscles in each. Although the nature of the analysis was rough, striking agreement was found between variation in muscle size and variation in torques.

ACKNOWLEDGMENTS

The author is grateful to the curators of the mammal collections at the American Museum of Natural History, the Yale Peabody Museum, and the Museum of Comparative Zoology (Harvard) for permission to study the specimens utilized in this project. The work largely represents an

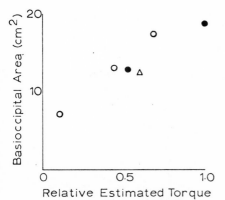

FIG. 5. Comparison of Basioccipital areas of insertion with estimated, relative dorso-ventral torque. $r = 0.942$.

undergraduate research project conducted at Yale University, first under the supervision of Dr. Charles A. Reed and later Dr. Keith S. Thomson. Their advice and suggestions were stimulating and beneficial. The comments of Dr. Henry S. Horn of Princeton University were also extremely helpful. The work was supported by an NSF (Undergraduate Research Participant) grant to the department of biology at Yale University, by a grant from the Sigma Xi, and by an NSF Pre-doctoral fellowship in biology.

LITERATURE CITED

ANTHONY, H. E. 1928. Field book of North American mammals. G. P. Putnam's Sons.

COLIAS, N. E. 1956. The analysis of socialization in sheep and goats. Ecology 37:228–239.

COUTURIER, M. 1938. Le Chamois (*Rupicapra rupicapra*). Private Publ. Grenoble.

——. 1962. Les bouquetins des Alpes. Private Publ. Grenoble.

GEIST, V. 1964. On the butting behavior of the mountain goat (*Oreamnos americanus*). J. Mammal. 45:551–568.

——. 1966a. The evolutionary significance of mountain sheep horns. Evolution 20:558–566.

——. 1966b. The evolution of horn-like organs. Behavior 27:175–214.

GRZIMEK, B. 1966. Wild animal, white man. Translated M. Glenny. Hill and Wang.

HAAS, G. 1959. Untersuchengen über Angeborene Verhaltensweisen bei Mähenspringern (*Ammotragus lervia* Pallas). Z. f. Tierpsychol. 16: 218–242.

HAEFEZ, E. S., AND J. P. SCOTT. 1962. The behavior of sheep and goats. In E. S. Haefez ed., The behavior of domestic animals. Ballier, Tindall Cox.

HOLBOURN, A. H. S. 1945. The mechanics of brain injuries. Brit. Med. Bull. 3:147–149.

HUTCHINSON, G. E. 1963. Natural selection, social organization, hairlessness and the Australopithecine canine. Evolution 17:588–589.

KATZ, I. 1949. Behavioral interactions in a herd of barbary sheep. Zoologica 34:9–18.

LYDEKKER, R. 1898. Wild oxen, sheep and goats of all lands. Rowland Ward.

McCANN, L. J. 1956. Ecology of the mountain sheep. Amer. Midl. Natur. 56:297–323.

MILLS, H. B. 1937. A preliminary study of the bighorn of Yellowstone National Park. J. Mammal. 18:205–212.

MURRIE, A. 1944. The wolves of Mt. McKinley. Fauna of the National Parks of the U.S., Fauna series no. 5.

PILGRIM, G. E. 1939. The fossil Bovidae of India. Palaeont. Ind., (new ser.) 26:1–356.

——. 1947. The evolution of buffaloes, oxen, sheep and goats. J. Linn. Soc. London 41: 272–286.

REED, C. A., AND W. M. SCHAFFER. 1966. Evolutionary implications of the cranial morphology in the sheep and goats (Caprini Simpson, 1945). Amer. Zool. 6:565.

SCHAFFER, W. M., AND C. A. REED. The structure, function, and evolutionary implications of the cranial morphology in the sheep and goats, in prep.

SCOTT, J. P. 1960. Comparative social psychology. In R. Waters et al., ed., Principles of psychology. McGraw Hill.

WALKER, E. P., ET AL. 1964. Mammals of the world, vol. 2. Johns Hopkins Press.

WALTHERS, F. 1961. Einige Verhaltens Beobachtung am Bergwild des Georg. von Opel Freigehege. G. von Opel Freigehege Jahrbuch, 1960/61, p. 53–89.

WARD, R. 1935. Rowland Ward's records of big game. African and Asiatic sections. Rowland Ward Ltd.

WELLES, R. E., AND F. B. WELLES. 1961. The bighorn of Death Valley. Fauna of the National Parks of the U.S., Fauna series no. 6.

RANGE-RELATED DIFFERENCES IN GROWTH OF DEER REFLECTED IN SKELETAL RATIOS

By David R. Klein

ABSTRACT: The skeletal ratio femur/hind foot was employed to identify growth differences existing between two island populations of deer (*Odocoileus hemionus sitkensis*) in southeast Alaska. Skeletal ratios are a more reliable measure of growth differences than measurements of body weight or length because the skeleton can be measured more accurately. Also, the differential growth of skeletal parts reflects physiological age essentially independently of body size; therefore, the skeletal ratio is not as greatly influenced by genetic differences as are measurements of body weight and length. The deer populations on the islands studied show growth differences which are apparently attributable to differing levels in their annual nutrition. The use of the femur/hind foot ratio supports the thesis that these growth differences are of nutritional rather than genetic origin.

Ratios of lengths of long bones were used to identify growth differences existing in deer (*Odocoileus hemionus sitkensis*) from Alaskan ranges of varying quality.

Body weights and measurements have long been the standard criteria for evaluation of growth in animals in the laboratory, among domestic stock and with wild species as well. Brody (1945), Von Bertalanffy (1938) and others have developed growth equations, which utilize such measurements of body "size," based on the assumption that animals grow toward an "ultimate" or "final" body size. Modifications of this concept of growth have been made by Parker and Larkin (1959) to more nearly relate individual growth stanzas in fishes to physiological age rather than chronological age. Wood *et al.* (1962) have shown that in deer a seasonally cyclic growth is imposed on 4 distinct growth stanzas that occur throughout their development. One of the major problems in the use of body measurements to quantify growth has been the possible unknown effects of genetic variation on individual animals or between populations. This is of particular importance in studies with large mammals where it is frequently not possible to secure large samples. Wood *et al.* (1962) found individual variation in growth of captive deer to be so great as to obscure inflections in the growth curve when mean values are obtained from several animals. They have met this problem by plotting the course of growth for individual animals.

Several workers in the field of animal ecology have employed body weights and measurements to reflect size differences in animals resulting from variations in the nutritive quality of their diet (Park and Day, 1942; Severinghaus and Gottlieb, 1959; Taber and Dasmann, 1958 and others). However, in most of such cases large numbers of animals were available for study from the populations under consideration. Individual variation was not an important factor because of the large sample sizes. In the present study large samples were not obtainable and techniques had to be developed to utilize most expeditiously the weights and measurements of the sample specimens.

JOURNAL OF MAMMALOGY, 1964, Vol.45, No.2, pp. 226 235.

This paper reports on a segment of a study conducted during the summers of 1959, 1960 and 1961 on 2 islands of different range quality located within the natural range of the Sitka black-tailed deer in southeast Alaska. The 2 islands, Woronkofski and Coronation, are each approximately 25 square miles in area, are vegetated with a western hemlock–Sitka spruce forest type and with varying amounts of muskeg and alpine areas. Woronkofski Island is located adjacent to the coastal mountains and experiences relatively warm summers and cold winters with heavy snowfall. Coronation Island, in contrast, lies on the western edge of the archipelago adjacent to the Pacific Ocean and has cool summers and mild winters of light snowfall. Average monthly temperatures in degrees Fahrenheit at Wrangell, 3 miles from Woronkofski Island, are 30.0 in January and 57.3 in July, while at Cape Decision, 4 miles from Coronation Island, the average for January is 33.9 and for July, 52.7° F. Monthly snowfall averages for November through March are 12.90 at Wrangell and 3.13 inches at Cape Decision (U. S. Weather Bureau, 1959). Over long periods of time these climatic disparities have had markedly different effects upon the deer populations of the 2 islands. On Woronkofski Island, deer have undoubtedly experienced wide fluctuations in numbers associated with series of relatively mild winters interrupted by severe ones. Heavy winter losses have been frequent and severe enough to prevent excessive overuse of the range. Even during the relatively mild winters, availability of forage is greatly restricted and protected from overuse at elevations above a few hundred feet by the accumulation of deep snows. On Coronation Island, deer populations have not been restricted by winter snow accumulation, and it is likely that a continuing heavy population pressure on the range has resulted in the elimination of important winter and summer forage species.

Conclusions of the comparative study of the two islands are as follows (Klein, 1962): (1) the deer range on Woronkofski Island, on a unit-area basis, has a greater quantity of forage and variety of species than the range on Coronation Island; (2) the forage available throughout the entire growth period of vegetation is of higher quality on Woronkofski than on Coronation Island; (3) rumen content analyses corroborate the observed differences in range quality; (4) the limited data on age structures suggest that the deer population on Woronkofski Island is younger and more productive than the Coronation Island population.

METHODS

Qualitative measurements were made of both the deer and the range on the two islands. Twenty-six deer were collected from Woronkofski and 37 from Coronation Island. Sex, age, weights and measurements were recorded, and rumen content samples were collected from all specimens. The range was evaluated through the use of line intercept transects located in the major cover types and correlated with chemical analyses of major forage species.

The total weights and field-dressed weights (viscera removed) of the deer collected were determined by a spring scale of 50-pound capacity. When necessary, specimens were cut into segments to facilitate weighing. Body and skeletal measurements were taken in millimeters, using a flexible steel tape. The length of the hind foot was taken from the tip of the hoof to the proximal end of the calcaneus. The total length of the femur was determined and the metatarsal was measured from the distal end to the base of the deepest facet on the proximal articulation. When possible, age, sex and femur length were obtained from deer dying of natural causes and these data have been included with other specimen data in the statistical analyses.

In the comparisons of growth rates between islands, weights, femur lengths and femur/hind foot ratios were plotted against age. Age was determined from the degree of tooth development and erosion and was adjusted to correspond to the seasonal growth of deer. This method of aging deer, while with obvious limitations in the older age categories, was considered accurate through the 4-year category where comparisons could be made with large numbers of specimens from hunter-killed deer. On the basis of observations of wild Alaska deer and those raised in captivity (Cowan, in corresp. 1962), a 5-month period of active growth of the skeleton and total body mass was assumed to approximate Alaskan conditions. This period of most active growth takes place during 15 May through 15 October. During the remainder of the year a state of physiological dormancy exists in which growth is greatly restricted; for the purpose of data comparisons the amount of growth from 15 October to 15 May was considered to be equal to the average growth during one month of the summer period.

In the statistical comparisons of sample means of weights, measurements and ratios from the 2 islands, variances are pooled in the calculation of standard errors of the means as described by Steel and Torrie (1960).

RESULTS AND DISCUSSION

Weight, the standard criterion for measuring growth, was tested as a basis for comparison of the 2 populations of deer being studied. Standard statistical techniques were employed to compare means of body weights for the various age-groups. Table 1 lists these comparisons made on male deer. It is apparent that significant differences exist between the means for all age-groups with the exception of the one-year-old animals. This would be expected in animals of genetically similar populations which are subjected to differing nutrient regimens throughout their lives. Growth differences become more pronounced as the animals grow older. Fig. 1a portrays the differential growth rates existing within male deer of the 2 islands which are reflected in body weight. The diverging slopes of the growth regressions suggest that animals from both islands are of equal body weight at or slightly before parturition. It is quite apparent from these data that male deer on both islands continue to grow in body weight through their fourth year.

TABLE 1.—*Comparison of weights and measurements of male deer from Woronkofski and Coronation islands, Alaska*

Measurement	Age (yr)	Island	Sample size	Mean	Standard error	t	Level of significance
Weight (lb)	1	W	5	62.4	3.112	1.33	n.s.[1]
		C	4	53.5			
	2	W	4	98.5	3.855	2.52	0.05
		C	5	79.6			
	3	W	3	115.7	2.431	3.52	0.05
		C	3	88.3			
	4+	W	5	143.4	5.253	3.75	0.005
		C	6	104.7			
Femur (cm)	1	W	5	20.68	0.2884	2.60	0.05
		C	2	18.90			
	2	W	4	24.05	0.2101	4.85	0.005
		C	5	22.14			
	3	W	4	25.58	0.2953	4.67	0.005
		C	5	23.02			
	4+	W	7	25.12	0.1057	6.78	0.001
		C	21	23.34			
Hind foot (cm)	1	W	5	39.12	0.4197	1.47	n.s.
		C	4	37.80			
	2	W	4	43.00	0.3700	2.55	0.05
		C	5	41.10			
	3	W	3	44.00	0.3261	1.84	n.s.
		C	3	42.83			
	4+	W	5	43.72	0.2349	4.52	0.005
		C	6	41.60			
Ratio of femur/hind foot	1	W	5	0.5286	0.01126	1.82	n.s.
		C	2	0.5165			
	2	W	4	0.5595	0.00830	3.20	0.05
		C	5	0.5364			
	3	W	3	0.5820	0.00897	5.15	0.01
		C	3	0.5487			
	4+	W	5	0.5778	0.00752	0.97	n.s.
		C	4	0.5713			

[1] Not significant at the 0.05 level.

Female deer, presumably because of slower growth and less total growth in mass than male deer, failed to show from one island to the other as clear a separation within age-classes as the male deer. Only by grouping female deer 3 years old and older was it possible to show a significant difference between the weights of the female deer from the 2 islands (Table 2).

195

Studies with captive deer (Cowan and Wood, *viva voce*, 1960) have demonstrated that male deer may continue to grow in weight for 4 years or longer, whereas female deer attain essentially all of their mature body weight during their first 2 years of life. In addition, growth rates of male deer must be more rapid than those of females to account for the difference in size of sexes in the one- and 2-year age categories (Klein, 1959).

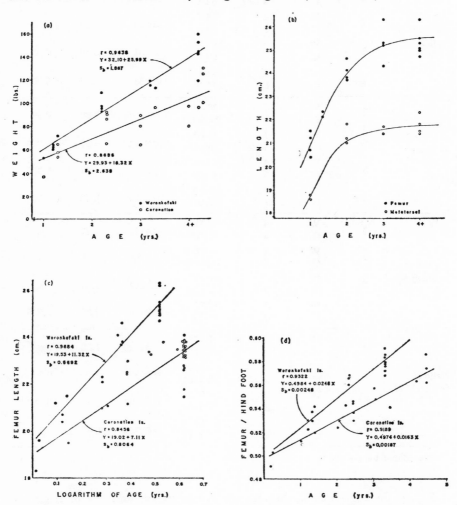

Fig. 1—Relationship of body weight and length of the bones of the hind leg to age in male deer. (a) Growth rates reflected in weight regressions. (b) Relationship of growth of the femur to that of the metatarsal bone in Woronkofski Island deer (curves fitted by eye). (c) Growth rates reflected in femur length regressions. (d) Growth rates reflected in regressions of femur/hind foot ratios.

TABLE 2.—*Comparison of weights and measurements of female deer from Woronkofski and Coronation islands, Alaska*

Measurement	Age (yr)	Island	Sample size	Mean	Standard error	t	Level of significance
Weight (lb)	3+	W	5	98.4	2.6618	2.34	0.05
		C	12	78.2			
Femur (cm)	2+	W	8	22.89	0.1381	3.69	0.005
		C	12	21.75			
Hind foot (cm)	2+	W	9	41.03	0.2066	4.02	0.001
		C	12	39.30			
Ratio of femur/hind foot	2+	W	7	0.5573	0.00275	1.40	n.s.[1]
		C	9	0.5493			

[1] Not significant at the 0.05 level.

Growth studies made by McKeekan (1940), Wallace (1948), Palsson and Verges (1952) and others, utilizing diets producing low and high planes of nutrition and repletion techniques, have clearly demonstrated the significance of physiological and chronological time in animal growth rates. These studies have shown that while a low plane of nutrition slows the growth rate and delays aging of the tissues, it may allow for the greater development of the digestive tract and other organ systems. Consequently, a poorly fed animal may actually have a greater potential for growth than an animal raised on a high plane of nutrition but of the same chronological age. The importance of this growth phenomenon in wild ungulates and its effect on their ultimate body size is difficult to determine. One possibility is that this would be a compensating factor allowing animals on poor quality range to continue to grow for a longer period, although at a slower rate, than comparable animals on higher quality range. Two factors, however, tend to prevent this "equilazation" of growth from being realized. First, growth hormones, primarily those associated with sexual maturation, control growth and can subvert the growth processes to assure reproductive success (Silberberg and Silberberg, 1949; Taber and Dasmann, 1958). Both somatotrophic and thyrotrophic hormones are associated with the limitation of skeletal growth with sexual maturity, thus possibly counteracting genetic growth potential (McLean and Urist, 1961). This is of greater consequence in female deer than in males because of the former's earlier and complete assumption of the reproductive burden in contrast to the males' slower reproductive development and more gradual involvement in breeding activity (Cheatum and Morton, 1946). Secondly, a continual, low quality diet may exist in the wild in which elements essential for more than minimal growth may be lacking. Deer on such a diet, while capable of surviving and possibly reproducing, could not fulfill their genotypic growth potential.

197

Skeletal measurements appear to be more reliable indicators of growth in wild ungulates than body weight. This is true partly because skeletal measurements can be taken more accurately and are not subject to variations due to degree of fullness of the digestive tract or loss of body fluids (Tables 1 and 2). Also the extreme fluctuations in body weight associated with accumulation of fat reserves in summer and fall and their catabolism during winter, and the weight loss in males associated with rutting activities, tend to mask sequence of growth. Cowan (*viva voce*, 1960) has found that male black-tailed deer in captivity stop eating and can lose up to 40% of their body weight during the rutting period. Correspondingly, wild female deer may lose 35% of their body weight during severe winters in Alaska. The skeleton does not undergo negative growth during periods of physiological stress as is the case for fat and muscle tissues and consequently serves as a more reliable indicator of growth in deer and other wild ungulates. Admittedly, among domestic ungulates the skeleton has been shown to have a higher priority for growth than muscle or fat tissue and is therefore less affected by nutritional deficiencies in the diet than total body mass (Hammon, 1944). However, under wild conditions a more complex relationship apparently exists between seasonal variations in the quality of the diet and priorities for growth of the various body tissues. The winter condition of growth cessation in deer in northern regions apparently extends to skeletal tissue. Therefore, in the spring when growth of body tissues is reinitiated, apparently through photo-stimulation (French *et al.*, 1960), and high-quality forage is often in short supply, skeletal growth may be inhibited along with the growth of muscle and fat tissues. In addition, growth of the long bones may be limited by closure of the epiphysial cartilages before the genetic growth potential of the skeleton has been realized.

Not only are the effects of growth inhibition on the skeleton reflected in reduced growth of the entire skeleton, but the growth of individual bones is affected differently. A sequence of growth priority is exhibited in the growth of the skeletal components just as variations in growth priorities exist between the various body tissues. This has been demonstrated in feeding experiments with domestic stock by McMeekan (1940) and others. Further-more, at birth there is considerable variation in the relative proportion of growth remaining to be made by the bones of the skeleton. McMeekan found that a positive correlation exists between the relative proportion of growth made by a bone prior to birth and its priority for growth after birth. For example, the skull, which has completed approximately 40% of its growth at birth, has an extremely high priority for growth immediately after birth, but the growth accomplished after birth is, of course, correspondingly less than that obtained by the pelvis or the late-maturing long bones. From Palsson and Verges' (1952) work with growth in lambs it is possible to list the approximate sequence of priority of growth of the major bones of the skeleton after birth as follows: skull, forefeet, hind feet, metacarpals, metatarsals, cervical and thoracic vertebrae, radius–ulna, humerus, tibia–fibula, caudal vertebrae, scapula, lumbar vertebrae, sacral vertebrae, femur, pelvis and ribs. It is apparent from this listing that a sequence of growth takes place from the extremeties (the head, feet and tail) toward the central portion of the body in the pelvis region. The lumbar and sacral vertebrae, proximal portions of the limbs, scapula and pelvis are late developing in contrast to the skull, lower legs and tail. The forelegs develop before the hind legs. In view of this knowledge the femur is perhaps the most suitable bone of the skeleton to use as a measure of relative growth accomplished after birth. In contrast, the metatarsals (cannon bones), which have accomplished a much larger proportion of their growth at birth, offer a suitable basis for comparison. This differential growth of the femur and metatarsal bones is demonstrated in Fig. 1b. In practice, however, hind foot length has been found to be simpler to obtain in the field than metatarsal length, and it shows less sample variation; it encompasses all of the skeleton of the lower leg, including the metatarsal bone. Therefore, hind foot length was used in preference to metatarsal length during the study.

Skeletal measurements appear to be useful criteria for comparisons between populations of deer or other animals. Variations in size of animals in different populations may be of genetic origin or a product of their nutrition. The deer populations on Woronkofski and Coronation islands are assumed to be genetically similar because there is a general exchange of deer between islands in this region of the Alexander Archipelago. If these deer are indeed genetically similar, than differences in length of the long bones between islands among deer of comparable age are attributable to nutritional factors. Data in Table 1 show the complete separation of the Woronkofski and Coronation Island male deer in all age-classes on the basis of femur length. This is in contrast to hind foot length which did not reflect as great a difference between the island deer; this is understandable in view of the above discussion of differential skeletal growth.

As in the case of the weight comparisons, the female sample, which was small, had to be grouped to include all age-classes of 2 years or older to yield significant differences between islands on the basis of femur and hind foot lengths (Table 2).

Fig. 1c shows the differential growth in femur lengths of male deer from Woronkofski and Coronation islands. In the Woronkofski deer the femur ceased to show measurable growth in length after the third year, thus all of the femur lengths from deer over 3 years of age have been included with the 3-year-old deer to obtain a straight-line relationship. In the case of the Coronation deer the femur ceased to grow in length after the fourth year, and a similar procedure was followed to enable comparisons of the growth regressions for the 2 islands.

On the basis of the phenomenon of differential growth priorities of skeletal parts discussed above, the ratio of femur length to hind foot length reflects the relative proportion of growth accomplished after birth and serves as a basis for relating physiological to chronological age. The value of this ratio lies in its usefulness in differentiating growth responses due to nutritional factors from size differences due to genetic factors. It should be emphasized here that direct comparisons are not being made between the physical dimensions of the deer; on the contrary, a series of femur/hind foot ratios, when plotted against chronological age, is merely an index to the rate and degree of fulfillment of genetic growth potential.

The femur to hind foot ratios, while not showing as high levels of significance in the differences between means (Tables 1 and 2), are less affected by genetic factors which may govern body size and are therefore more reliable for reflecting nutritional effects. Correspondingly, skeletal ratios used in conjunction with body or linear measurements should be effective in isolating genetic effects. In Fig. 1d rates of completion of skeletal growth among male deer from the two islands are compared. Again, a much more rapid growth of the skeleton is evident among the Woronkofski deer.

Among female deer the femur to hind foot ratio did not show a clear difference between islands, perhaps because of small sample size as well as the reduced rate and magnitude of growth of females.

CONCLUSIONS

The use of skeletal ratios to measure growth differences in mammals where nutritional regimens may vary is a technique suitable for use in field ecology. The femur/hind foot ratio appears to be a more reliable measure of growth than body weight or linear measurements and is less subject to genetic influence. This ratio is also adaptable to conditions where only small samples are obtainable.

The deer populations on the study islands showed growth differences attributable to differing levels in their annual nutritional regimens. The use of the femur/hind foot ratio supports the thesis that these growth differences are of nutritional rather than genetic origin.

ACKNOWLEDGMENTS

The investigation was financed through Federal Aid in Wildlife Restoration funds, Projects W-3-R and W-6-R, U. S. Fish and Wildlife Service and Alaska Department of Fish and Game, and is a segment of research toward the Ph.D. degree at the University of British Columbia. The author appreciates the technical advice of Drs. I. McT. Cowan and A. J. Wood of the University of British Columbia and Mr. D. B. Siniff, biometrician with the Alaska Department of Fish and Game. Drs. R. B. Weeden and C. F. Herreid kindly consented to read and criticize the manuscript.

LITERATURE CITED

BRODY, S. 1945. Bioenergetics and growth. Reinhold Publishing Co., New York. 1023 pp.

CHEATUM, E. L. AND G. H. MORTON. 1946. Breeding season of white-tailed deer in New York. J. Wildl. Mgmt., 10: 249–263.

FRENCH, C. E., L. C. McEWEN, N. D. MAGRUDER, T. RADER, T. A. LONG AND R. W. SWIFT. 1960. Responses of white-tailed bucks to added artificial light. J. Mamm., 41: 23–29.

HAMMON, J. 1944. Physiological factors affecting birth weight. Proc. Nutrition Soc., 2: 8–14.

KLEIN, D. R. 1959. Sitka black-tailed deer studies. U. S. Fish & Wildlife Serv. Unpubl. P–R report, Alaska W-3-R. 37 pp.

————. 1962. Rumen contents analysis as an index to range quality. Trans. N. Am. Wildl. Conf., 27: 150–164.

McLEAN, F. C. AND M. R. URIST. 1961. Bone. Univ. Chicago Press. 261 pp.

McMEEHAN, C. P. 1940. Growth and development in the pig, with special reference to carcass quality characters: Part II—the influence of the plane nutrition on growth and development. J. Agr. Sci., 42: 1–92, 93–149.

PALSSON, H. AND J. B. VERGES. 1952. Effects of the plane of nutrition on growth and the development of carcass quality in lambs: Part I—the effects of high and low planes of nutrition at difference ages. J. Agr. Sci., 42: 1–92.

PARK, B. C. AND B. B. DAY. 1942. A simplified method for determining the condition of white-tailed deer herds in relation to available forage. U. S. Dept. Agr. Tech. Bull. No. 840. 60 pp.

PARKER, R. R. AND P. A. LARKIN. 1959. A concept of growth in fishes. J. Fishery Res. Bd., 16: 721–245.

SEVERINGHAUS, C. W. AND R. GOTTLIEB. 1959. Big deer vs. little deer; food is the key factor. N. Y. State Conservationist, 14(2): 30–31.

SILBERBERG, M. AND R. SILBERBERG. 1949. Some aspects of the role of hormonal and nutritional factors in skeletal growth and development. Growth, 13: 359–368.

STEEL, R. G. D. AND J. H. TORRIE. 1960. Principles and procedures of statistics. Mc-Graw-Hill Book Co., New York. 481 pp.

TABER, R. D. AND R. F. DASMANN. 1958. The black-tailed deer of the chaparral. Calif. Dept. of Fish & Game, Game Bull. No. 8. 163 pp.

U. S. WEATHER BUREAU. 1959. Climatological data—Alaska. Vol. 45 (1–13), U. S. Dept. Commerce.

VON BERTALANFFY, L. 1938. A quantitative theory of organic growth. Human Biology, 10: 181–213.

WALLACE, L. R. 1948. The growth of lambs before and after birth in relation to the level of nutrition. III. J. Agr. Sci., 38: 367–401.

WOOD, A. J., I. McT. COWAN AND H. C. NORDAN. 1962. Periodicity of growth in ungulates as shown by deer of the genus *Odocoileus*. Canadian J. Zool., 40: 593–603.

Alaska Cooperative Wildlife Research Unit, University of Alaska, College, Alaska. Received 2 January 1963.

A *MICROTUS* POPULATION WITH SUPPLEMENTAL FOOD

By Charles J. Krebs and Karl T. DeLong

ABSTRACT: A low density population of the California vole was provided with unlimited food supplementing the natural forage for 11 months. Numbers at first increased very slowly, then rose abruptly to only a moderate density and then declined rapidly in spite of excellent individual growth rates and a sustained high reproductive rate among the adults. Thus supplemental food was not sufficient to produce a rapidly expanding population or to prevent a decline to low numbers.

INTRODUCTION

Periodic fluctuations in small mammal populations could be caused by variations in food supply but whether in fact this occurs is controversial (Pitelka, 1964; Kalela, 1962; Chitty, 1960; Krebs, 1964). The present experiment was therefore planned to show whether a superabundance of high-quality food was sufficient to promote exponential growth in a low density small mammal population. A low density *Microtus californicus* population was given supplemental food for 11 months and it demographic changes were followed by intensive live trapping. This species shows periodic fluctuations with peaks every 3–4 years (Pearson, 1964).

METHODS

The experimental area was a 0.82 acre grassland on the east side of San Francisco Bay in the Richmond Field Station of the University of California. It was bounded on one side by a drainage ditch and a street, and on the other three sides by live-trapping grids being used for other studies. The area was divided into 25-ft squares with a stake at each corner (9 rows, 7 columns). The only other small mammal on this area was the house mouse (*Mus musculus*), and information on this species will be reported elsewhere by DeLong. Food supply was increased in two ways. First, crimped oats were placed evenly over the area in 126 pint or quart jars laid on their sides and covered by boards. The number of feeding stations was always in excess of the number of mice. This was begun on 21 October 1963 and continued throughout the study. Second, on 14 January 1964 one-half of this grid was fertilized with 8N/10P fertilizer in pellet form at the rate of 400 lb per acre. The vegetation responded strongly in appearance to this fertilization, becoming dark green. Corn and chick-starter mash were also supplied but the mice appeared to eat little of these compared with the oats. The experiment was discontinued on 15 September 1964 because the population had become very sparse. The population was followed by live trapping with 126 Longworth traps for 2–3 days every 2 weeks. The number of traps was always in excess of the number of animals.

The area used for comparison was a 1.73 acre grassland in Tilden Park at the east side of Berkeley, California, about 6 miles away from the Richmond grid. This area was trapped with 200 live traps on the same schedule as the

JOURNAL OF MAMMALOGY, 1965, Vol.46, No.4, pp.566-573.

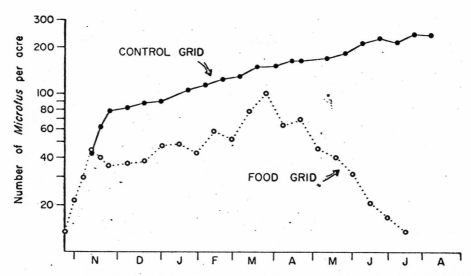

Fig. 1.—Number of *Microtus* known to be alive per acre for the Tilden Control grid (1962–1963) and the Richmond Field Station food grid (1963–1964).

Richmond area. The Tilden population increased from fall 1962 to summer 1963, and provided an example of a population in the expanding phase of a cycle. There are many differences in vegetation, and probably microclimate, between the Richmond and Tilden areas, but these differences are not considered important for this study. We wish to compare a *naturally* expanding population as a standard and a population experimentally supplied with food in excess of demand. If the experimental population had been food limited, and if oats, chick feed and fertilized natural vegetation represent an adequate dietary supplement, then we would expect this experimental population to increase and to be similar demographically to the standard expanding population.

RESULTS

The changes in population density on these two areas are shown in Fig. 1, and the separate data for males and females are given in Table 1. These data were obtained by direct enumeration of the population. The Tilden population showed a steady increase from late November to August, averaging 3% per week. The experimental population did not show this type of increase. Initially there was a large spurt of growth for 3 weeks in late October and early November, probably a result of immigration from surrounding areas, Between 29 October and 25 November eight adult mice were known to have moved onto this area from an adjacent grid which began 75 ft to the south; similar movements of untagged juveniles might have occurred.

After this intial spurt there was only a slow increase in the experimental

203

TABLE 1.—*Minimum number of* Microtus *known to be alive per acre*

Week	Tilden Control (1962–1963)		Richmond Experimental (1963–1964)	
	Males	Females	Males	Females
29 Oct.			5.0	8.3
5 Nov.			6.6	14.9
12 Nov.			11.6	18.2
19 Nov.	17.4	24.9	18.2	26.5
26 Nov.	27.8	34.7	18.2	21.6
3 Dec.	38.8	40.0	15.9	19.5
17 Dec.	38.8	42.8	13.4	23.2
31 Dec.	43.4	44.0	15.9	22.0
14 Jan.	42.8	46.9	22.0	25.6
28 Jan.–4 Feb.	47.5	59.6	22.0	26.8
11–18 Feb.	52.1	65.4	19.5	23.2
25 Feb.–4 Mar.	57.3	69.5	26.8	31.7
10–17 Mar.	62.5	68.3	18.3	34.2
24–31 Mar.	65.4	85.7	26.8	52.5
6–13 April	64.8	88.0	47.6	53.7
20–27 April	70.1	96.1	29.3	35.4
4–11 May	63.1	103.6	34.2	35.4
18–25 May	60.8	110.6	25.6	19.5
1–8 June	67.2	120.4	23.2	17.1
15–22 June	82.2	132.0	18.3	13.4
29 June–6 July	104.2	128.0	9.8	11.0
13–20 July	106.0	111.7	8.5	8.5
27 July–3 Aug.	123.9	119.9	4.9	8.5

population for 16 weeks from 18 November to 11 March. Then suddenly within 2–4 weeks the population doubled, reaching a density slightly over 100 per acre on 6 April. This increase seemed to occur 2 weeks earlier in the females than in the males (Table 1). From 6 April until the experiment was terminated on 15 September, the population decreased rapidly, at a rate of about 13% per week, and finally reached the same low density from which it had started the previous September.

Growth rates of individuals in these populations were measured by weighing each animal at each capture. Fig. 2 compares the seasonal changes in instantaneous relative growth rates for males on the two areas. These adjusted growth rates were obtained by linear regression, adjusting the observed data for each month to a hypothetical 35 g mouse. The growth rates of the experimental mice which received supplemental food were higher than those found in the Tilden animals. The growth rates of these experimental mice were the highest growth rates we have observed in eight different populations of this species from which we have extensive measurements (Krebs, unpubl. data).

In contrast to these high growth rates, the mean body weight of adult males in the experimental population was relatively low. The highest mean

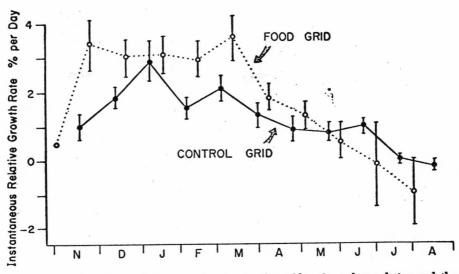

Fig. 2.—Instantaneous relative growth rates for the Tilden Control population and the Richmond Field Station population which was provided with excess food. The growth rates are adjusted by linear regression to an average 35 g mouse for both areas.

weight achieved by males in this population was 46.9 ± 2.7 g on 10 February, whereas the Tilden males at the same time of year averaged 51.2 ± 1.2 g. In every month except November the average weight of Tilden males was greater than that of experimental males.

Reproduction was measured indirectly by the condition of the external sexual characters; position of testes, perforation of vagina, relative size of nipples and relative separation of pubic symphysis. Table 2 compares some of these reproductive measures for the experimental and Tilden populations. These data include only animals from the main breeding season (November to May). There are slight differences in the proportion of adult males with scrotal testes and adult females with perforate vaginas, the experimental population showing slightly less reproductive activity than the control. These differences do not appear in the proportion of adult females with medium-to-large nipples or in the proportion of adult females with open pubic symphyses (these bones are widely separate or open for only a short time before and after parturition). Much larger differences appear in the proportion of subadults in breeding condition; fewer subadults were breeding on the experimental area compared with the Tilden area, and males were apparently more strongly inhibited than females. These reproductive effects, particularly the inhibition of breeding in young animals, have been described in peak and declining populations of small mammals (Kalela, 1957; Krebs, 1964; Chitty, 1952).

TABLE 2.—*Reproductive measures of the Richmond and Tilden populations during the main breeding season (November to May)*

	Tilden Control		Richmond Experimental		Significance level[a]
	N	Proportion[1]	N	Proportion	
Testes scrotal					
Adults	960	0.98	95	0.92	$P < 0.01$
Subadults	190	0.68	90	0.36	$P < 0.01$
Vagina perforate					
Adults	1,216	0.92	132	0.86	$0.05 > P > 0.01$
Subadults	396	0.78	81	0.54	$P < 0.01$
Nipples medium or large					
Adults	1,216	0.69	125	0.74	$P > 0.05$
Pubic symphysis open					
Adults	1,216	0.35	125	0.39	$P > 0.05$

[1] Proportion of animals examined having attribute.
[a] Adjusted chi-squared test for homogeneity.

None of the reproductive measures in the experimental population showed any change during March and April when the population spurted to a moderate density and began its decline. The difference between the sexes in the timing of the March increase also suggests that changes in reproductive rate were not the cause of the population changes during this period.

Survival rates are compared for these two populations (Table 3) using the life table calculation for expectation of further life given by Leslie et al. (1955). The mice from the Tilden population had an expectation of life about two to three times that of mice from the experimental population; this effect occurred in both sexes and all age groups. On both areas males survived less well than females.

Early juvenile survival may be measured indirectly by an index comparing the number of new juveniles caught in a given week with the number of females having medium or large nipples 4 weeks previous. The average index through the entire breeding season for the experimental population was 1.6 mice per lactating female, while the average index was 0.6 for the Tilden population. The absence of recruitment of juveniles into the population is thus not responsible for the failure of the experimental population to increase.

The sudden increase of the experimental population in March and April was produced by an interaction between early juvenile survival rate and survival rate of the trappable population (Table 4). Periods of rapid increase in both males and females coincided with times of high juvenile survival and high adult survival, and these periods did not occur at the same time for the two sexes.

Localizing some of the food resources of the Richmond area did not seem to produce any large changes in the movement patterns of the mice. Mean

TABLE 3.—*Expectation of further life in weeks (±1 SE) at time of first capture for mice from the two populations during the breeding season*

	Tilden Control	Richmond Experimental
Males		
Adults[1]	7.77 ± 0.44	2.78 ± 0.62
Subadults	6.78 ± 0.40	3.94 ± 0.57
Juveniles	8.62 ± 0.86	4.26 ± 0.49
Females		
Adults	12.51 ± 0.84	5.25 ± 0.85
Subadults	11.32 ± 0.60	4.37 ± 0.72
Juveniles	12.67 ± 1.29	4.84 ± 0.63

[1] Animals classified at time of first capture as adults (≥ 40 g), subadults (26–39 g), or juveniles (≤ 25 g).

length of movements between trapping periods was 53.0 ft for adult males on the food grid during the breeding season; the means of five comparable populations ranged from 39.5–51.2 ft (Krebs, unpubl. data). For adult females comparable data were 31.4 ft, and 15.9–29.1 ft. Artifical feeding did not decrease movements, as revealed by live traps, but may have increased them slightly.

CONCLUSIONS

The provision of supplemental food to this low population of *Microtus californicus* did not allow exponential growth as usually occurs in a naturally expanding population. In spite of excellent individual growth rates and a sustained high rate of reproduction in the adults, the artificially fed population either increased very slowly or declined in numbers during most of the experiment. The doubling of the experimental population which occurred in a 2–4 week period in late March shows that the potential for population growth was present. There was no clear indication why the experimentally

TABLE 4.—*Minimum survival rate (per 14 days) for males and females of the experimental population and index of early juvenile survival during the period of sudden increase. High survival rates in each series are underlined*

	28 Jan.	11 Feb.	25 Feb.	10 Mar.	24 Mar.	6 Apr.	20 Apr.	4 May	18 May
Minimum survival rate—males	0.65	0.60	0.33	0.23	<u>0.91</u>	0.31	0.75	0.52	
Index of early juvenile survival	0.3	1.7	0.5	<u>2.8</u>	<u>3.0</u>	1.4	1.1	1.0	
Minimum survival rate—females	0.67	<u>0.78</u>	<u>0.76</u>	<u>0.77</u>	0.57	0.39	0.50	0.40	

fed population of this area increased rapidly at this point or why it then declined through April, May and June in the presence of a dense growth of grass and with favorable weather. There was no indication of heavy predation on the experimental area during this study, nor did any of the live-trapped animals show obvious disease symptoms. Emigration from the area onto the surrounding three live-trapping areas was slight; 13 individuals were known to have emigrated from the experimental area between March and May, out of 127 known losses during this period. Artificial feeding increased growth rates but did not raise survival rates. Some factor other than food shortage must have been causing the low survival of these mice.

Low mean body weights, poor individual growth rates and decreased reproduction are some of the characteristic features of declining small mammal populations (Chitty, 1952). In this experiment we had excellent individual growth rates and reproductive rates, but still low body weights and no continued population response on the area which was provided with supplemental food. The data reported here suggest that the growth-rate response which characterizes periodic fluctuations is not a necessary part of the mechanism which restrains the population from increasing.

Bendell (1959) showed that an island which did not support a *Peromyscus leucopus* population could be made habitable and even support a high-density population by adding artificial food. Our experiment was carried out on an area which already supported a natural population of *Microtus*, and to this extent differed from Bendell's experiment. We do not know whether this difference between a vacant area and an occupied one is sufficient to explain the opposite conclusions reached in these two experiments, or whether species differences must be invoked.

ACKNOWLEDGMENTS

We thank the Museum of Vertebrate Zoology for the use of its facilities, the Miller Institute for Basic Research for support of the senior author and the Union Foundation Wildlife Fund for partial support of the junior author.

LITERATURE CITED

BENDELL, J. F. 1959. Food as a control of a population of white-footed mice, *Peromyscus leucopus noveboracensis* (Fischer). Can. J. Zool., 37: 173–209.

CHITTY, D. 1952. Mortality among voles (*Microtus agrestis*) at Lake Vyrnwy, Montgomeryshire in 1936–9. Phil. Trans. Roy. Soc. London Ser. B, 236: 505–552.

————. 1960. Population processes in the vole and their relevance to general theory. Can. J. Zool., 38: 99–113.

KALELA, O. 1957. Regulation of reproduction rate in subarctic populations of the vole *Clethrionomys rufocanus* (Sund.). Ann. Acad. Sci. Fenn. Ser. A, 4(34): 1–60.

————. 1962. On the fluctuations in the numbers of arctic and boreal small rodents as a problem of production biology. Ann. Acad. Sci. Fenn. Ser. A, 4(66): 1–38.

KREBS, C. J. 1964. The lemming cycle at Baker Lake, Northwest Territories, during 1959–62. Arctic Inst. N. Amer. Tech. Pap. 15, 104 pp.

LESLIE, P. H., J. S. TENER, M. VIZOSO AND H. CHITTY. 1955. The longevity and fertility of the Orkney vole, *Microtus orcadensis*, as observed in the laboratory. Proc. Zool. Soc. London, 125: 115–125.

208

PEARSON, O. P. 1964. Carnivore-mouse predation: an example of its intensity and bioenergetics. J. Mamm., 45: 177–188.

PITELKA, F. A. 1964. The nutrient-recovery hypothesis for arctic microtine cycles. I. Introduction, pp. 55–56. In "Grazing in Terrestrial and Marine Environments," ed. by D. J. Crisp, Brit. Ecol. Soc. Symp. No. 4. Blackwell, Oxford.

Museum of Vertebrate Zoology, University of California, Berkeley. (Present Address: C. J. KREBS, *Department of Zoology, Indiana University, Bloomington;* K. T. DELONG, *Biology Department, Ripon College, Ripon, Wisconsin.) Accepted 12 April 1965.*

An Ecological Study of Mobility and Settlement Patterns Among the Belcher Island Eskimo

MILTON M. R. FREEMAN[1]

ABSTRACT. A complex of ecological factors favours the development of individual production techniques on the Belcher Islands; settlement formation, therefore, does not result from the requirements of collective economic activity. Economic factors are mainly responsible for changes in settlement composition and location, though at some seasons, social pressures have a strong influence. Settlement composition is based largely on kinship, although personality factors play an important role. Acculturation influences both mobility and settlement patterns.

RÉSUMÉ. *Etude écologique de la mobilité et du dessin des établissements chez les Esquimaux des îles Belcher.* Dans les îles Belcher, un complexe de facteurs écologiques favorise le développement de techniques individuelles de production; c'est pourquoi la formation des établissements humains ne résulte pas des nécessités d'une activité économique collective. Les facteurs économiques sont les principaux responsables des changements dans la composition et la localisation des établissements, bien qu'en certaines saisons, les pressions sociales aient aussi une forte influence. La composition des établissements est largement basée sur la parenté, bien que des facteurs de personnalité jouent aussi un rôle important. L'acculturation a une influence tant sur la mobilité que sur le dessin des établissements.

РЕЗЮМЕ. *Экологическое изучение форм миграции и оседлости среди ескимосов островов Белчер.* Комплекс экологических факторов содействует развитию личной промысловой техники на островах Белчер; поэтому образование поселков не является следствием нужд коллективной экономической деятельности. Экономические факторы влияют главным образои на изменение состава и расположения поселков, хотя в некоторые времена года социальные факторы тоже имеют большое влияние. Состав поселков обусловливается главным образом родственными связями, хотя вопросы личности тоже играют важную роль. Подъем культуры влияет как на формы миграции, так и на формы оседлости.

INTRODUCTION

Traditional Eskimo settlement patterns indicate a correlation between population numbers and game *availability*, rather than game *abundance*. For example, seals are no more abundant in winter than they are in summer, yet among many Eskimo groups, settlements are large in winter and small in summer. Paradoxically also, the largest population concentration is at the season of most severe environmental pressure. The answer to this paradox is that a scattered summer population exploiting low-density game resources comes together at certain seasons to increase the effectiveness of resource-harvesting through collective activity. Collective hunting is not practised on the Belcher Islands. This is most likely the result of ecological factors, particularly the long open-water season and winter sealing conditions favouring extensive hunting from the kayak. In the absence of collective techniques, the *raison d'etre* of large seasonal settle-

[1]Northern Co-ordination and Research Centre, Ottawa, Canada. Present address: Biology Department, Memorial University of Newfoundland.

ARCTIC, 1967, Vol.20, No.3, pp. 154-175.

ments diminishes; furthermore, other factors in combination favour the establishment of small settlements on the Belcher Islands. The first of these factors is the almost complete dependence of the natives on marine resources, mainly seals and seabirds. The second is the kayak hunters' dependence on favourable weather, with the Belcher Islands experiencing some of the least favourable weather in the eastern Arctic. The third is that the individual game animal available to the hunter most of the year, and especially in winter, is small in size; ringed seal, for instance, are usually smaller on the Belcher Islands than they are elsewhere in the Arctic. These factors combined tend to prevent the individual from accumulating food surpluses; in addition, they appear to favour the establishment of small economic units whose unrestrictive organization facilitates opportunistic action on the part of the individual. This flexibility and the variety of productive techniques suggest that an ecological study should attempt to rationalize variations in the observed settlement behaviour, rather than seek rules governing settlement.

PROCEDURE

General Methodology. The author visited the Belcher Islands from May to September 1959, April to October 1960, and February to April 1961. Although most time was spent in one settlement only on each visit, more than one thousand miles of travel on the islands allowed visits to all settlements and to regions of the archipelago habitually travelled by the Islanders. Companions on these occasions freely volunteered information on hunting, travelling, and living conditions, with a minimum of formal questioning. This study is based on data obtained from discussions, observations, and published accounts.

Settlement Coefficient. A quantification of actual occupation of, and hence considered suitability of, a settlement area may be approximated by the following equation:

$$S.C_s = \frac{H_s.t_s}{C_s}$$

where $S.C_s$ = settlement coefficient for a given season (s),

H_s = number of households present at season s,

t_s = length of seasonal occupancy in weeks,

and C_s = seasonal constant, viz., number of weeks constituting the season.

Acculturation Index. Four sets of criteria were used to assess the relative positions of male heads of households along a continuum from those traditionally oriented to those with a high degree of alien-culture aspiration or achievement. These independently variable criteria, with assigned scores, are listed below:

211

Ownership or utilization of sealskin kayak	10
Non-ownership or non-utilization of sealskin kayak	0
Winter dwelling a snowhouse	10
Winter dwelling a canvas tent	0
Winter parka of skins	10
Winter parka of imported cloth	0
Third class trapper	10
Second class trapper	6
First class trapper	1

In the first three sets of criteria, intermediate scores of 5 were awarded when individuals were in the process of becoming oriented to an alien culture. Rank as a trapper was assessed by actual performance (number of skins obtained) during the two "good" fox years, 1959-60 and 1960-61, and was verified by comparison with recent trading records.

Scores ranged from 1 (highly acculturated) to 40 (traditionally oriented). Each individual's assessment could be subjectively verified by considering his attitudes (where known) to wage employment, hunting, trading, and food choices, religious and recreational activities, and the result of a material culture survey.

The acculturation index of each settlement was the mean score of the constituent household heads. Data from thirteen settlements regarded as "normal" (i.e., with no fluctuation of population through hospitalization or other abnormal cause) has been represented graphically on page 170. For convenience, a semi-logarithmic plot has been employed. Calculation of the correlation, r, follows normal statistical procedure.

THE ENVIRONMENT

The Belcher Islands consist of a number of low-lying Precambrian outcrops covering an area of about 2,000 square miles in southeast Hudson Bay. Past glacial activity has eroded the underlying hardrock to produce a landscape characterized by extensive areas of smooth ridges, with countless lakes of all sizes filling the depressions between them.

In winter, strong winds and temperatures of –10° to 15°F. prevail for several months. Summer temperatures average 50°F., but wind, rain, fog, and overcast are common. These meteorological conditions influence subsistence activities; wind is probably the most important single physical factor limiting the effective hunting of animals in the Arctic, particularly marine mammals. The expectation of weather suitable for open-water hunting in this region is seldom more than 10 per cent of the daylight hours at the beginning of summer, and a gradual deterioration occurs as the season advances (McLaren 1961). Snow falls in October and persists till May. Lakes freeze in November and by mid-December sea-ice formation is extensive around all but the most exposed coastal sections. From January till mid-May in most years, an ice bridge connects the Belcher Islands to the Ungava mainland, 80 miles to the east.

Although trees are entirely absent, there are several woody species important as fuel; prostrate willows are widespread, dwarf birch and arctic heather are local. Lichens ("reindeer moss") are also gathered, and burn with an intense though short-lived flame. Driftwood, occurring mainly in the west of the Islands, is a principal source of fuel and workable wood. Berry-bearing plants are found throughout the Islands, the fruit ripening in the autumn.

Animal life on the Belcher Islands, like the plant life, is characteristically arctic, although because of the low latitude and other factors the bird fauna is unusually rich. The fish fauna is decidedly poor: one fresh-water species only, the arctic char, has economic importance. During the downstream and upstream "runs" good catches are made using nets, though only on a few days of the year; no river system on the Belcher Islands seems to have the capacity for intensive annual exploitation. Mussels and sea urchins are found at certain locations, and these as well as shore fish, such as cod and sculpins, can be of value during bad weather, when hunting is not possible.

On land, there are few species of mammals, and none is plentiful. There are no longer any caribou, and arctic and red fox are generally scarce, though when fat, they may be used for food. The arctic hare is not abundant, but a few are killed by most households each year.

Birds remaining throughout the winter and used for food are snowy owl, ptarmigan, eider duck, old squaw, and guillemot. Eider ducks are especially important, as apart from their abundance and relatively large size, they provide skins still extensively used for clothing by the Islanders. In spring, geese, ducks, and loons of several species arrive; the eggs of geese, ducks, and seabirds are eaten whenever available.

Of the fauna, however, marine mammals are the most important from the Eskimo's viewpoint. Ringed seal and, to a lesser extent, bearded seal are ubiquitous. Harbour seal, harp seal, walrus, and white whale are seasonally present, but, with the exception of the white whale, these species make only infrequent contributions to the local economy (for a fuller discussion, see Freeman 1964). The polar bear is seen infrequently, and is generally restricted to the western part of the archipelago.

The seasonal behaviour of marine mammals is of the utmost relevance in considering the settlement patterns among maritime Eskimo groups. The subject is treated elsewhere from the anthropological viewpoint (e.g., Weyer 1932). Critical studies of seal bionomics with particular bearing on the Belcher Island situation have also been published (McLaren 1958, 1962).

The ringed seal (*Phoca hispida*) is a small, widely distributed inshore species, forming the principal quarry of Eskimo hunters throughout the

Canadian arctic littoral. Belcher Island specimens attain a weight of about 60 pounds. An important feature of this seal's biology (and of probable consequence to Eskimo hunting practice) is the variation in size with latitude. A hunter in northern Baffin Island, for example, will probably obtain seals of twice the average weight of Belcher Island specimens. This seal is not especially gregarious, and the scattered population favours sheltered locations; at any season, complex indented coasts with offshore island or skerry development will have a greater seal population than will simple exposed coasts.

During spring, when ringed seal come to lie on the surface of the ice, their population density (and availability to the hunter) increases with the erosion of the landfast ice.

The bearded seal (*Erignathus barbatus*) is large, averaging about 500 pounds. The meat yield alone makes it important economically, and, in addition, the tough hide has considerable value for a variety of uses. This species is less numerous than the ringed seal. During winter, the bearded seal is generally found away from areas of landfast ice, in the pack ice, or at the floe edge, as it rarely maintains breathing holes.

The white whale (*Delphinapterus leucas*) is of importance also for its size, adult specimens being about 900 pounds in weight. However, the occurrence of this species is almost exclusively limited to the open-water season. Only rarely is it found near the Belcher Islands during winter, though small numbers may occasionally be trapped under rapidly forming sea ice in some deep sheltered bays.

HISTORICAL FACTORS

Trading visits by Islanders to the mainland at the end of the nineteenth century brought them knowledge of Christianity, and by the time of the first visit by Euro-Canadians (in 1915), firearms and imported tools and clothing were in evidence. A population of 150 was reported for 1910; at that time, the Islanders' trade with the mainland was in products of hunting, particularly polar bear skins, seal skins, and walrus ivory (Freeman 1964).

In 1928, a winter trading operation was established in the southwestern part of the archipelago in an effort to encourage fox-trapping. This venture was judged successful, and the trading post moved to the eastern part of the Islands with a resident Euro-Canadian manager. In 1938, the population of the Islands was reported to be 189. About a third of this number became attracted to the vicinity of the trading post and their settlement patterns were altered accordingly. Most of the remainder of the population was distributed in the northern part of the Belcher Islands, with perhaps half as many in the south. The northern segment, living in three or four mutually interacting groups, was some distance logistically, and a progressively increasing distance culturally, from the more acculturated central segment of the population, which resided much nearer

214

the trading post. This period of intense culture contact for the central groups saw the rise of a messianic movement; following a number of ritual killings, the population numbered 164 in 1941.

The Euro-Canadian trader was withdrawn in 1943, and operations at the post reverted to seasonal trading only. A number òf social changes resulted as a succession of local and mainland Eskimos were placed in control of essential supplies. This new "elite" began a series of preferential trading transactions known to have continued up to the present. Under this system, not only successful trappers became favoured by the trader, but also kin and non-related families who aligned themselves with his actions or his expressed wishes.

In 1953, the population was 170, with the same general disposition as in the days of full trading operations a decade earlier. There were now, however, approximately equal numbers occupying several locations in the north, south, and east of the archipelago.

During the summer and autumn of 1954, culture contact of un-precedented intensity resulted in many socio-political and economic changes which directly affected settlement behaviour (Desgoffe 1955). In summary, the new influences included economic subsidy, disruption of the annual cycle through limited wage employment, and the re-establishment of the trading post for year-round operation under the control of a mainland Eskimo. These various factors produced, in effect, a centralization of population in the eastern part of the Islands for many months of the year, delayed dispersal to winter settlement areas, and hastened the return of households to the eastern regions early in the spring.

In the years following 1955, most of the northern and southern groups gradually returned to earlier winter settlement areas (see Fig. 1). Despite steadily increasing culture contact since 1953, the Eskimo trader, by making only a few subsidy payments at irregular intervals, discouraging the production of handicrafts during the winter months, and living as a hunter-trapper himself, probably helped to prevent a marked devaluation of current cultural norms. Increased income resulting from the new economic opportunities that had been locally available since 1954 was not sufficient to finance technological improvement in resource-harvesting (for details, see Freeman 1964). Thus, for most of the population ecological pressures continued to influence settlement patterns in much the same way as before.

DEMOGRAPHY

During the twentieth century, the Belcher Island population appears to have fluctuated between 150 and 190 persons. A net annual increase of natality over mortality in most years, combined with periodic migrations and epidemics, have caused these fluctuations. Epidemics occur sporadi-cally and are of considerable social and economic moment in a society where adult males and females are almost invariably complementary partners of an economic dyad (see Table 1).

215

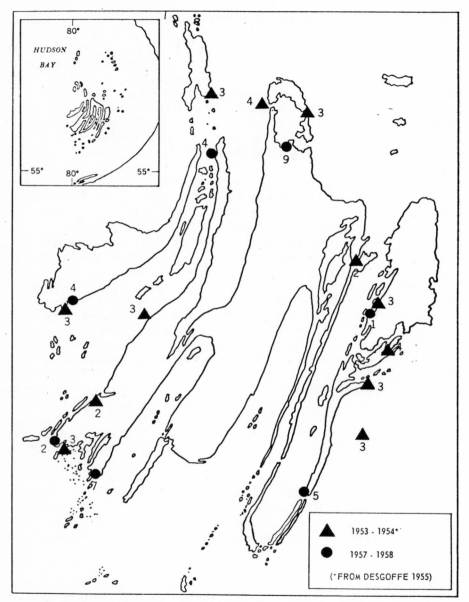

FIG. 1. Number of constituent households and location of winter settlements, Belcher Islands.

Since the early years of this century, there appears to have been a decrease in large scale movements of people between the Islands and the Ungava mainland. The reason for lessened emigration from the Islands appears to have been the increasing scarcity of caribou on the mainland

216

TABLE 1. Mortality occurring during two epidemics, Belcher Islands.

Date	Ages of males deceased	Ages of females deceased	Cause
Winter 1953-54	54, 30, 28, 18, 1, 1	69, 57, 40, 38, 22, 20, 1	Influenza
Autumn 1961	61, 49, 1	54, 40, 29, 23, 1, 1	Measles

and the establishment of trading facilities on the archipelago.

The last large migration occurred in 1953, when 20 Ungava Eskimos settled on the Islands; by the winter of 1961, only 3 remained, emigration and mortality accounting for the decrease. The motive for this large immigration (which would be considered large at any stage in the Islands' history) was the expectation of better hunting.

Since 1953, immigration has been slight: 4 people in 1954; 4 in 1959; and 1 in 1960. These included the families of both the Eskimo trader and the Eskimo catechist; both of these men were, in fact, born on the Islands, but had spent most of their lives on the mainland.

Hospital treatment is the main reason for emigration from the Islands (see Table 2), but many return after a year, and some after two or even more years of treatment; more than half of the individuals hospitalized receive treatment for tuberculosis or related diseases. Fluctuating frequency of hospitalization resulted from the irregularity of visits by health teams. The large 1960 evacuation (Table 2) was suspiciously linked to a recurrence of the harmful culture-contact situation analyzed by an earlier writer (Desgoffe 1955).

TABLE 2. Ages of Belcher Island Eskimos recently hospitalized.

Date	Ages of Males	Ages of Females
Summer 1954	64, 55, 54, 24	55, 50, 43, 35, 22
Summer 1959	30, 16	16, 11, 9
Summer 1960	62, 31, 17, 10	60, 54, 44, 34, 33, 30, 17, 12, 7, 5

Migration to mainland settlements, with their greater wage-earning, recreational, educational, and welfare services, accounted for only two instances of emigration in the 3 years (1959-61) for which there are data. In both cases, the emigrants were young unmarried adults.

HOUSEHOLD COMPOSITION

Households are formed at or shortly after marriage, though lack of capital (represented by dogs, sled, tent, etc.) may delay the establishment of a discrete household for an indefinite period.

Residence after marriage appears to be initially uxorilocal, in agreement with the pattern observed among other Ungava Eskimo groups (Willmott 1961; Honigmann 1962; Graburn 1964).

Households may be simple or compound; the former consists of a single nuclear or stem family in a dwelling, whereas the latter is composed of two or more family units living in a multiple dwelling and sharing a common entrance. Compound households result from the absence or incapacity of an otherwise irreplaceable contributing adult member; they also result, though less frequently, from the loss of a male adult. The reason appears to be that whereas a male is dependent on the full-time attention of a capable woman for daily domestic tasks, a female alone or having dependents can maintain a household by relying on the gifts of food and raw materials any successful member of a settlement is obliged to provide for the less fortunate. Thus, elderly couples or widows with small children will continue to maintain separate households, though their economic autonomy has largely disappeared. (Government subsidy had yet to be made regularly available before the autumn of 1960).

Household sizes during the winter of 1959-60 ranged from 3 to 8 persons, with a mode of 5 and mean of 5.5 persons.

During 1959 and 1960, 97 per cent of the households in summer and 91.4 per cent in winter were simple rather than compound. An analysis of these 89 simple households showed that the nuclear family comprised 54 per cent of the summer households, and 66 per cent of the winter households; in a further 22 per cent of summer and winter households, one or both elderly parents of one of the spouses resided in that household. In 7 out of 8 cases where this occurred, the parents lived with the eldest of their married children. In one case, the parent lived in the household of her youngest married daughter; this may be taken as continuing (initial) uxorilocality of the young couple (who had been married 3 years before) owing to their continued economic dependence on that parent for household property.

SETTLEMENT COMPOSITION

From a study of Ungava Eskimo kinship terminology, Graburn (1964) concluded that the basis of settlement was co-residence of male siblings after marriage (following initial uxorilocality) and that there is at all times only one norm of residence for all individuals in the society. The co-residence of married brothers in the same settlements on the Belcher Islands agrees to a large extent with the pattern established by Graburn. Thus, during the winter, at the time of greatest dispersal, from a total of 6 pairs of married brothers, 5 pairs co-resided in 1959, and 4 pairs in 1960 and 1961.

The largest winter settlement was that of Kritusuk (Fig. 2). The nucleus of this group was the patrilocal extended family. The breakdown of this large settlement was due to certain personality differences, aggravated by

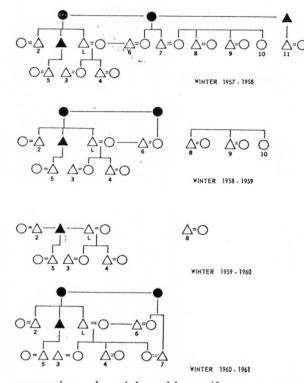

FIG. 2. Yearly variation in composition of Kritusuk's settlement, 1957-61. Numbers refer to constituent households; L is leader.

WINTER 1957 - 1958

WINTER 1958 - 1959

WINTER 1959 - 1960

WINTER 1960 - 1961

economic and social problems (for summary, see Freeman 1964). The first stage of the breakdown was through the kin link 7, and the subsequent movement away of the extended sibling group, now unrelated to the core family.

The importance of kin linkage to settlement composition is further seen by reference to the destination of the families leaving Kritusuk's settlement; 7 and 8 join their respective brothers, 11 goes to his wife's brother (who is also his sister's husband's brother), and 10 goes to live at the settlement of his sister's husband's brother.

From these considerations (see also Fig. 3), it is evident that there is flexibility in settlement composition from year to year. Only rarely does a settlement remain constant for more than 2 years; families less closely related to the leader are generally the least permanent. Economic liaisons to finance joint ownership of a whaleboat, for example (cf. Balikci 1964; Willmott 1961), were nowhere apparent on the Belcher Islands, and no other potentially permanent liaisons outside of kinship were present. However, though flexibility is apparent, moves are to some extent predictable along recognized lines of kinship.

The presence of an unrelated kin group established with Kudlayok's winter settlement (Fig. 3) was the result of his recent immigration to the Belcher Islands from Ungava, and the consequent need for local guidance

219

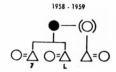

TADLEROKUT
1957 - 1958

○=△   △=○
   L

1958 - 1959

○=△ ○=△ △=○
  7   L

FIG. 3. Settlement composition in consecutive winters, Belcher Islands. L is leader's household; numbered households, as in Fig. 2.

KUDLAYOKUT

1957 - 1958 - 1959

○=△−△=○   ᴸ△=○−△=○
        ○=△

A'ALUKUT

1958 - 1959

○=△   △=○ ○=△   ○=△
  L   11

△ = ○

1959 - 1960

○   ○=△ ○=△   △=○   ○=△   ○=△
       L   11

and for crew members for his whaleboat. However, there was no question of permanence in the association; in the autumn of 1960, for example, Kudlayok's wife's brother left the settlement (see below). The factor which initially established the liaison between immigrant and native families is unknown; however, the bond was strongly maintained by personality factors, the leader being full of praise for the younger member of the associated sibling group. (The importance of personality factors in Iglulik Eskimo social organization is stressed by Damas 1963; see also Balikci 1964). The nature of the link between the two families in Tadlerok's winter settlement in 1957-58 (Fig. 3) was similarly based on personality preference.

LEADERSHIP

At each settlement, during winter dispersal, one man is regarded as the leader. His influence in day-to-day affairs may be imperceptible, especially if economic conditions are favourable. His judgement is accepted when a decision is made to move the settlement; indeed, in several cases it was discovered that in all such matters his was the only opinion voiced. Settlement composition can also be influenced by the leader; this happened once in 1959 and again in 1960, when in each case a family moved from

220

a settlement at the express wishes of the leader. In one case, the brother-in-law of the leader said he had heard (from another): "K. doesn't want me in camp this winter." He blamed this on his poor hunting the previous fall whilst recovering from an injury.

As is generally reported for other Eskimo groups, the leader excels as a hunter (however, cf. Damas 1963, p. 186); this was indirectly verifiable by certain other accomplishments in the Belcher Island situation. These included the size of the leader's dog team, the number of dependents he supported, and his standing as a trapper. In each case, the leader was the oldest active member of the settlement. These data are summarized in Table 3 for the sample winter 1959-60; each of the 5 settlements referred to had 5 or more households.

TABLE 3. Some leadership qualities, Belcher Islands, 1959-60.

Leader	Number of dogs	Dependents supported	Trapping returns
Kritusuk	—	††	††
A'aluk	††	—	††
Kudlayok	†	—	††
Tadlerok	†	†	—
Sanikiloak	—	†	†

†† Appreciably largest number in settlement ·
† Largest number in settlement
— Fewer compared to some others in settlement

Leadership was strongest among the northern settlements: Kritusuk was elder kinsman of a large extended family; A'aluk was the senior member of an extended sibling group with associated affines; and Kudlayok, although a recent (1953) immigrant from Ungava, had, by possessing a motorized whaleboat and by heading his own large kinship group at the time of his arrival, established his immediate importance on the Belcher Islands (see Figs. 2 and 3 for composition of these settlements). The two southern settlements were led by men whose authority was partly derived from outside the community. Tadlerok was formerly in charge of camp trading arrangements, and subsequently became recognized as a leader by various Euro-Canadian agencies. In similar fashion, Sanikiloak was placed in charge of a government-owned communal whaleboat; in this capacity he was frequently called upon to make decisions for those in his own and in other settlements. These southern settlements have weak kin linkage and experience the greatest compositional variation from year to year.

SETTLEMENT AREAS

The location of settlements varies both seasonally and annually; however, a consistent pattern of preference by individual households and by

221

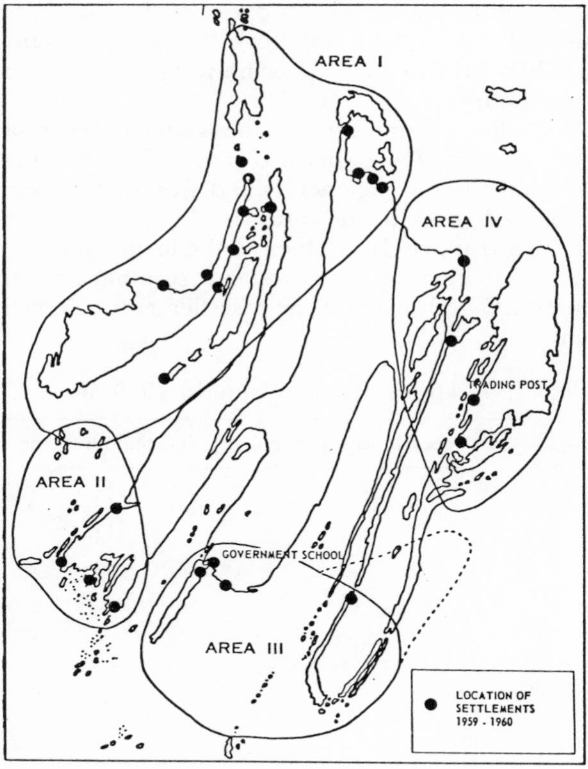

FIG. 4. Settlement areas on the Belcher Islands.

groups of households suggests an underlying rationale behind actual choice of settlement areas. In matters of settlement, a marked conservation is evident; for example, the community appears to be divided into "northerners" and "southerners," two groups which claim to have geographic knowledge of only the northern or southern parts of the archipelago respectively. The few men who have knowledge of the whole archipelago are among the most acculturated of the Islanders.

Two factors reflect the suitability of an area for settlement: the first is the size of the population supported, and the second is the length or frequency of occupation. Both these characteristics were combined to give a *settlement coefficient*, due allowance being made for varying lengths of the different seasons. By use of this coefficient, one obtains empirically derived assessments of the preference for, and hence supposed suitability of, given settlement areas. Assessments based on biogeographic considerations and on the opinions expressed by Islanders were used to delimit the 4 major settlement areas shown in Fig. 4; each of these areas possesses distinct ecological characteristics and is habitually frequented by particular households. Settlement coefficient data for several winters are presented in Table 4. Despite variation, the overall pattern shows a statistically

TABLE 4. Settlement coefficient data, Belcher Islands.

Winter	Area I	Area II	Area III	Area IV
1953-54*	16	5	3	12
1957-58	16	9	5	1
1958-59	22	3	3	2
1959-60	16	6	6	3
1960-61	9	6	7	9
	$CHI^2 = 27.42$		(12 d.f.)	P<0.01

*1953-54 data from Desgoffe 1955

significant association (p. <0.01), which suggests that the observed population disposition reflects a consistent preference by groups of households for particular regions of the archipelago having distinct ecological characteristics.

Proximity to good hunting was given in almost every case as the prime reason for choosing a particular winter settlement area. This was to be expected in a region where food shortage was a constant threat and where, at that time, there was no outside subsidy to reduce anxiety. Other considerations, such as proximity to driftwood supplies or good trapping, or historical precedent, were not generally voiced, even though some answers received suggested that consideration was given to such matters. The point here is that the individual hunter, or leader of a group, makes a purely personal assessment of a settlement area based on his knowledge of several alternatives. In many cases, an individual's ecological knowledge is both limited and strongly biased. The bias is due to a strong preference for living in a particular ecological milieu. However, is there, in fact, any objective basis for settlement in relation to food resources? Certainly there is no reason to question the importance of food availability as an influence in demographic matters among subsistence hunters in general, and among the Belcher Island Eskimos in particular. The availability of driftwood or foxes may be prime motives in some cases; however, the need to hunt, for dog food especially, is mandatory.

Values for available biomass (food, oil, and dog food) for each settlement area are given in Table 5. Only those species of animals that contribute in a potentially constant (and hence potentially predictable) manner to the winter economy are considered. Estimates of seal abundance are according to the theoretical considerations of McLaren (1958, 1962); other estimates are from local knowledge. The errors inherent in any census such as this make absolute estimates of questionable significance, but it is believed that relative estimates are fairly realistic (Fay and Cade 1959).

223

TABLE 5. Estimates of biomass available to hunters in winter, Belcher Islands.

Species	Approx. Wt.	Area I		Area II		Area III		Area IV	
		Abundance	Biomass	Abundance	Biomass	Abundance	Biomass	Abundance	Biomass
Ringed seal	28 kg.	7.3×10^3	20.5×10^3	2.6×10^3	7.4×10^4	4.6×10^3	12.9×10^4	4.1×10^3	11.5×10^4
Bearded seal	212 kg.	3.65×10^3	15.5×10^6	1.3×10^3	5.4×10^6	2.3×10^3	9.8×10^6	2.05×10^3	8.7×10^6
Polar bear	400 kg.	1×10^1	4.0×10^2	1×10^1	4.0×10^2	1×10^1	4.0×10^2	0	0
Walrus	600 kg.	1×10^1	6.0×10^2	0	0	0	0	0	0
Eiders	2.5 kg.	1×10^3	2.5×10^3	1×10^3	2.5×10^3	1×10^2	2.5×10^2	1×10^2	2.5×10^2
Old squaw	.75 kg.	1×10^2	7.5×10^1	1×10^2	7.5×10^1	1×10^1	$.75 \times 10^1$	1×10^1	$.75 \times 10^1$
Black guillemot	.4 kg.	1×10^3	4.0×10^2	1×10^3	4.0×10^2	1×10^2	4.0×10^1	1×10^2	4.0×10^1
TOTAL BIOMASS		17.6×10^6		6.2×10^6		11.1×10^6		9.85×10^6	
Density kg./sq. km.		1.3×10^4		1.2×10^4		8.0×10^3		1.1×10^4	

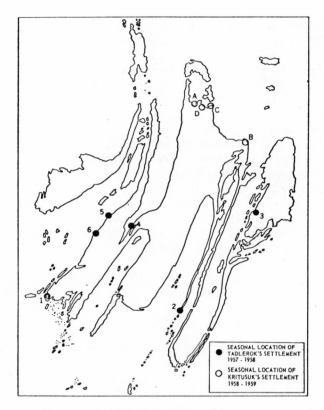

FIG. 5. Examples of settlement mobility patterns, Belcher Islands.

SEASONAL LOCATION OF
TADLEROK'S SETTLEMENT
1957 - 1958

SEASONAL LOCATION OF
KRITUSUK'S SETTLEMENT
1958 - 1959

Comparisons of Tables 4 and 5 show certain correspondences in area ranking. Area I, for example, with consistently heavy settlement, is seen to contain the most resources. Area II, although having low total biomass, appears on the average to be the second most favoured settlement area. The explanation for this apparent anomaly is probably the favourable density of biomass, which makes it a good hunting area.

In summary, we might cautiously conclude that a consistent pattern of winter settlement can be demonstrated from our data, and that this settlement pattern appears to correlate, at least in part, with the potential availability of dominant food species.

SETTLEMENT MOBILITY

Settlements fluctuate in composition, in location, and in their degree of interaction with other settlements. Movement is, in fact, an adaptive device allowing fuller exploitation of the economic potential of the total environment. Fig. 5 illustrates two types of settlement behaviour; numbers 1 to 6 correspond to the locations of Tadlerok's settlement in winter, spring, summer, early autumn, late autumn, and winter, respectively, for the year 1957-58. This large annual migration (175 miles) allows consider-able interaction with other settlements. In contrast is Kritusuk's settlement in 1958-59, where locations in winter-spring, summer, autumn, and winter are indicated in Fig. 5 by the letters A to D, respectively. Kritusuk's annual migration was small (40 miles) and took place at the peripheries of two adjacent settlement areas (I and IV.), thus allowing negligible inter-action with other settlements.

For a variety of historical and psychological reasons, certain individuals now require resources that are widely scattered and were either not avail-able or not considered of such importance in earlier times (e.g., wage employment, foxes, driftwood, etc.). To illustrate this statement, it was necessary to assess objectively the degree of acculturation of each house-hold; the *acculturation index* of each settlement was the mean household score at that settlement (see page 155). The correlation coefficient, r, calculated from acculturation indices and lengths of annual migration obtained from all settlements for sample years between 1957 and 1960 inclusive, indicates a definite relationship ($r = -0.809$) between the degree of acculturation and mobility among settlements on the Belcher Islands (Fig. 6).

THE SEASONAL ECONOMIC CYCLE

Whether seeking seals at breathing holes (or elsewhere) during winter, stalking them on sea ice in spring, or hunting them from a kayak in summer and autumn, the Belcher Islander rarely seeks or has the advantage of co-operation with others during the productive phases of the hunt. For company or safety, two men may choose to travel together to any given hunting place, but on arrival, each man hunts on his own.

Mutual co-operation is as well marked at the distributive phase as it is lacking at the productive phase of economic activity. Sharing follows a pattern that depends mainly on the type of game and the needs of

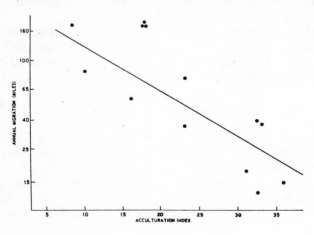

FIG. 6. Relationship between acculturation and mobility. Belcher Islands, 1957-60.

settlement members. Gifts of food may be made to kin in other settlements, but day-to-day sharing is only among co-resident members of the settlement.

In early winter, sealing occurs most frequently at the edge of the land-fast ice, (i.e., at the "floe edge"). Seals are shot in the water and retrieved with the kayak, which is a hunting technique considered more comfortable and rewarding than waiting motionless at the seal's breathing hole, and is also safer than hunting at current-maintained open water in the fast ice. Thus in early winter, nearness to the floe edge is a factor in the location of winter settlements. During late winter, the distance from some settlements to the floe edge increases considerably because of the steadily increasing ice cover, particularly in the eastern part of the archipelago. This does not very often result in a move, but rather in a change in hunting technique; at this season of less intense cold, many prefer to hunt at seal breathing holes.

However, as with all other sealing methods practised locally, this is an individual activity and therefore requires no changes in either settlement composition or attitudes. The south coast of the Belcher Islands is relatively poor for this type of hunting, and open water where alternative techniques could be employed is a long distance away, so there is a low incidence of settlement along this coast, apart from the extreme southeast and southwest where especially favourable local situations prevail. At these especially favourable locations, current-maintained pools occur in the fast ice; these pools are generally small in size, but may provide a surprising yield of seals and, in some years, whales also. However, sustained hunting soon exhausts the supply of seals, and no settlement of size can be supported by hunting only at such locations. Small settlements can benefit from nearness to these open-water places, particularly in the southeast where other forms of hunting can be disappointing. The presence of mussel beds in the pools, and the frequent visits of eider duck throughout the winter are added factors favouring nearby settlements.

During May, seals are stalked as they sleep at their breathing holes or elsewhere on the fast ice. The best areas for winter sealing are also most productive at this time. However, during June, open coastlines become less suitable as it is there that the earliest break-up of sea ice occurs. The best spring sealing, which depends on safe ice, may continue several weeks longer in sheltered areas, thus settlements at that time are in the more landlocked, sheltered coastal sections.

Once the sea ice disappears, three factors are important. The first is the continued need for sheltered or landlocked sealing areas to increase the possibility of hunting from boats in windy weather. The second is the need to reduce the distance to the trading post, as travel is not as easy by boat as it is by sled. The third factor is strictly social: after a winter of living in small dispersed settlements, reduced ecological pressures during spring allow increased social contacts through visiting and the joining together of certain settlements. Unfortunately, the summer density of seals is no greater than it is in winter, and, in addition, losses from sinking are maximal in summer. This threat of reduced hunting returns, compounded by logistic difficulties, is countered by a number of households' leaving spring settlements and constituting a summer grouping in the vicinity of the trading post. These particular households include those that more readily accept Euro-Canadian values, and are consequently not too discouraged by the knowledge that hunting is meagre in the over-exploited region adjacent to the trading post. Those remaining in the spring settlements' may now find local hunting adequate, but sometimes households move to other localities (especially favourable for fish, wildfowl, or whales) during the open-water season.

Settlements situated at or near a river or lake containing char disperse to winter settlement areas after the autumn fishing season. Frequent storms at this season make it an absolute necessity for those with large boats to seek a sheltered harbour. Sealing is very uncertain owing to the poor weather, but occasional whales may be taken, and sometimes walrus. Usually, however, food is scarce in the autumn, and at that season the most marked inland orientation occurs: men and women fish in lakes, women and children spend much time gathering berries and woody plants and lichens for fuel. Fuel now becomes very important, and for this reason, as much as for any other, the autumn settlement is unlikely to be sited in exactly the same place from year to year.

Conditions are usually favourable for building snow houses from late November, though in some years not until January. If a household decides to remain in a tent during the winter months, proximity to abundant driftwood for heating is imperative; 3 households had abandoned the use of snow houses for winter habitation by 1958. Some other households in the west and southwest of the Islands move from snow houses to tents before the end of winter (starting in March), when less intense cold, longer days, and a lessening interest in trapping makes it easier to do so. All are forced to move from snow houses to tents by the end of April, although by then driftwood is not so important as fuel, since tundra plants are sufficient for heating purposes.

Whereas hunting is a traditional activity intimately connected with the Eskimo value system, trapping is a relatively recent innovation and has produced, in varying degrees, marked economic and political changes among Eskimo groups (see Balikci 1964). However, on the Belcher Islands, owing largely to the very real scarcity of foxes, changes for the most part are slight, though they affect some individuals much more than they do others. Trapping is again a highly individual activity; pelts are not normally shared even within households, though the meat of the fox is, and food obtained from trading the pelt is shared in the same way as is other food.

There does not appear to be any notion of territorial rights based either on trapping or on other resources. In 1959 and 1960, two recent immigrants from Ungava set traps widely in the regions trapped by long-standing residents, and a number of other settlement moves in these two seasons were accompanied by corresponding alterations in trapping locations. Men trap in a mosaic pattern over the same area of land and are unaware of the proximity of traps of even members of their own settlement, a situation entirely inconsistent with the notion of personal rights to a given resource. It is maintained by some informants that the best trapping is to be had in the west of the Belcher Islands. Only one man asserted that he was positively influenced in his choice of settlement area by the promise of good trapping; this man was an immigrant from Ungava, where for several decades trapping has been systematic, rather than marginal (as it is on the Belcher Islands).

CONCLUSION

Settlements on the Belcher Islands are composed of a number of interacting households. The ideal household corresponds to the nuclear family. Households can be considered potentially stable in time, insofar as certain non-ideal circumstances (including kinship obligations) permit the maintenance of an ideal composition. The formation or reconstitution of an autonomous economic unit is the rationale underlying changes in household composition.

Patrilocal residence of male siblings after marriage is the basis of settlement composition. Seasonal or annual changes in settlement composition result from economic pressures; in the latter case more particularly, personality factors are additionally important. Fragmentation of settlements occurs across the weakest kin linkages (in relation to the leader) and illustrates the importance of kinship as a solidary mechanism in settlement structure.

The household functions as the basic economic unit in acquisitive phases of the hunting economy; generally, distribution occurs on a settlement-wide basis, though sharing practices depend on a number of variables. Trapping is a marginal economic activity, with the household functioning as both the unit of production and the unit of major distribution.

An awareness of historical background, and particularly of acculturating influences, is considered basic to an understanding of settlement mobility patterns. The end point of increasing acculturation among several arctic and subarctic hunter-trapper societies appears to be the formation of large sedentary and possibly permanent villages situated at the point of trade and subsidy. In progressing to this state, as are a number of Canadian Eskimo groups (including the Belcher Islanders), there is a stage of increased nomadism which appears to vary in intensity with the level of acculturation reached or the degree of "alien-culture aspiration" possessed. The seasonal distribution of "income" on the archipelago results in extended migration: in winter to the west, where foxes are considered most abundant, and in summer to the east, where there is the greatest opportunity for wage employment. Thus the movements of settlements or households with no particular aspirations towards a cash economy are irregular and small scale in contrast to the regular east-west •migrations of the more acculturated members of the community.

The location of seasonal settlements conforms in general outline to bio-geographic features; coastal characteristics are important in influencing the actual numbers of seals, as well as in influencing their availability to the hunter.

The presence of seemingly well-defined settlement areas that are habitually frequented by particular groups of households is partly explained by earlier historical influences combined with limited ecological knowledge (the result of patrilocal residence).

There are no prescribed territorial rights to natural resources, but behavioural norms maintain social distance between non-related individuals in Eskimo society (e.g., Weyer 1932; Petersen 1963). This, too, restricts free intercourse between settlement areas; such interaction as occurs takes place at the seasons of least ecological pressure, namely spring and early summer.

ACKNOWLEDGEMENTS

I should like to thank Drs. Asen Balikci, David Damas, and I. A. McLaren for helpful discussion. Grateful acknowledgement is also made to the Arctic Institute of North America and the McGill University Carnegie Arctic Program for supporting the field studies.

REFERENCES

BALIKCI, A., 1964. Development of Basic Socio-economic Units in Two Eskimo Communities. *National Museum of Canada Bulletin*, 202. 114 pp.

DAMAS, D., 1963. Igluligmiut kinship and local groupings: a structural approach. *National Museum of Canada Bulletin*, 196. 216 pp.

DESGOFFE, C., 1955. Contact culturel: le cas des esquimaux des îles Belcher. *Anthropologica* 1. 45-83.

FAY, F. H., and T. J. CADE., 1959. An ecological analysis of the avifauna of St. Lawrence Island, Alaska. *University of California Publ. Zool.*, 63(2): 73-150.

FREEMAN, M. M. R., 1964. Observations on the Kayak-Complex, Belcher Islands, N.W.T. *National Museum of Canada Bulletin*, 194. 56-91.

GRABURN, N., 1964. Taqamiut Eskimo kinship terminology. *Canada Department of Northern Affairs. NCRC* 41-1. 222 pp.

HONIGMANN, J. J., 1962. Social networks at Great Whale River. *National Museum of Canada Bulletin*, 178. 110 pp.

MCLAREN, I. A., 1958. The economics of seals in the eastern Canadian Arctic. *Fisheries Research Board Canada Arctic Unit Circular No. 1*. Montreal, 94 pp.

————, 1961 (ms). Fisheries Research Board of Canada. Manuscript Report. (Biological). No. 716. Montreal.

————, 1962. Population dynamics and exploitation of seals in the eastern Canadian Arctic, in *The Exploitation of Natural Animal Populations,* ed. E. D. Le Cren and M. W. Holdgate. Oxford.

PETERSEN, R., 1963. Family ownership and right of disposition in Sukkertoppen District, West Greenland. *Folk,* 5: 269-81.

WEYER, E. M., JR., 1932. *The Eskimos: Their Environment and Folkways.* Yale University Press. 491 pp.

WILLMOTT, W. E., 1961. The Eskimo community at Port Harrison, Quebec. *Canada Department of Northern Affairs. NCRC* 61-1. 197 pp.